D1465650

THE FRUIT GROWER'S HANDBOOK

APPLES—*Belle de Boskoop* (*top*) and *Cox's Orange Pippin* (*bottom*)

THE
FRUIT GROWER'S
HANDBOOK

MODERN CULTURAL METHODS

By

N. B. BAGENAL, B.A.(Cantab.)

Wye College, Kent

FRONTISPIECE IN COLOUR
30 PHOTOGRAPHIC ILLUSTRATIONS
and MANY DIAGRAMS

WARD, LOCK & CO., LIMITED

LONDON AND MELBOURNE

First Published . . . *1949*

MADE IN ENGLAND
Printed in Great Britain by Butler & Tanner Ltd., Frome and London

CONTENTS

CHAPTER   PAGE

I   GENERAL CONSIDERATIONS 13

II   SOILS FOR FRUIT GROWING 19

III   MANURING 23

IV   PROPAGATION OF FRUIT TREES AND BUSHES . . . 26

V   PRUNING 39

VI   FORMS OF FRUIT TREES 50

VII   FORMING AND TRAINING: THE "DELAYED OPEN-CENTRE"
      TREE 63

VIII   PLANNING AND PLANTING 77

IX   GATHERING AND STORING FRUIT 87

X   GRADING AND PACKING FOR MARKET 91

XI   THE CONTROL OF PESTS AND DISEASES 97

XII   THE CULTURE OF PARTICULAR FRUITS 113

      The Apple 113

      The Apricot 151

      The Blackberry and its Hybrids 153
        (*Japanese Wineberry, Laxtonberry, etc.*)

      Bush Fruit 157

      The Cherry 157

      The Cobnut and Filbert 169

      Currants, Red and White 173

        ,,   Black 175

      The Damson 185

      The Fig 186

      The Gooseberry 189

      The Loganberry and Phenomenal Berry . . 198

      The Medlar 203

      The Mulberry 204

      The Peach and the Nectarine 205

5

CHAPTER   PAGE

XII THE CULTURE OF PARTICULAR FRUITS—*continued*

The Pear 215

The Plum 233

The Quince 250

The Raspberry 252

The Strawberry 259

The Walnut 271

INDEX 275

LIST OF ILLUSTRATIONS

Apples—*Belle de Boskoop* and *Cox's Orange Pippin*

Frontispiece in Colour

Facing Page

1. Standard Apple Tree " Lord Derby "—Young Standard Cherry Tree 16

2. Influence of Rootstock on Size of Tree : Sixteen-year-old " Worcester Pearmain " Apple on Malling Number IX, a very dwarfing stock—Sixteen-year-old " Worcester Pear-main " Apple on Malling Number II, a semi-dwarfing stock 17

3. Influence of Rootstock on Size of Tree : Sixteen-year-old " Worcester Pearmain " Apple on Malling Number XVI, a very vigorous stock 32

4. Dwarf Pyramid Apple *before* and *after* pruning . . . 33

5. Espaliers : Fan-trained trees of Apricot and Greengage . 80

6. Branch of a " Worcester Pearmain " Apple, showing " tip-bearing " habit—Branch of a " Cox's Orange Pippin," showing close self-spurring habit 81

7. Apple Sawfly : Adult Sawfly—Larva—Attacked Fruitlets— Apples scarred by larva 96

8. Apple Capsid : Apples attacked by Apple Capsids . . 97

9. Winter Pruning : Bush Apple " Lane's Prince Albert " (six years old) *before* and *after* pruning 144

10. The Root-system of a ten-year-old Apple Tree on a vigorous stock excavated from medium loam and reconstructed to show the actual positions occupied by the roots in the soil 145

11. Red Currant Bush *before* and *after* Winter Pruning . . 160

12. Shoot of a Black Currant showing typically distorted leaves— the chief symptom of " Reversion " 161

13. The Root-system of an eight-year-old Gooseberry Bush excavated from sandy soil and reconstructed to show the positions occupied by the roots when in the soil 192

Facing Page

14. Winter Pruning : Apple " Cox's Orange Pippin " Bush Tree
    (three years old) *before* and *after* Winter Pruning . . 193

15. Winter Pruning : Apple " Cox's Orange Pippin " Bush Tree
    (six years old) *before* and *after* Winter Pruning . . . 208

16. Influence of Stock on Growth of Tree : " Victoria " Plum
    (thirteen years old) on Common Plum Stock—" Victoria "
    Plum (thirteen years old) on Myrobolan Plum Stock . . 209

DIAGRAMS IN TEXT

		PAGE
1.	Soil Auger	19
2.	Budding	31
3.	Whip or Tongue Grafting	33
4.	Rind or Crown Grafting	34
5.	Stub Grafting	35
6.	Side Grafting	36
7.	Inarching—Fig. 1. Wedge-shaped cut in Scion. Fig. 2. Incision on Stem. Fig. 3. The Scion inserted and nailed	37
8.	Pruning Stool	41
9.	Single Long Summer Pruning (Apples and Pears) . . .	43
10.	Multi Short Summer Pruning (Apples and Pears) . . .	44
11.	Making the Cut (Pruning)	45
12.	Removal of Branch	46
13.	Making an Undercut before Removal of Branch . . .	46
14.	Bark-ringing and Protecting the Cut	47
15.	Bush Form : Shaping and Training	51
16.	Standard	52
17.	Half-Standard	52
18.	Standard : Shaping and Pruning in Early Years . . .	53
19.	Pyramid	54
20.	Pyramid : Shaping and Training in Early Years . . .	54
21.	Single Vertical Cordon	55
22.	Training Oblique and Horizontal Cordons	56
23.	Showing Successive Positions for Oblique Cordons . .	57
24.	Double Vertical Cordon	58
25.	Triple Cordon	58
26.	Espalier : Shaping in Early Years. Fig. 1	59
27.	Espalier : Shaping in Early Years. Fig. 2	59
28.	Fan : Shaping and Training. Figs. 1–4	60
29.	Fan : Shaping and Training. Figs. 5 and 6 . . .	61
30.	Delayed Open Centre Tree : Shaping and Training. Figs. 1 and 2	63
31.	Notching to Promote Shoot Growth	65

PAGE

32. Feathered Maiden 66
33. Arrangement of Shoots 67
34. Two-year-old Tree after Pruning 68
35. Nicking to Prevent Extensional Growth 69
36. Shortening and Removing Branches 70
37. Pruning Young Leading Shoots 71
38. Pruning Laterals to Form Blossom Buds 72
39. Pruning Laterals to Form Blossom Buds 73
40. Pruning Weak Growing Tree 74
41. Pruning Laterals to Form Blossom Buds 75
42. Pruning Spur Systems 76
43. Marking out the Ground for Planting 79
44. Planting Board 81
45. Erecting Wire-netting to keep out Rabbits . . . 82
46. Staking : Oblique 83
47. Tying the Tree to the Stake. Figs. 1, 2 and 3 . . . 84
48. Tying the Tree to the Stake. Figs. 4 and 5 . . . 85
49. Protection of Wall Fruit from Hail 85
50. Home-made Fruit Picking Bag 87
51. Grading Box for Apples 91
52. Rope method of Training Blackberries 154
53. Shaping Red and White Currants. 173
54. Currant Cuttings 175
55. Training Loganberries 199
56. Fan-Trained tree at end of four years' growth . . . 206
57. Peaches and Nectarines : Removal of Fruit-bearing Shoot and
    Training in of " Replacement " Shoot 207
58. Peach Pruning : Pinching and Disbudding 208
59. Supporting Raspberry Canes 253
60. Supporting Raspberry Canes. Simple Method . . . 255
61. Block Method of Raising Strawberry Runners . . . 260
62. Apparatus for Warm Water Treatment of Strawberry Runners 268

PREFACE

My book entitled *Fruit Growing*, first published by Messrs. Ward, Lock & Co., Limited, in 1935 and revised in 1945, has firmly established itself as the *Standard* work.

In view of the continued requests from students and those interested in fruit culture, for a cheaper version of *Fruit Growing*, I have now prepared a new, popular, abridged volume. Here it is—entitled : *The Fruit Grower's Handbook*.

The chief aim of the book is to show the amateur fruit-grower and the student of horticulture how to apply the principles underlying the growth and cropping of fruit trees to fruit-growing practice on a small as well as on a large scale.

The section dealing with the control of diseases and pests, written by my late colleagues at East Malling Research Station, Mr. H. Moore and Mr. W. Steer, has been revised by them to include the latest information on this subject, and this section should prove of special value both to professional gardeners and to commercial fruit-growers.

Readers who require more detailed information on cultural matters are referred to *Fruit Growing*.

N. B. BAGENAL,

Wye College, Kent.

1949

FRUIT CULTURE

CHAPTER I

GENERAL CONSIDERATIONS

Success in growing fruit is based on two main principles, the first to maintain in the tree a balanced and steady rate of growth, and the second to keep the tree free from diseases and pests. If growth is too slow, the tree becomes stunted and crops prematurely; if growth is too fast, the tree produces more leaf and wood growth and less fruit than it should.

Selection of soil, site and aspect, choice of kinds, varieties and forms of trees and bushes, and methods of planting, pruning, cultivating, manuring and spraying, are important in so far as they help to keep the fruit trees in a state of balanced and healthy growth.

SOIL

Fruit soils cannot be judged by the same standards as those employed in choosing a site for flowers and vegetables. There are, for instance, many shallow soil series overlying solid chalk or sticky clay with as little as 9 to 12 inches of surface soil which in the process of digging or ploughing have been brought into a comparatively fertile and friable condition.

In such soils certain vegetables and flowers might be made to flourish, but if fruit trees or bushes were planted, their roots would very soon penetrate to the solid chalk or clay layers in the subsoil and perish.

Other soil series which may appear most disappointing on the surface have a layer of better soil lower down, and as soon as the roots reach this layer, the trees begin to grow more strongly.

In subsequent chapters mention will be made of the special soil requirements of different kinds and varieties of fruits. It might be noted here that what may prove admirable for one kind or variety may be unsuitable for another.

A deep, fertile soil is good in so far as it will always give the young tree or bush a better start than it would get in a thin, sandy loam or in a wet, sticky clay. But too rich a soil may produce too rapid growth, and this is bad for the tree.

SITUATION AND ASPECT

Some shelter from severe or prolonged winds is important for all fruits, however hardy. In exposure to the south-west there is a double danger ; in the late summer the fruits may be blown from the trees, and in the autumn a heavy strain is put on the anchorage, especially of newly-planted trees which are not yet firmly rooted in the ground.

Shelter from east winds is important for quite another reason. These winds are usually at their worst in April, and sometimes last well into May. This is the flowering time for most fruit trees and bushes, and it is, therefore, one of the most critical periods in the whole season. Many kinds of fruits depend on insects for cross-pollination, and if the trees or bushes are exposed to the full force of the easterly gales, the pollinating insects cannot fly freely from flower to flower. Apart from this, the force of the wind may be so great as to bruise the flower petals, thus making them less attractive to insects. Then, again, easterly winds, if prevalent for any length of time during the period after blossoming, may seriously upset the balance of the plants by causing a sudden check to growth, which should at this period be continuous. The tiny fruitlets, instead of making steady development, remain small, often change colour, shrivel up and drop to the ground. This frequently happens in the case of black currants, gooseberries and cherries, and although such " running-off " is often attributed to insufficient pollination or to frost damage, it may be caused by cold winds.

Thus, at almost any season of the year there is risk of damage of one sort or another from undue exposure to wind. Nevertheless, when looking for a sheltered situation, it is important not to choose the lowest site available, since this may be dangerously subject to frost. It is no use making the orchard safe for insects if the flowers are to be frost-bitten before they open or just as they come into bloom. To escape frost the situation should have free air drainage beyond and below it, and should not be too closely overtopped by higher land whence frosts or cold mists can descend upon it.

Having, then, successfully compromised between undue exposure to winds and to frost and cold mists, the next important consideration is to choose a situation with as much sunlight as possible. A site directly overshadowed by tall trees or buildings should be avoided, since it is impossible for healthy fruit-bud formation to take place under such conditions. A southern slope gets more direct sunlight per day than any other, but where bad winds have to be reckoned with, a gentle slope to the north or north-east is by no means to be despised.

For spraying, a plentiful water supply will be required, easily accessible to the orchard or fruit garden, and there should be a good hard path or roadway on which the fruit can be carried smoothly and securely to the packing shed and store.

TYPES OF FRUIT CULTURE

THE WALLED GARDEN

Apart from the danger of frost a really good walled-in garden is the best place for growing fruit. The soil has been transformed by use into a friable loam, full of humus. The garden is sheltered on all sides from winds ; as a rule water has already been laid on, and there are good paths. The one real risk is that in seeking a sheltered situation for flowers and vegetables, the original planner of the garden may have unwittingly provided a frost-trap.

But if fruit is to be grown successfully and economically in a walled garden, if the trees are to be grown at their normal rate and kept free from disease, the grower must be free to cultivate or grass down just where and when he wishes ; to apply the kinds of manure which the trees want, and to withhold those which they do not want. Above all, he must be free to take his spraying machine where he will, and use the sprays that are most likely to control the diseases and pests of fruit without worrying about what effect they will have on delphiniums or lettuces or anything else.

Since most walled gardens are already planted up with many other crops besides fruit, there must always be some compromise between the varying requirements of the fruit trees and bushes, and of the flowers, vegetables and shrubs. So long as this situation is accepted from the outset, and a certain amount of give and take is provided for, there is no reason why all the crops should not do reasonably well.

THE KITCHEN GARDEN

The kitchen garden, as its name implies, is primarily devoted to the growing of vegetables for use in the kitchen. Fruit is bound to be a secondary consideration here, and spraying and manuring are possible only in so far as they can be made to fit into the scheme of vegetable culture. Tar-oil sprays in the winter and lime-sulphur sprays in the spring or early summer are usually out of the question in a kitchen garden ; and such manures as are generally used for vegetables, whilst they may be suitable for some kinds of fruits, are not desirable for others. So that in the kitchen garden as in the mixed wall garden, the two cardinal principles of fruit-growing, the growing of the plants at their normal rate and keeping them free from disease, are always going to be difficult so long as vegetables continue to be the main consideration.

But the kitchen garden has certain obvious advantages. It is fairly certain to be more sheltered than an open field, and since the trees and bushes are likely to be confined in a comparatively small space, it is possible to give them much more individual attention than they could ever hope to receive in a large orchard or plantation.

THE FRUIT GARDEN

The fruit-garden pure and simple, where only fruit is grown without vegetables or flowers, is undoubtedly the next best thing to the walled garden already mentioned, and for many people a more practical proposition.

Here the distribution of kinds and varieties of fruits can be planned to ensure that spraying, pruning, manuring and cultivating can be carried out economically and efficiently. Top fruits such as plums and cherries, which need fairly heavy dressings of organic nitrogenous manures, can be planted with bush fruits such as black currants, logan-berries and blackberries, which have similar manurial requirements. Fruits such as apples, which require a large amount of potash, and may have to be grassed down for a time to reduce nitrogen, can be planted by themselves.

A third part of the garden can be left for such fruits as strawberries, gooseberries, red currants and raspberries, which require feeding with potash and nitrogen and constant cultivation to produce well-balanced growth.

In the fruit-garden, small to medium-sized trees will usually be found planted fairly closely on dwarfing or semi-dwarfing stocks according to the kind and variety of fruit, and in various forms—bushes, pyramids, espaliers, cordons and the different forms of wall-trained trees. Since space is bound to be more or less limited, the standard and half-standard trees will not usually be welcomed in the fruit-garden.

THE PLANTATION

A plantation is any unit of fruit trees or bushes larger than that usually contained within the boundaries of a garden. The term " plantation " usually implies that some degree of cultivation is being given, however intermittently, to the soil. It is this last characteristic which distinguishes the plantation from the orchard, in which the trees should have the greater part of their root area covered with a permanent sward of grass.

In a plantation there may be fruit of all kinds and sizes ; bush, half-standard, three-quarter standard or standard trees, on various types of stock, may be planted with or without an undercrop, or soft fruits may be planted by themselves.

THE ORCHARD

Until recent years a grass orchard was intended to provide grazing for stock as well as fruit and the trees had to have long stems to keep the branches up and out of the way of the stock. High-headed trees of this kind are called " standards," " three-quarter standards " or " half standards " according to the length of the stem from ground

STANDARD APPLE TREE "LORD DERBY"

YOUNG STANDARD CHERRY TREE

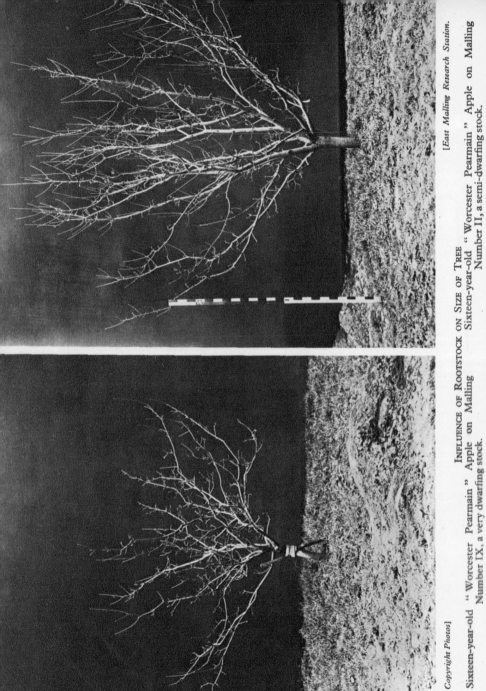

[East Malling Research Station.

INFLUENCE OF ROOTSTOCK ON SIZE OF TREE

Sixteen-year-old "Worcester Pearmain" Apple on Malling Number IX, a very dwarfing stock.

Sixteen-year-old "Worcester Pearmain" Apple on Malling Number II, a semi-dwarfing stock.

level to the lowest branches. In the west, where cattle and horses are grazed, standard trees may have a stem or leg of 6 feet 6 inches to 7 feet; in poultry runs half standards may have a stem of 4 feet 6 inches.

The most satisfactory form of grass orchard consists of cherries or plums, with poultry or sheep to keep the grass short, or some form of cylindrical mowing machine to keep it cut at regular intervals throughout the summer.

WHAT IS AN ECONOMIC UNIT ?

When planting-up fruit for market, one of the most difficult things to decide is what constitutes an economic unit of production. In other words, which pays best—to plant up a comparatively small acreage on a highly intensive system of cordon, or dwarf-pyramid culture, or to spread the same amount of capital over a comparatively large area on a more extensive system of fruit culture ?

There is no simple answer to this question, but the smaller the unit, the more will success depend upon the skill and industry of the individual cultivator.

There is no more fascinating form of hobby-farming than a small area devoted to intensive fruit plantations, provided the owner has independent means, plenty of reserve capital and the services of a really competent manager who has had experience in this particular type of fruit culture.

As a means of supplementing a pension or small fixed income, intensive fruit-growing, or, indeed, any form of farming, must be regarded as highly speculative, especially for a man who has had no previous experience.

The most important factor in deciding the success of such a venture is the temperament and business ability of the man who is going to run the concern. If he can contemplate with equanimity the idea of giving up most of his time throughout the year to the problems of growing and marketing his fruit to the best advantage, he will probably make a success of it; if not, he would be well-advised to put what spare cash he has into gilt-edged securities rather than invest it in the roots of fruit trees.

When it comes to the question of planting fruit on a more extensive scale, the problem is not so much whether it pays to plant fruit under these conditions, as the extent to which it is profitable to invest capital in the business.

There are those who say that a unit of fifty acres of fruit under one management is likely to produce the highest gross income, because such an acreage is large enough to allow of certain important economies of large-scale production in the way of spraying machines, tractors and grading machines, and yet small enough to allow of specialization in fruit-quality, packing and marketing. Others maintain that, over a long period, the highest profits per acre are made by factory fruit farms, run either privately or by limited companies, where the acreage is so large that the overhead expenses are cut to a minimum, and economies are effected in all the most expensive factors of production.

There can be no doubt that extensive fruit plantations on any scale from fifty acres upwards can be made to pay a profit at the present time, provided there is enough capital available to buy and plant the land with fruit under reasonably favourable growth-conditions, and to keep it going under good management until the trees or bushes come into bearing.

After that period, the question of how much interest it will yield on the capital invested is, as in all farming enterprises, partly a matter of luck, but mainly one of business ability on the part of the farmer or farm manager.

The most important practical point for the prospective fruit grower to note is that in addition to the initial capital required to buy and plant up the fruit, enough reserve capital must be available to keep him and the farm going until the fruit is in bearing and can pay for itself.

CHAPTER II

SOILS FOR FRUIT GROWING

SOIL TYPES

The most certain way to find out the soil formation in any one place is to go to the Geological Survey Museum and ask to see the 6-inch Geological Survey and Drift Maps of the area. These maps should also be available at the office of the National Agricultural Advisory Service in the area. From the solid geology survey maps one can learn the nature of the underlying rock. The Drift Maps will show the approximate boundaries of the transported soils which from the fruit grower's point of view may be very important.

But all map knowledge should be always supplemented by information about the prevailing soil series. This can generally be got from the Soil Chemists' Department of the N.A.A.S., and in any case the intending planter should get the village blacksmith to braise an ordinary carpenter's awl on to an iron rod with handle, to make a soil auger (see figure).

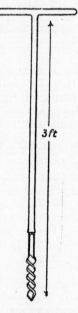

3 ft

SOIL AUGER.

With this tool he can vet any soil to a depth of 3 feet ; in so doing he will get as much exercise as in a round of golf, and learn more about soils than any map or book can teach.

To use the soil auger, clear away rough grass and loose earth, then screw half a dozen turns and pull out. Unscrew the first soil sample from the auger with the forefinger and thumb of the left hand, and repeat until the soil has been penetrated to the full depth of the auger.

When soil sampling in this way the following points about the chief soil types should be borne in mind :

Clay.—If the geological map indicates London Clay, Gault, or Weald Clay as the geological formation, there will be no difficulty in recognizing it in the chunks of grey, yellow or bluish clay of cheese-like texture which may be reached at any depth from 10 or 12 inches to 3 feet below the surface. The soil particles in this type of clay are so fine, and stick together so closely,

19

that the soil very quickly becomes impermeable in rainy weather, and remains waterlogged for long periods ; moreover, in the summer such soils crack badly, so that the roots of plants are subjected to the two-fold danger of rotting in winter and of being torn apart in summer.

While clay soils on level ground can seldom be properly drained, those on a slope can have a system of pipe-drains inserted at a depth of from 2 to 3 feet to drain the winter rains away into the ditches, and so prevent the soil from becoming entirely waterlogged.

Some of the best-grown fruit trees in this country are on sloping clay soils which have been pipe-drained in this way. In general, however, from an economic aspect, stiff clay soils stand condemned, since so much money has to be spent to improve their drainage and texture. They can be made very good at a price, but as cheap natural fruit soils they are to be avoided.

Chalk.—Chalk on the geological map covers a wide range from thin bare chalks on the top of the Downs, through chalk loams of varying depth and texture to chalk marls overlying clay at the bottom of the Downs.

When the auger strikes solid rocky chalk at a depth of anything under 18 inches, fruit of any kind, with the possible exception of strawberries, is almost bound to be a failure. When roots penetrate the chalk layer, a condition known as lime-induced chlorosis is set up in the plant and this is due to the large quantities of lime present in the chalk. The leaves turn a sickly yellow colour, and, being deprived of chlorophyll, are unable to perform their natural functions on which the health of the tree depends.

Local deposits of " clay-with-flints " on the top of the chalk Downs often may have 3 feet or more of red clay loam above the solid chalk. Here fruit of all kinds can be grown successfully if the drainage is good enough. But when solid chalk occurs at anything less than 3 feet below the surface, top fruits are always liable to chlorosis, although bush fruits may prosper. When chlorosis does occur the trees should be grassed down and generously manured through the grass ; under such conditions they have been known to recover and to remain healthy.

Chalk loams on the more gradual slopes of the Downs where erosion has not been too severe, and chalk marls, often overlying Gault clay, on the foothills are by no means to be despised. The chalk loams are apt to dry out in dry summers, especially under grass, and the chalk marls, unless very well-drained, are apt to be waterlogged, but on deep chalk loams, plums, cherries and dessert apples can all be made to do well and on chalk marls, plums, especially greengages and damsons, can be grown.

To sum up, the thin chalk soils should be avoided, but deep chalk loams and well-drained chalk marls will grow good quality fruit under skilled management, especially plums and to a less extent cherries.

Brick Earth.—The term brick earth is generally applied to soils which contain a moderately high percentage of clay particles and are thus fairly retentive of moisture. They have also a nicely-balanced proportion of the coarser soil particles, which provide good natural drainage.

On really deep soils of this type fruit trees and bushes of all kinds grow with remarkable vigour. Cherries and pears in particular seem to revel in it, and for strong growth in all fruits it is, perhaps, the best natural soil in the country.

To sum up, in looking for soils in this country on which to grow hardy fruits with the minimum of effort, the first thing is to buy Drift Maps of the district and discover all the soils of a brick earth type shown on them. Many of these, by nature of their alluvial origin, are liable to be in low-lying situations peculiarly susceptible to late spring frosts, and this point must be carefully borne in mind when selecting the site for fruit.

Gravel.—If the auger or spade strikes a solid bed of gravel with nothing but coarse sand between the pebbles, it should be realized that in such a soil every drop of rain water will rapidly drain away in winter, and there will be little or no chance of moisture being drawn upwards from below during the summer. It will, in fact, be too well drained.

In assessing the value of any gravelly soil for fruit-growing, the most important points to consider are the nature of the gravel itself, and the amount and nature of the soil between the gravel.

Plateau gravels are found in high places, and valley gravels where rivers run or have run in the past.

The amount and nature of the soil in the gravel depends on how the beds came to be laid down. Some of the valley gravels which have plenty of soil of a medium to stiff texture between the stones form ideal soils for fruit-growing. The stones provide a natural drainage system, while the soil between the stones contains sufficient clay particles to retain the moisture in a dry summer.

To sum up, a soil containing a fair proportion of small gravelly stones is suitable for fruit-growing, whereas a soil in which there seems to be more gravel than earth, or in which the earth in the gravel consists of nothing but coarse sand, is to be avoided on account of its poor drought-resisting qualities.

Sand.—The chief advantages of sandy soils are ease of cultivation and ease of rooting ; chief disadvantages are that they will not hold moisture and are often very deficient in potash.

Generally speaking, the darker the colour of the sand the more humus it contains ; whitish coloured sands should be avoided at all costs. From the economic point of view very sandy soils are no good for fruit-growing because they require so much humus putting in to make them hold the moisture and so much manure added to make them fertile.

MAKING THE CHOICE

All the soil types already mentioned have certain merits, and in any mixture of these, provided no one type is present in excess, it is fairly certain that fruit trees and bushes can be made to grow successfully without too much money being spent on soil improvement.

Soils most naturally suitable for fruit culture are those which combine depth with good but not excessive drainage, and which have a smooth, silky texture. Soils naturally unsuitable are those which are shallow, badly-drained or excessively drained, and which have a texture which is either too close or too open.

If balanced and healthy growth is to be maintained, it is important that fruit trees and bushes should be planted, wherever a choice is possible, in the soil conditions most suitable to them. Further reference will be made to this when dealing with the different kinds of fruit.

SOIL CULTIVATION IN RELATION TO GROWTH

Before planting any fruit the soil should be thoroughly well cultivated by means of ploughing, subsoiling where necessary, digging, double-digging, or trenching. And for the first few years after planting, digging or ploughing in early winter, levelling in early spring with cultivators, and hoeing in early summer seldom fails to benefit all young fruit trees and bushes. Thereafter there is no hard and fast rule to guide the grower in deciding on the amount of cultivating that should be done to the soil. Bush fruits and strawberries will always do best under conditions of " clean " cultivation, which means keeping the surface soil loose and free from weeds or grass. Some top fruits will do best when no attempt is made to cultivate the soil, and when weeds or grass are allowed to grow over the tree roots. The governing principle underlying successful soil management is that cultivating tends to encourage shoot growth, and lack of cultivation tends to check it. Thus between clean cultivation at one end of the scale, and grass or weeds at the other the fruit grower has at his disposal an extremely wide range of controlling factors which he can apply in maintaining a correct balance between shoot growth and fruit-bud formation.

CHAPTER III

MANURING

The main manurial requirement of dessert apples, red currants and gooseberries is potassium.

Cooking apples, pears, raspberries, loganberries, blackberries and strawberries, although requiring potassium as a permanent part of their manurial treatment, need in addition nitrogenous manures.

Plums, damsons, peaches, nectarines, apricots, cherries, black currants, cobnuts and filberts require plentiful supplies of nitrogen to keep up a regular supply of annual shoot growth and to give size and quality to the fruit. They fare all the better for regular applications of potassium in moderate quantities, but their main need is for nitrogen. Within the same class of fruit, varieties differ in their manurial requirements. Thus among cooking apples, *Grenadier* is specially dependent on ample supplies of potassium, whilst *Bramley's Seedling* gives the finest crops of fruit from heavy dressings of nitrogenous manures *after the necessary basis of potassium has been secured.*

Again, among dessert apples *Worcester Pearmain* will give its best-coloured fruits only when receiving relatively low amounts of nitrogen in proportion to potash, while *Cox's Orange Pippin* when in full bearing responds to moderately high amounts of nitrogen in proportion to potassium. The kinds and approximate amounts of nitrogenous, phosphatic, and potash manures recommended for different fruits will be given in the chapters dealing with each fruit.

The application of manures to fruit is one part of the general process of tree-nutrition. Trees will require less or more of any particular plant food according to the condition of growth prevailing at that time and in that place.

In grass orchards, once a potassium basis has been determined, the balance can usually be adjusted by one or more of the three methods of increasing shoot growth, i.e., by the application of nitrogenous manures, by hard pruning, or by ploughing up and cultivating under the trees.

In cultivated plantations the problem is generally not so simple. When a serious deficiency of potassium must be rectified for trees with well-established root systems, the first difficulty is that of getting the potassium down to the deeper parts of the soil where the roots are, and the second, of having to wait for several years before the trees get enough potassium for it to have any marked effect. The main symptom of the lack of potassium is a burnt-up appearance of the margins of the leaves, known as " leaf-scorch." There are various forms of leaf-scorch, as for instance, the damage caused by sprays used at too high a concentration, or that caused by severe and sudden droughts, or by growing the trees under waterlogged conditions, or through a deficiency of available magnesium in the soil. By far the most common form of leaf-scorch, however, is that seen on apples, gooseberries and red currants as a result of lack of potassium.

Leaf-scorch seldom occurs on trees growing in grass, and this is generally attributed to the " low-nitrogen " condition of such trees.

Hence, with apple trees in an established plantation where leaf-scorch is severe, an obvious remedy is to give up clean cultivation either partly or wholly, and to apply heavy dressings of potassium as sulphate of potash. With gooseberries and red currants, however, this is out of the question, since such comparatively shallow-rooting plants soon succumb under these conditions from lack of moisture. This is one of the main arguments against growing top fruits and bush fruits together if they can possibly be kept separate.

SOIL IN RELATION TO MANURING

If trees are growing in rich, highly nitrogenous soil, they will need less manuring with nitrogen than if they were growing in poor soils low in nitrogen.

If trees are growing in wet, badly-drained soils, some roots will be killed and the tree will be under-nourished because it has not enough roots to supply it with the raw materials of plant foods.

Trees of this kind will need more manuring rather than less.

Trees growing in thin sandy soils will need more manuring with potash and more organic manures to keep the soil from getting too dry.

CLIMATE IN RELATION TO MANURING

Fruit trees growing in areas of high rainfall (40–50 inches a year) need smaller applications of nitrogenous manures than in areas of low rainfall (18–20 inches a year). Fruit trees growing in areas of high sunshine make smaller growth and can make better use of nitrogenous manures than those in areas of low sunshine.

PRUNING IN RELATION TO MANURING

Very severe pruning tends to promote new shoot growth, and in this respect it has much the same effect as heavy dressings of nitrogenous fertilizers.

It follows that when the process is reversed and little or no pruning is done, the trees will tend to produce a relatively small amount of new growth. Thus, where new growth is required to keep the balance, more nitrogen will be necessary than in the case of the severely pruned tree in order to produce the same result.

CULTIVATION IN RELATION TO MANURING

When trees are grown under grass, there is always a tendency towards what may be called a " low-nitrogen " condition, but when they are grown under clean cultivation, there is the reverse tendency.

ROOTSTOCKS IN RELATION TO MANURING

Trees on very vigorous rootstocks have a natural urge to make strong growth, while those on dwarfing or semi-dwarfing rootstocks are much less inclined to do so. One or two apple rootstocks produce trees which suffer severely from potassium or nitrogen deficiency unless very well looked after in this respect.

DISEASE CONTROL IN RELATION TO MANURING

If the leaves of an apple tree are badly eaten by caterpillars, curled up by aphis or blackened by the scab fungus, they cannot perform their natural function of manufacturing food for the tree. In consequence, growth is checked and the nutrition of the tree suffers, whatever the manurial programme may be.

To sum up, modern research has shown that the study of the manuring of fruit trees cannot be limited to mere consideration of the kinds and amounts of manures to apply, but must be regarded as part of the much larger subject of nutrition. In the complex process of fruit tree nutrition, many different factors play their part, and if trees are to be kept in a condition of healthy and balanced growth, each one of these factors must be taken into consideration.

NOTE.—Readers should also consult " Manuring Fruit Crops in War Time " (Growmore Bulletin No. 4 M.O.F.) and " The Diagnosis of Mineral Deficiencies in Plants " (H.M. Stationery Office), both by Dr. T. Wallace, Long Ashton.

CHAPTER IV

PROPAGATION OF FRUIT TREES AND BUSHES

Where large numbers of trees or bushes are to be planted, and when early cropping is the main requirement, the best source of supply for planting material is a reliable nursery.

On the other hand, for those with plenty of time, leisure and money, or for those who wish to try their hand at raising new varieties, or who require only a few trees or bushes of very select varieties, the propagation of fruit trees and bushes is a fascinating hobby.

HYBRIDIZATION AND PROPAGATION FROM SEED

With few exceptions, all new varieties of fruit are obtained as the result of hybridizing, i.e., the transferring of pollen from the stamens of the flower of one variety to the style of another. This may be done naturally through the passing of insects from flower to flower, collecting pollen from one and brushing it off against another. This is known as "open pollination." But when plant breeders set out to raise new varieties they take pollen from the flower of one selected parent and put it on to the flower of the other selected parent in such a way as to make sure that cross-fertilization takes place. The flower sets and in due course the fruit ripens its seed.

These seeds should be sown in autumn in shallow wooden boxes or earthenware pans containing one-third leaf-mould, two-thirds good loam and a little sharp silver sand. The boxes or pans must be well-drained with plenty of broken crocks at the bottom. They are placed in cold frames and need not be pampered until after the seeds have germinated the following spring, when they will need protection from frost.

The seedlings are potted up when a few inches high and gradually hardened off ready for planting out when the late frosts are over. The seedlings can either be left to grow on their own roots or, in the case of tree fruits, after two or three seasons' growth the shoots may be cut off and grafted in the spring on to rootstocks, or budded in the summer. There is a likelihood that the seedlings will display one or more of the characteristics of either or both parents, but further than that, it would not be safe to forecast. Nor does it appear to make any difference which of the two parents supplies the pollen to the flower of the other.

This method of hybridizing can be used with minor modifications for raising new varieties of all our hardy fruits.

Where opportunity offers, it is advisable to pot up the parent plants and bring them under glass some months before they are due to flower. This is comparatively easy in the case of the soft fruits such as straw-berries, raspberries, currants and gooseberries ; in the case of apples, pears, plums, peaches, nectarines, apricots, cherries and walnuts, if the parent plants are too big to be potted up, hybridizing can be done out of doors.

To ensure germination, the seeds of all hardy fruits require a resting period of from three to four months in fairly low temperatures. Seeds of the stone fruits which find it difficult to break through the hard outer shell are sometimes deliberately cracked at the time of sowing. Or alternatively the outer shell can be softened by half-burying the seeds in moist sand for periods of from three to nine months, varying with the hardness of the shell. This process is technically known as " stratification."

PROPAGATION FROM HARDWOOD CUTTINGS

Currants and gooseberries are raised in thousands every year from hardwood cuttings, and are very easy to propagate in this way. The ideal growth conditions for hardwood cuttings are those which encourage quick rooting and unchecked growth through the growing season. The best results are obtained from soil of a brick earth type, well-aerated, well-drained and yet retaining ample moisture through summer. But with early autumn planting and constant hoeing throughout the growing season a good " strike " of cuttings may be obtained on practically any soil that is not either pure sand or solid clay. Since the technique of taking and inserting cuttings is not quite the same for all kinds of currants and gooseberries they will be considered separately in the sections dealing with each fruit.

VEGETATIVE PROPAGATION—ROOTSTOCKS

Apples, pears, plums, peaches, nectarines, apricots and cherries are usually budded or grafted on to rootstocks belonging to the same species as the scion. These rootstocks can be raised either from seed by the methods described above, or by means of vegetative propagation. Rootstocks are generally raised from seeds more easily and more cheaply than by vegetative propagation, but when they are raised from seeds of " open-pollinated " flowers it is impossible to know for certain what their parentage is and what their effect will be when used as rootstocks. At the present time most rootstocks raised in this country are produced vegetatively either from stoolbeds or from layers. By these methods a single rooted stock can be planted, and from it almost any numbers of "clonal" rootstocks can ultimately be produced, every one of which will be perfectly true to type, since each contains the same genetic characters as the parent "clone."

METHOD OF STOOLING

Most of the commonly-used apple and quince rootstocks can be raised quite easily by this method. The rooted stocks which are to form the stool-beds are planted upright in the autumn in well-manured ground in rows at least 3 feet apart, leaving one foot between the stocks in each row.

The stocks are cut down to within 2 feet of ground level and are left to grow for one year, the ground being kept well hoed throughout the season. In the following spring, about February, the stocks should be cut down level to the ground. The buds at the base will push out young shoots, and as soon as these are 5 or 6 inches long, earth should be mounded up in a stool to a depth of 2 or 3 inches around their base.

This process is repeated again after a further flush of growth has been made, the base of each shoot being ultimately buried in 6 or 8 inches of soil. From this buried portion adventitious roots are formed in the moulded soil which forms the stool-bed. In November the soil is scraped away from the stool, and the young stocks are cut off at the point from which they started growth in the spring. Those which are well-rooted can then be planted out in nursery rows in readiness for budding the following summer. Any stocks which are not sufficiently well-rooted to be worth planting in the nursery for budding can be bedded out an inch or two apart in nursery rows for one season, after which they are known to nurserymen as "bedded" stocks.

METHOD OF LAYERING

This is the method used for the vegetative propagation of most of the plum, cherry and pear rootstocks. The stocks are planted in the autumn, sloping at an angle of about 45 degrees, in rows at least 4 feet apart, leaving about 3 feet between the stocks in each row. For the first season there is nothing to do beyond keeping the ground well hoed. At the end of the year, during the winter, any weak side shoots that may have grown out are cut back to within an inch of their base, leaving the main stem and strong laterals full length. Then a shallow trench a few inches deep is made down the middle of the row, as though for sowing peas, and into this trench the stocks are bent down in a horizontal position and held in place by strong wooden pegs and wire hoops. Fine soil is heaped over the entire length to the depth of about one inch above the layers just before buds are due to open in the spring. The essential difference between the stooling and layering methods of vegetative propagation of rootstocks, is that in layering the parent stocks must receive a covering of earth in the dormant season before growth begins, whereas in normal stooling no earthing up takes place until the young shoots have made 5 or 6 inches of growth from the base of the stool. In layering, success depends on preventing the base of the shoot from becoming hard by exposure to light, and on forcing the young shoots to push through the soil as in natural suckers. When these young shoots have grown 4 or 5 inches, the layer beds are earthed again, taking care to leave at least 2 inches of growth above soil level.

Earthing up continues periodically throughout the season until the layers are covered to a depth of at least 6 or 7 inches of soil, care being taken to see that after earthing, the soil does not get washed off again by heavy rains. In November the soil is removed with a fork, and the rooted layers are cut off and planted out in the nursery for budding the following summer. Any coarse unrooted shoots are pegged down again alongside the parent layer, and the whole bed is earthed over again during the winter to a depth of one inch in preparation for next year's crop of layers.

BUDDING AND GRAFTING

THE OBJECT OF BUDDING AND GRAFTING

Although all kinds of fruit trees, once they can be made to strike root, will grow and eventually crop on their own roots, the practice of budding or grafting has become universal for various reasons. The fruit tree that has been budded or grafted on a selected rootstock will come into fruiting several years before the tree that has grown on its own roots and has never been grafted.

It is now generally recognized, moreover, that apart from the time which it takes a tree to come into bearing, the ultimate size of the tree and the quality of the fruit can also be influenced in varying degrees by careful choice of rootstocks. This is especially the case with apples, and to a less extent with pears, plums and cherries.

BUDDING

Budding is in itself a simple operation, but one which needs a good deal of practice to make perfect. The percentage of buds which take will depend partly on weather conditions during and after budding, and partly on the speed and dexterity with which the operation is carried out.

The principle underlying budding and grafting is the same, namely, to bring into close contact portions of the cambium layer of stock and scion, and to keep them together until fresh tissue forms to unite them into a single growth.

TIME FOR BUDDING

Budding of fruit tree stocks is usually done some time in July or August, the order of budding roughly corresponding with the date of flowering. Thus cherries, plums and quinces come first and apples follow after. The best way to decide if the stocks are fit for budding is to run the budding knife lightly down the base of one of the stocks and insert the knife handle under the bark. If it lifts easily and comes clean away from the wood, budding can be begun at once. If the bark sticks or tears when lifted, the stock is not fit for budding.

CHOOSING THE BUDS

A healthy shoot of current year's growth having been chosen (Fig. A), the leaves should all be removed from it close to the leaf-stalk, only a piece of the latter being left on (Fig. B). With a sharp knife the bud is then cut out of the wood, the knife making a curve behind it, leaving the bud midway on a thin strip of bark and wood (Fig. C). The woody part may now be removed, and in order to do this, the piece is held by the leaf-stalk and bud, while the bark is started away from the wood at the top end with the tip of the knife, and is then given a sharp pull, when the bark should peel cleanly off the slip of wood.

Experiments have shown that removing the woody portion of the bud in this way is not always essential, and should it prove difficult to do so without spoiling the bud, it would probably be as well to make the cut as thin as possible with a very sharp knife and to leave the wood in. In some seasons, however, and with some kinds of buds, the wood comes away so easily that no difficulty is found in performing the full operation.

PREPARING THE STOCK

The bud being ready, the stock must next be dealt with. A clean, smooth spot on the stem is chosen 4 to 6 inches above ground level, and with the budding knife a cut about $1\frac{1}{2}$ inches long is made, only just sufficient pressure to pierce the bark without penetrating the wood beneath being employed. At the top of this a cross-cut half an inch long should be made with equal care (Fig. D), the bark on either side of the first cut then being raised from the wood by means of the blade of the knife, or its thin handle, slipped in between bark and wood. The point of the " shield " containing the bud is then inserted at the cross-cut, and is gently pushed down under the bark until the bud is well down below the level of the cross-cut. When the bud is well down, the projecting tip of the shield should be cut off with a cut exactly on a level with the cross-cut in the stock, so that the tip of the shield fits inside the bark, see diagram (Fig. E).

TYING

Tying can be done either with raffia or with narrow rubber strips and should finish with one or two half-hitches. In either case the tie should be made to the full extent of the slit, its object being to keep the cambium layers of stock and scion in close contact until the union is completed (Fig. F).

AFTER-CARE OF THE BUD

About a fortnight or three weeks after the buds have been inserted the raffia should be untied and the buds carefully examined. If the leaf-stalk has fallen off or drops at a touch, the union is pretty certain to be complete. But if the leaf-stalk

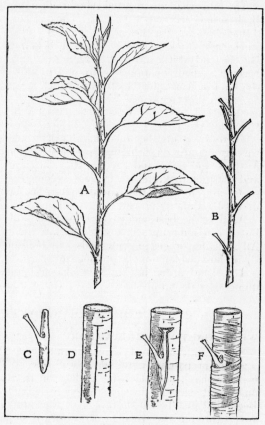

BUDDING.

is stiff and adheres firmly to the bud, the chances are that union has not taken place and that the bud will die. In this case, the stocks can either be budded again at once, or if large enough can be grafted the following spring. Buds can usually be inserted successfully on stocks of diameters not exceeding about half an inch; on stocks larger than this grafting is generally to be recommended in the following spring.

If raffia is used for tying in the buds, there is always a certain risk of its causing constriction if the stem swells rapidly. After untying to examine the buds, those that have taken should be lightly retied to prevent the rind curling back from the bud-shield.

The buds that are inserted remain dormant until the following spring. In February the stocks are cut back either to the bud or leaving a " snag " of 3 or 4 inches above the bud. Many people prefer to cut the stock right back to the bud at the beginning of the growing season. By the end of the growing season the bud will have grown out and become a shoot of anything from 3 to 8 feet of growth according to the kind of fruit and the stock in which it was inserted. This is called a " maiden " tree.

GRAFTING

There are a number of different ways of grafting, all depending for success mainly on bringing together portions of the cambium layer in stock and scion and keeping these in close contact until they unite, and the rootstock and scion shoot become one plant. For grafting the scions are cut from the parent tree in the dormant season and heeled in until required for use.

April is the best month for most kinds of grafting in this country, but it can sometimes be started earlier and carried on later than this. All splitting or clefting methods can be started earlier in the season than those which involve lifting the bark.

The usual order in which stocks are grafted is : plums, cherries, quinces, pears, apples.

FORMS OF GRAFTING

WHIP- OR TONGUE-GRAFTING

Stocks in the nursery are generally grafted by this method. The scion is prepared by taking a well-ripened one-year-old shoot some 6 inches long, and selecting a place on it where two good buds come on opposite sides of the shoot, one a little higher than the other (Fig. A). Beginning just below the upper of the buds, make a clean cut at one sweep through the wood in a downward slope, coming out just below the lower bud.

It is essential that there should be a good bud just above the cut at each end. This cut should be made firmly and evenly, otherwise the scion will not fit closely to the stock and its chance of a perfect union will be lessened.

The stock should have been cut back late in January to about 8 inches from the ground.

Remove all side growth from the base and cut the stock cleanly off about 3 or 4 inches above the surface of the ground.

                    [*East Malling Research Station.*

INFLUENCE OF ROOTSTOCK ON SIZE OF TREE
Sixteen-year-old " Worcester Pearmain " Apple on Malling Number XVI, a very
vigorous stock.

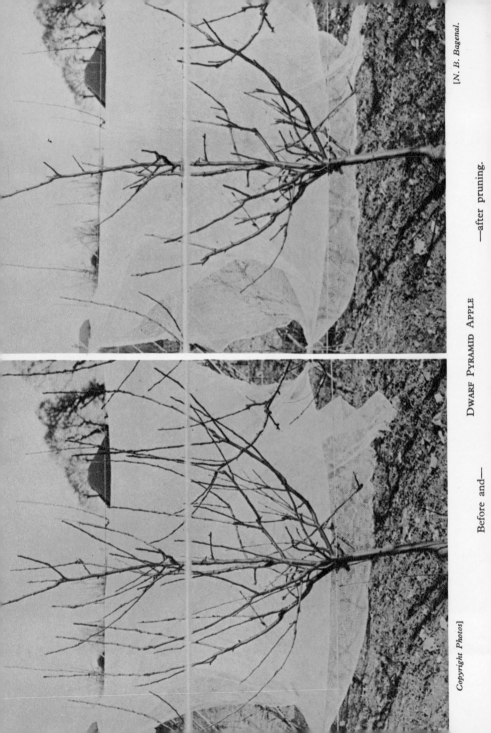

Before and— DWARF PYRAMID APPLE —after pruning.

The cut surfaces of the inner bark of both stock and scion should touch as much as possible. If it is found impossible to make these layers of bark meet on both edges, make them match exactly on the one.

When both scion and stock fit perfectly, a further security may be obtained by making a small upward cut in the tail of the scion, in order to obtain a slip projecting towards the stock (Fig. A). In the stock itself, opposite this slip, should be made an incision (Fig. B) into which the slip will exactly fit, thus holding stock and scion together (Fig. C) during the operations of tying and covering with wax. This slip should be thin, or it may cause the junction to bulge, and the scion to be pushed away from the stock. When these two latter are fitted closely together, and it is found that their layers of inner bark are fitting closely and neatly, the junction should be made firm by tying tightly with raffia.

The last process is the secure covering of the whole junction—scion and stock, with grafting wax—and the graft is complete.

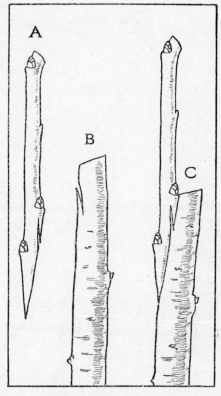

WHIP OR TONGUE GRAFTING.

RIND OR CROWN GRAFTING

This is one of the most popular and easiest methods of grafting on to mature trees when the stock is comparatively large. The scion is prepared much as for tongue-grafting, with a sloping cut about $1\frac{1}{2}$ inches in length. The stock should be cut off cleanly, and with a sharp knife a slit should be made in the bark of the same length as the tail of the scion. While the knife is still in the cut, the blade should be gently pressed from side to side so as to loosen the bark in the immediate neighbourhood of the cut, and on withdrawing the knife, the scion is slipped in between the wood and the bark, and pressed down until the surface left by the cross-cut at its head lies on the top of the stock. From two to four scions may be placed on each branch over 4 inches in diameter so treated. When the grafts are growing well, they may be supported by being tied to sticks fastened securely to the branches of the stock.

Until the grafted tree has developed a good head of new grafted wood, it is a great mistake to remove all the shoots and twigs of the old stock.

OTHER METHODS OF TOP GRAFTING

Three other methods of top-grafting mature trees may be briefly mentioned here.

OBLIQUE CLEFT GRAFTING

Cleft grafting, in which the branch to be grafted is cleft down the middle, has always been popular for cherries, plums and old trees of apples and pears in which the bark is rough and difficult to lift. This method, however, is open to criticism because of the dangers of infec-

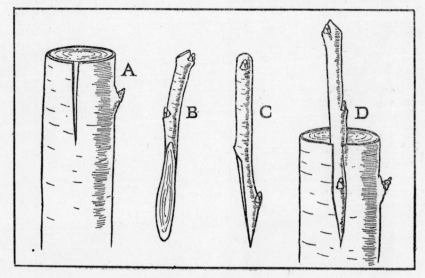

RIND OR CROWN GRAFTING.
A. The prepared stock. B and C. The scion. D. The scion inserted in the stock.

tion from fungus
diseases in the
deep gash made
by the cleft. In
oblique cleft
grafting instead
of splitting the
branch straight
down through
the middle, one
or more small
splits are made
with a special
grafting tool at a
tangent at equal
distances round
the circumfer-
ence of the
branch.

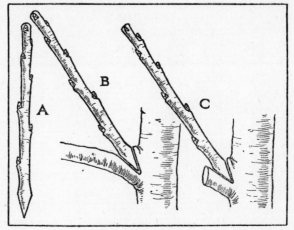

STUB GRAFTING.

The scion is cut to the shape of a thin wedge and inserted cambium
to cambium at the outside edge of the cleft, where it is held firmly
without having to be tied. A piece of clay or " pug " is generally
pushed into the cleft behind the scion before all the cut surfaces are
waxed over.

FRAMEWORKING—STUB AND SIDE GRAFTING

In the frameworking methods the leading branches are left intact
and scions of the new variety are grafted on to them all the way up.
In stub grafting, one of the clefting methods, the scion, cut wedge
shape (Fig. A), is inserted from above into the base of a lateral by
means of an oblique cut made half-way through the lateral about half
an inch from its base (Fig. B).

As soon as the cut is made, the lateral is bent back, the scion inserted,
and the lateral then springs back and is cut off, leaving the scion held
firmly in the cleft (Fig. C). All cut surfaces are then sealed with
grafting wax ; no tying is necessary.

SIDE GRAFTING

A clefting method for frameworking branches of an inch or so in
diameter. The scion is cut to a wedge at the base with one side slightly
longer than the other (Fig. A, page 36). Driving the knife into the side
of the branch at the required place at an angle of 20 to 25 degrees,
and about $\frac{1}{4}$ inch deep, bend the branch to open the cut and insert

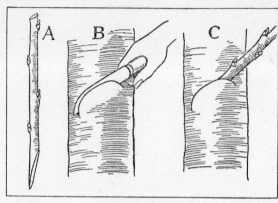

SIDE GRAFTING.

the scion cross-ways at an angle of 45 degrees with cambiums matching (Fig. C). Seal with wax without tying.

Framework grafting can be begun in February, and by using a combination of stub and side grafts almost any shape or size of established tree can be changed from one variety into another in the course of a season.

INARCHING AND BRIDGE-GRAFTING

If a fruit tree has been partly or wholly girdled by canker, if the stem has been badly gnawed by animals, or if the tree is unduly stunted as a result of being grafted on an unsuitable rootstock, or because it has been planted in an unsuitable soil, it is always worth trying to restore its vigour.

A tree that has been injured by canker or by gnawing can be inarched. If there are one or more strong shoots growing out from below the injury, or stock suckers growing from ground level close to the stem, one or more of these can be inarch grafted above the injury, in late March or any time in April. Press the selected shoot inwards against the stem in a vertical position, and mark a place on the stem well above the injury, where it can conveniently be inserted. Next prepare the top end of the shoot or sucker for grafting by making a long sloping cut about $1\frac{1}{2}$ inches long on the under side, and a similar cut about one inch long on the upper side, forming a wedge (Fig. 1, page 37). At the place on the stem already marked, make a vertical incision downwards, about three-quarters of an inch long, and at the base of this draw the knife away to the right, at an angle of about 150 degrees, cutting obliquely into the bark. This cut is also about three-quarters of an inch long (Fig. 2). Lift the bark under these two cuts with the handle of a budding knife, and push the top end of the scion gently into place under the bark. To hold the graft in position, a small-headed nail is driven clean through the bark and scion into the wood, at the point of insertion under the bark (Fig. 3). Finally seal thoroughly at the point of insertion with a good grafting wax.

For badly stunted trees, and for trees on which there are no low-growing shoots or rootstock suckers suitable for inarching, it will be necessary to dig up rootstock suckers from elsewhere, or to buy some rootstocks.

These rootstocks must be of the same species, i.e., apple for apple, and should be as vigorous as possible. One or more of these stocks is planted in autumn or winter close to the base of the tree to be inarched.

If the tree stem measures over 3 inches in diameter, it may be necessary to plant more than one stock, at equal intervals round the base of the tree. The inarch grafting is then done the following spring as described above. In the event of there being an injury in the stem, the inarch will be made a few inches above the injured area. Where there is no injury, but the tree is stunted, the inarch should be made about 9 to 12 inches above ground level.

Bridge Grafting.—Another way of saving a tree stem that has been badly girdled is by means of bridge grafting. Scions long enough to span the girdled area with ease are cut in winter as described on page 32. The scions can be of any variety, but must be the same species as the tree into which they are to be bridge-grafted.

In April inarch the bottom end of the scion into the stem below the injured area, and the top end of the scion into the stem above the injured area, nail in position and seal as already described. In making the bottom graft the L-shaped cut should be made in the

INARCHING.

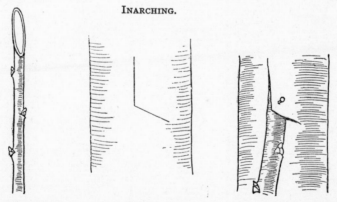

FIG. 1.—WEDGE-SHAPED
CUT IN SCION.

FIG. 2.—INCISION ON
STEM.

FIG. 3.—SCION INSERTED
AND NAILED.

reverse position to that for the top graft described on page 36 under inarching (Fig. 2). A stem of 3 inches or more in diameter will require more than one scion, and these should be inserted at equal intervals round the stem to make an effective bridge across the girdled area. If the girdle has been caused by canker, the diseased tissue should be cut out as described on page 130 before the grafting is done.

NOTE.—For a detailed description of different methods of grafting see *The Grafter's Handbook*, by R. J. Garner.

CHAPTER V

PRUNING

PRUNING A DIFFICULT ART

The pruning of the bush fruits is a comparatively straightforward operation, which can soon be mastered with a little practice. Nor do the stone fruits present much difficulty when grown in the more natural forms, though when trained on walls or wires they are by no means simple trees to prune.

But with all forms of apples and pears, pruning is a difficult art and one which can never be fully learnt from a book. It calls for practical experience.

THE OBJECTS OF WINTER PRUNING

For the pruner there are three main stages in the life of the tree. In the first stage he aims at building up a branch framework for the fruit by comparatively *hard* pruning, in the second stage he encourages the tree to come into fruiting by *light* pruning, and in the third stage he has to keep the tree balanced in a state of healthy growth combined with regular cropping, by hard or light pruning according to circumstances.

FIRST STAGE—FORMING AND SHAPING THE FRAMEWORK

Hard Pruning for Shoot Growth.—To form the framework of the tree strong extension shoots are needed from which to select the main branches or "leaders." Thus, the first object of the pruner in this stage is to promote healthy growth of strong wood shoots. This is done by the hard pruning back of some shoots on the young tree to within a few inches of their base, since *the first general principle of winter pruning is that hard cutting back encourages the growth of strong new shoots from all parts of the trees.*

The pruner's second object is to shape the framework according to the form required, by cutting out unwanted shoots, and making the others grow in the right direction. This is comparatively simple in the case of the more natural shapes such as bush and standard, but espalier, pyramid and other artificial forms of trees require a good

39

deal of skill, and for these forms it is usually cheaper in the long run to buy three- or four-year-old trees which have been trained by a nurseryman.

Naturally, the price of such trees is higher than that of one- or two-year-olds, but for those who have not the time nor the inclination to carry out the shaping of these more complicated frameworks, it is worth paying the extra price to get well-trained trees to begin with.

SECOND STAGE—BRINGING THE TREE INTO BEARING

Light Pruning for Fruit-Bud Formation.—In this stage the second general principle of pruning must be borne in mind, namely, that *the less winter pruning a young tree receives, the more quickly it will come into bearing.*

Hence, at this stage pruning should be as light as possible consistent with healthy growth. The extension shoot at the end of each " leader " should either be left full length or only " tipped " lightly, according to kind and variety, and the lateral or side shoots should be left as long as possible. The subsequent treatment of these lateral shoots must depend to a large extent on the kind of fruit and on the form of the tree. With the stone fruits, most of them are best left full length, those which are actually touching each other being cut off at the point of contact. In the case of bush and standard forms of apples and pears, the shoots on the inside of the tree must be shortened back to let the light in, whilst those on the outside of the tree can safely be left quite long for a year or two until the tree comes into fruiting.

With the more artificial forms of tree, cordon, espalier, etc., in which the number of main branches is limited, the second stage of pruning is immensely important if quick fruiting is required. Only too often the period of fruiting is delayed indefinitely because, in order to preserve the trim appearance of the tree, all the shoots are clipped off close at the very time when they should be left long for a season or two.

THIRD STAGE—PRUNING THE FRUITING TREE

Hard or Light Pruning, according to Growth and Cropping.—When the tree has come regularly into bearing, the degree of pruning has to be decided in accordance with what the tree is doing. If it has carried a normal crop of good-sized fruits, and at the same time has made a fair amount of new wood growth during the season, the winter pruning should aim at keeping this balance. With apples and pears, the extension shoots will need shortening in differing degrees according to variety, and lateral shoots will be " spurred back " or shortened to visible fruit buds reasonably close to their base.

If the tree has carried an abnormally large crop, and has made little or no fresh wood-growth, the winter pruning must be definitely severe. With the idea of restoring the balance of growth, the extension shoot on each main branch should be cut hard back to within a few inches of the base, and all lateral shoots or spurs which are then showing numerous fruit-buds must be drastically shortened.

On the other hand, if the tree has carried little or no fruit or flowers and has made a large number of strong new shoots, then the less winter pruning that is done, the better. In such cases, if the tree continues to make strong growth even when unpruned, it is clear that some other method of checking growth must be tried, such as summer pruning, ringing, or rootpruning (in the case of stone fruits) or grassing down to check nitrogen supply to the tree.

With stone fruits, pruning in this third stage is best confined to cutting clean out at the base any shoots that are badly placed, and shortening back crossing branches to allow free passage of light and air between them.

It is very seldom necessary or desirable to shorten the extension shoot on the main branches of plums, cherries, peaches or any of the stone fruits once the tree is established. And since these fruits bear short natural spurs with mixed wood and fruit buds arising on two-year-old shoots, there is no need for regular shortening back of the side shoots in order to form artificial spurs as in the case of apples and pears.

DEHORNING

When fruit trees have become too tall and straggly for pruning, spraying, thinning and picking, they may be dehorned. This operation consists of cutting back the main branches in the winter, each to a small branch terminating in a strong young shoot of the previous season's growth, pointing in the required direction. In this way it is possible to remove two or three storeys from the top of the tree and at the same time to preserve the framework in its proper shape.

PRUNING STOOL.

PRUNING VERY OLD TREES

Fruit trees over fifty years of age have to be treated with caution when pruning. If they are dehorned too drastically, they may die back, a branch or two at a time. If the trees have been long neglected, the first thing to do is to cut out all the dead branches.

After that, the actual pruning back of the straggling main branches is an operation which in a very old tree is best spread over two or three winters so as not to cause too severe a shock to the roots of the tree.

SUMMER PRUNING

There is an important distinction between winter and summer pruning. Winter pruning is done when there are no leaves on the tree, and provided the root-system is not disproportionately small, the result will be to stimulate the growth of strong shoots from well-developed wood-buds on the pruned parts of the tree in the following spring.

Summer pruning, on the other hand, is done when the tree is in full leaf.

The removal of green shoots and leaves is bound to result in an immediate check to the food supply going down to the roots, because there are less leaves to do the work. A check in the growth of new roots means a check in the growth of new shoots, so that the net result of summer pruning must always be a check to shoot growth. How long the check will continue and what the effect will be on the rest of the tree will depend on the time of summer pruning, the severity of pruning, the weather following the pruning, and other conditions such as cultural and manurial treatments.

It is no wonder that the subject of summer pruning is highly controversial, and one which commercial fruit-growers of bush and standard trees are inclined to fight shy of, except as a means of letting light in to colour up the fruit.

Summer pruning, however, is of the utmost importance as a means of preserving a healthy balance of shoot and root growth in the more artificial forms of tree such as cordons, pyramids, fans and espaliers, or even in very closely-planted bush trees.

The main point to note is that summer pruning tends to *check growth* of roots and shoots, whereas the chief object in winter pruning is to stimulate the growth of new shoots.

The three methods most worth describing are what may be described as the orthodox English method of the Single Summer Pruning and the two Multi Summer Pruning Methods of Long and Short Summer Pruning of Apples and Pears.

SINGLE LONG SUMMER PRUNING OF APPLES AND PEARS

This consists of shortening all lateral shoots of any size to within about 5 or 6 inches of their base in July (see diagram), pears usually being done in the first half, and apples in the second half of the month. The one certain effect of this is to let the sun and air into the tree to colour the fruit and ripen the wood. Some contend that the check to growth resulting from this wholesale reduction of the leaf area has the effect of producing fruit-buds more quickly at the base of the pruned lateral shoots than if those shoots had been allowed to grow unchecked throughout the season.

Whether this is so or not, it often happens that if the weather continues wet, one or even two buds at the end of the summer-pruned shoots

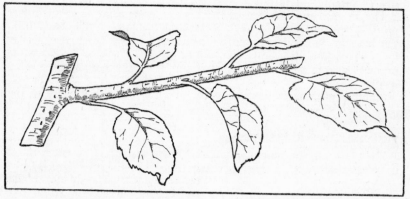

SINGLE LONG SUMMER PRUNING (APPLES AND PEARS).

start growing out into weak secondary shoots, which often become infected with one or other of the bad fungus diseases, such as canker, scab or mildew.

Single summer pruning of this kind is usually followed in the winter by the cutting back of the summer-pruned shoots to whatever length of spur is considered suitable.

MULTI-SUMMER PRUNING—LONG PRUNING OF APPLES AND PEARS

Beginning about June, all strong shoots that are going woody at the base and are a foot or more in length, are pruned back to within 5 or 6 inches of the base.

This operation is continued or repeated as and when shoots or secondary shoots reach this stage. In a dry summer it may have to be done only once ; if rain sets in or if the tree is growing very strongly in an off season, it may have to be repeated two or three times. In the winter unripened secondary growth is cut out at the base.

This method is rather more elastic than the Single Summer Prune, but takes longer. It is particularly associated at the present time with the training and shaping of closely-planted dwarf pyramid apple trees.

MULTI SHORT SUMMER PRUNING OF APPLES AND PEARS

The French Lorette system of pear pruning provides for the hard pruning back to their base of all new shoots as they attain a certain size at intervals of about a month throughout the summer.

The English modification of the Lorette system is a single summer pruning, cutting new lateral shoots back to two visible buds from the base at the end of June for pears and about three weeks later for apples (see diagram). Secondary growth, where it occurs, is pruned back to within one or two buds from the base the following winter.

Summer pruning in relation to the other fruits is dealt with in the paragraphs devoted to the individual fruits.

PRUNING INSTRUMENTS

For the winter pruning of extension shoots where a clean cut without bruising is desirable, a sharp pruning knife of really good steel is to be recommended. The blade should be slightly curved. A knife that shuts up is the more handy for the pocket ; on the other hand, a knife with a fixed handle and a sheath is much stronger and more durable. For winter pruning of lateral shoots and for all summer pruning the modern forms of secateurs are very popular.

MULTI SHORT SUMMER PRUNING (APPLES AND PEARS).

Parts of these secateurs wear out rather quickly and have to be replaced, but spare parts are easily got and should be bought with the secateurs.

For cutting off branches which are too big for the knife or secateurs, a small pruning saw is useful.

This may be either straight or curved, but should be fairly coarse in the teeth for cutting green wood across the grain.

PRUNING CUTS

The perfect pruning cut begins on the side of the shoot opposite to the selected bud, and slants slightly upwards across the shoot, to end above the base of the bud as in the diagram (Fig. A).   When the cut surface is large, it should be covered over with a good lead paint or with some shellac preparation such as painter's knotting to keep the surface dry whilst callousing over.   When sawing off large branches, undercut first by making a small cut on the underside before starting to saw through from the top (see diagram, page 46).

A

MAKING THE
CUT.

EXCESSIVE WOOD GROWTH

Restoring the Balance by Bark Ringing or by Root Pruning.—The balance between shoot-growth and fruit-bud formation may be upset in the other direction.   In this case, owing to excessive winter pruning or cultivating, or to unbalanced manuring or because the tree is on a very vigorous rootstock, there is a tendency for growth to be too strong with a consequent scarcity of fruit-buds.   Mention has already been made of the different ways of attempting to restore the balance in a case of this kind, either by leaving the extension shoots unpruned or lightly "tipped," by withholding all nitrogenous manures, and by giving up cultivation and letting the ground go down to weeds or grass.

Where it is impossible to try these remedial measures, or in cases where they have all been tried unsuccessfully, the practice of *Stem or Branch Ringing* may often be worth trying as a last resort with apples and pears.   In the case of the stone fruits which are liable to gum when ringed, the same result may be obtained by means of different degrees of *Root Pruning*.

BARK-RINGING ON STEM OR BRANCH

The operation of "ringing" has long been familiar to cultivators of the vine in Europe, and the principle underlying the practice is made use of by gardeners in many different ways to check growth and induce fruitfulness.

A fruit tree may be accidentally ringed when we forget to remove a label which has been tied round the stem with wire, or when a rabbit gnaws right round the stem on a cold winter's night, or again, when the canker fungus gets in and girdles the stem completely.   In all three cases the nutrition of the tree is interfered with in such a way as to

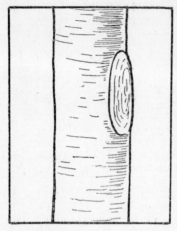

REMOVAL OF BRANCH: CUT FLUSH WITH TRUNK, SO THAT NO STUB IS LEFT.

cause a distinct decrease in growth and increase in fruit-bud formation above the ring, and the reverse tendency below the ring, in the season immediately following the ringing.

The reason for this sudden change is ascribed to the removal in the process of ringing of a complete band of bark tissue together with the living cambium cells immediately below the bark.

When only a narrow band of bark tissue is removed, for instance, by the tying round of a piece of wire or by a single incision with the edge of a knife, the check to growth lasts only for a very short time because the gap soon callouses over. But when a wide band of bark tissue is removed, the check to growth may be so severe as to cause the death of the tree. From this it may be seen that ringing is a dangerous operation and only to be used as a last resort, and when there is a reasonable chance that the gap will callous over the same season. The safest way is to remove two half-rings on opposite sides of the stem or branch a few inches apart (Fig. C, page 47). The width of the band to be removed varies with the diameter of the stem or branch to be ringed, but for safety it is probably best that the band taken out should not exceed half an inch in width (Fig. A, page 47).

In the case of an extremely vigorous young tree it is usually safe to take out a complete narrow ring provided the wound is immediately covered with adhesive tape (Fig. B, page 47). This prevents the exposed tissue from drying out and encourages rapid callousing.

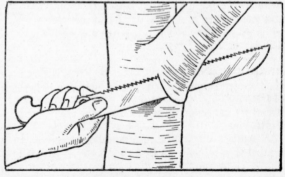

MAKING AN UNDERCUT BEFORE REMOVING A LARGE BRANCH, TO PREVENT SNAPPING.

The operation is best performed with a sharp pruning knife some time in May when the bark lifts easily from the wood.

ROOT PRUNING

The simplest form of root pruning for young trees which are growing too strongly is to dig the tree up in the winter, prune back the roots to within about 2 feet of the stem and replant. With older trees the operation is performed by digging a deep trench half-way round the tree in the winter and severing the main roots about 4 or 5 feet from the stem, completing the process the following winter round the other half of the tree.

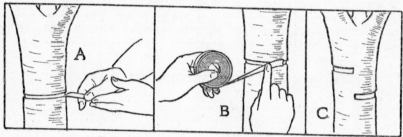

BARK-RINGING AND PROTECTING THE CUT.

When root pruning " scion-rooted " trees, it is best to dig a trench all round the tree first to discover the position of the scion roots and the condition of the original root-system. In the case of pears on quince stocks, for instance, the pear may have sent out one or two very large roots, and the quince roots may be dead. In such a case care should be taken not to root-prune too severely or the tree may lose its grip and fall down in the next high wind that blows.

THE BEST TIME TO PRUNE

In this country winter pruning of apples and pears can be carried out at any time between leaf-fall in the autumn and bud-burst in the spring, but it should not be attempted immediately before or during a severe frost.

Branch thinning of plums, cherries and other stone fruits is best done in June, July, or August, when large wounds so made are not vulnerable to the silver leaf fungus.

PRUNING AND PLANTING

There is an old controversy on this subject between those who maintain that if you do not prune the first season, the tree will make insufficient new shoot growth, and others who contend that if you do prune the first season, the tree will invariably make insufficient new root growth.

Since, in either case the question becomes important only in the case of four- or five-year-old trees which have had a large part of their root-system cut off at time of lifting, the obvious solution is to plant maidens and two-year-olds whenever possible.

Trees of this age are not at all likely to have lost a large proportion of their root-system, and it should, therefore, be quite safe to prune them at or soon after planting with the idea of getting strong new shoot growth.

When trees over three years old are bought in or transplanted, there will be a certain check whether they are pruned or not, and since the weather conditions cannot be foreseen, it seems best to leave them unpruned during the first season's growth in their new positions.

FRUITS AND THEIR METHOD OF BEARING

Fruit	On One-year-old Wood	On Wood more than One-year Old	Best Time to Prune
Apple		*	Winter and sometimes Summer
Apricot	*		Late Spring or Early Autumn
Blackberry and hybrids	*		Late Spring or Early Autumn
Cherry		*	Late Spring or Early Autumn
Cobnut		*	Winter and Summer
Currants	*		Winter and Summer (for Reds and Whites only)
Damson	*		Late Spring or Early Autumn
Fig	*		Late Spring
Filbert		*	Winter and Summer
Gooseberry	*		Late Spring or Winter
Loganberry	*		Late Spring or Autumn
Medlar		*	Winter
Mulberry		*	Winter
Nectarine	*		Late Spring and Summer
Peach	*		Late Spring and Summer
Pear		*.	Winter and Summer
Plum	*		Late Spring or Early Autumn and Summer
Quince		*	Winter
Raspberry	*		Winter and Late Spring
Veitchberry	*		Winter
Walnut	*		Late Spring or August

NOTE.—For detailed instructions for pruning the different kinds and varieties of fruit trees, see under the various headings, Apple, Pear, etc. See also Chapter V.

FRUIT THINNING

Where size of fruit is an important consideration, fruit thinning is to be recommended. Dessert apples may be spaced from 4 to 6 inches apart, and cooking apples from 6 to 9 inches. Plums on a tree which has set a very heavy crop may be spaced from 1 to 2 inches apart.

Pears of most varieties grow large enough without any thinning, but when they are to be exhibited on plates at a Show, or in the case of such small-fruited varieties as *Doyenné d'Eté*, *Fertility*, *Hessle* and *Seckle*, it is as well to thin out the young fruits, spacing them from 5 to 6 inches apart.

Hand thinning may be done by hooking the first two fingers round the fruit and pushing it gently but firmly off its stalk with the thumb.

In commercial practice, pears, plums and apples on bush or standard trees are usually thinned out some time in June.

The thinning of large-fruited gooseberries when about half an inch in diameter, will give good results in increased size of ripe fruit.

CHAPTER VI

FORMS OF FRUIT TREES

The most certain way to procure trees in any of the artificial forms is to buy them already trained from the nursery. The training of a fruit tree in any but the simplest artificial form is a comparatively long process, needing skill and experience, and trees trained in these forms are always older and more expensive than the more natural forms.

Trees which have stood in the nursery for four or five years whilst in process of training feel the shock of transplanting more than a young tree, and will need great care for a year or two after they are transplanted into their permanent quarters.

THE MORE NATURAL FORMS OF FRUIT TREE NOT NEEDING SUPPORTS

BUSH OPEN CENTRE

This form is suitable for all the hardy fruits with the possible exception of the apricot and nectarine, and may be used for all sizes of tree in garden, plantation or orchard.

Distance of planting varies from 10 to 40 feet, according to the kind and variety of fruit, the rootstock, the soil and other growth conditions.

Shaping and Pruning in Early Years.—A well-grown maiden * is cut or "headed" back in the winter to a wood bud about 30 inches above ground-level (Fig. A). Several strong shoots grow out spirally round the stem, just below the terminal bud. The following winter three or four of these shoots are selected to make a symmetrical, open, vase-shaped framework, and the remainder are cut clean out at the base. The framework branches or "leaders" are then cut hard back to within a few inches of their base to wood-buds pointing either outward or upwards, according to whether the variety is drooping or upright in its natural habit of growth (Fig. B).

Next winter the extension shoots from each of the leaders, together with any others that may be required to complete the framework of

---

* A maiden tree is one which has made a single season's growth from the bud or graft.

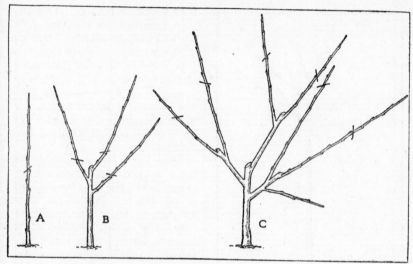

BUSH FORM: SHAPING AND TRAINING IN EARLY YEARS.

the tree, are again cut back to within 6 or 8 inches of their base (Fig. C). Shoots arising from these main branches or leaders in early years are treated differently according to the kind or variety of fruit. Notes on the pruning of these side shoots or "laterals" are given in the sections dealing with the various fruits.

DELAYED "OPEN-CENTRE"

In the Open-Centre form the main branches are trained out close together from a common point of origin on the stem known as the crotch.

The Delayed Open-Centre form differs from this in that the main branches are spaced out over a distance of from 2 to 4 feet of the stem according to the size of tree required. The chief advantage of this is that the strain of carrying the crop is not concentrated at one point as it is in the Open-Centre.

Both forms can be used for the same purposes and planted at the same distances (see diagrams and instructions given on page 52 and in Chapter VII, page 63).

As the Delayed Open-Centre form of tree, or D.O.C. as it is generally called, is now attracting considerable attention among up-to-date fruit growers, we have devoted an entire chapter (see Chapter VII), to the Forming and Training of this particular form of tree.

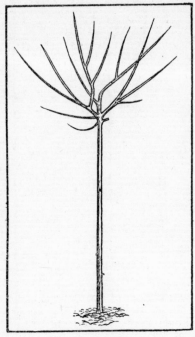

STANDARD.

HALF-STANDARD, THREE-QUARTER-STANDARD AND FULL-STANDARD OPEN-CENTRE

In the Standard forms the head of the tree is formed well above ground level at heights varying from about 4 feet 6 inches for the Half-standard, to about 7 feet for the tallest Full-standard (see diagrams).

These forms are used mainly for trees worked on vigorous rootstocks to be planted in the orchard or plantation. In general, they are not to be recommended for tree fruits in any but the largest gardens, but it is sometimes convenient to grow gooseberries and red and white currants as stand-

ards in gardens. Distances of planting for the tree fruits in the Half-standard, Three-quarter-standard and Standard forms vary from 15 to 40 feet, according to the kind and variety of fruit, rootstock, soil and other growth conditions.

Standard forms of gooseberries and currants may be planted at from 6 to 8 feet apart.

Shaping and Pruning in Early Years.—To shape the standard forms, heading back is delayed until the stem is well above the height at which the head is to be formed. During the years in

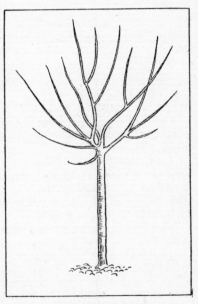

HALF-STANDARD.

which the single stem is growing to the required height the leading or extension shoot is left unpruned (Fig. A) and all side shoots are kept spurred back in winter to within an inch or two of their base (Fig. B).

This provides additional leaf area and ensures proper thickening of the stem during the nursery stage.

In the winter after the stem has reached the required height, it is headed back to the point at which it has been decided to form the head (Fig. B).

Subsequent treatment is the same as that for the bush form (Fig. C), but the hard pruning of the leaders is carried on for a considerably longer period than in the case of the bush, in order to make sure of providing a rigid framework of leading branches.

In strong-growing varieties of apples and pears the laterals on the *outside* of the tree should be left full length after a year or two.

DWARF PYRAMID

A form for apples on dwarfing stocks, which should also be suitable for certain pears on quince stock.

Distances of planting vary from 6 to 9 feet between the rows and from 3 to 9 feet between the trees in the row, according to kind and variety of fruit, stock and growth conditions.

The method of shaping and pruning has not yet been standardized, but the following method can be adapted to suit varying conditions of tree growth.

STANDARD: SHAPING AND PRUNING IN EARLY YEARS.

Shaping and Pruning in Early Years.—A maiden tree, preferably without " feathers," is planted in the autumn, and cut back the following spring to a bud about 30 inches above ground level (Fig. A, page 54). At the end of the first season's growth the terminal bud should have

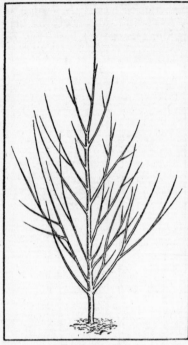

PYRAMID.

developed into a strong shoot growing vertically upwards. This extension shoot should be cut back in winter to about one-half its length. In the summer, four or five strong lateral shoots should have grown out spirally round the stem. These are cut back in the winter to a bud on the under side of each shoot, about 5 or 6 inches from their base. The tree should then appear as in Fig. B. The following summer any strong maiden lateral shoots arising from the original four or five side branches should be summer-pruned, cutting each back to a leaf about 5 or 6 inches from the base of the shoot in July. In the following winter the central leader extension shoot is again cut back by about a half, and the terminal extension shoots on the original side branches are also cut back to an under bud about 5 or 6 inches from their base. Should any secondary shoots have grown out from the summer-pruned laterals, these should be cut right back in winter to the point from which they came.

During the summer a second tier of side branches should have grown out spirally round the stem above the first tier, and these should be treated in the same way.

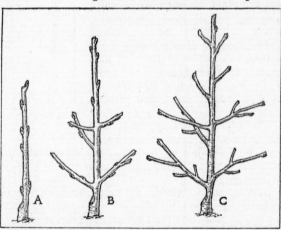

PYRAMID: SHAPING AND TRAINING IN EARLY YEARS.

ARTIFICIAL FORMS OF TREES REQUIRING SUPPORTS

SUPPORTS

Special galvanized fittings can be bought with straining bolts and nuts for each end, and intermediate eyes to fix along each line of wire. On walls, these fixtures may be driven into the cement between the bricks, or two-inch-wide wooden battens may be fixed upright to the wall at intervals of 12 to 15 feet, to which the wires may be fastened. Where there is no wall or fence, the wires are carried on iron or wooden posts, which should be bedded firmly in the ground. The straining wire, 12 or 13 gauge, should be galvanized, and is fastened horizontally to the uprights at distances varying with the type of training to be adopted.

Vertical and oblique branches of artificially-trained trees are usually tied to bamboo canes in order to keep them rigidly in position and to prevent rubbing against the wire. The canes may be fastened to the supports with thin wire or with paper-covered wire, and the branches fastened to the canes with soft fillis-string, or with raffia. If trees are tied direct to the wire, great care should be taken to prevent chafing as this may cause canker in apples and pears, and gumming in stone fruits. The ties should be examined yearly in the winter, after winter washing, and should be either re-tied or replaced with a new tie.

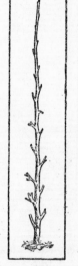

SINGLE VERTICAL
CORDON.

SINGLE CORDON

This form consists of a single-stemmed tree trained in a vertical, oblique, or horizontal position. It is used mainly for apple and pear trees, and sometimes for gooseberries and red and white currants. The trees are planted in rows 6 to 9 feet apart, the distance between the trees in the row varying from 2 to 3 feet for vertical and oblique cordons, and from 10 to 20 feet for horizontal cordons, according to circumstances.*

Shaping and Pruning in Early Years (Single Cordon).—A maiden tree, either clean stemmed or feathered, forms the cordon and no shaping is required for this form. The central leader extension shoot should require no pruning, at any rate in early years, but if the young tree makes abnormally weak growth, it would be wise to prune the leader, shortening it by about one-half.

* Gooseberry and Currant vertical and oblique cordons should be spaced one foot apart in the row.

All lateral shoots arising from the stem should be summer-pruned from the first season.

The most usual method of summer pruning cordons is to cut the laterals back to a leaf 5 or 6 inches from the base when they are about 12 inches long. (See section on Summer Pruning, page 42.)

Training of Single Oblique Cordons.—The tree is planted in a vertical position and allowed to grow thus for one season.

(If the tree is on a very dwarfing rootstock it can be planted at an angle of 45 degrees.)   A bamboo cane is then fixed to the horizontal wires at an angle of 45 degrees, and the tree is tied to the cane in its new position, keeping the stem straight throughout its whole length.

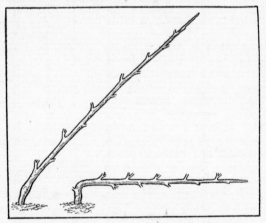

TRAINING OBLIQUE AND HORIZONTAL CORDONS.

The tree should be kept at this angle until the leading shoot has reached the top of the wire, about 6½ feet above ground level.

After that, the tree is untied, the position of the cane is adjusted to a slightly more horizontal position, and the whole tree is then bent down and tied to the cane.   In this new position the tree is allowed to continue until the leading shoot again reaches the top wire, when yet another alteration must be made in the position of the cane and tree.

The object of bringing the whole tree gradually down into a more and more horizontal position in this way (see diagram), keeping the stem always in a straight line, is to keep the balance between growth and cropping.

If the tree is allowed to bend in the middle or near the top, there will be too much growth in one part of the tree, and all the fruit will come in the other.

DOUBLE VERTICAL CORDON OR SIMPLE U-FORM

This form is suitable for apples and pears, in garden or plantation, and for gooseberries and red currants in gardens.

Apples and pears grown in this form should be planted at 6 to 9 feet between the rows, and at from 5 to 6 feet between the trees in the row.

Shaping and Pruning in Early Years.—The single maiden shoot is headed back to a bud 12 or 15 inches above ground level. During the following summer the top two shoots are trained out horizontally to right and left on canes to a length of from 6 to 8 inches, after which each is bent round into an upright position and allowed to grow up vertically (see diagram, page 58).

In the winter the two leading shoots are pruned back, removing about one-third of the growth of each to an upward bud. The next year these leading shoots are again allowed to grow unrestricted through the season, being tied in to upright canes as they grow.

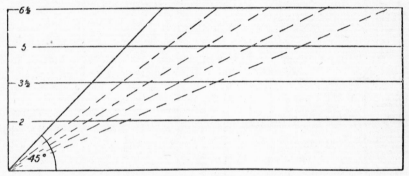

SHOWING SUCCESSIVE POSITIONS FOR OBLIQUE CORDONS.

The following winter both leaders are again tipped, the degree of severity of tipping being regulated in accordance with the vigour of their growth. Meanwhile all side shoots are spurred back in the normal way.

TRIPLE VERTICAL CORDON OR GRID IRON

This form is suitable for apples on dwarfing stocks, pear on quince or pear, gooseberries and red currants.

Shaping and Pruning in Early Years.—The single maiden shoot is headed back to a bud pointing vertically upwards, 12 to 15 inches above ground level, care having been taken in planting the maiden tree to see that there was such a bud in the required position. When the terminal bud and the buds immediately below it, on the right and left, have each made about 6 inches of growth, the terminal shoot is trained vertically upwards by tying it to a cane, while the other two are tied out either horizontally or better still to two canes bent

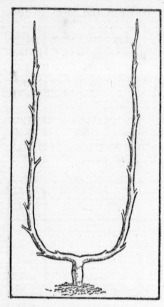

DOUBLE VERTICAL CORDON.

each in the shape of a bow. If the central shoot grows much more vigorously than the other two, the tip should be pinched out when it is about 2 feet long. At the end of the growing season, the two side branches are untied and trained more or less vertically, equidistant from and parallel to the central shoot and at a distance of from 6 to 8 inches from it. In the winter all three leaders are tipped by between one-third and one-half their length. Subsequent treatment is the same as for Double Cordons.

ESPALIER *

This is one of the most popular forms for apples and pears grown in borders in the garden, and is also used for red and white currants and for gooseberries.

Apples on dwarfing and semi-dwarfing stocks should make suitable-sized espalier trees for most varieties. For all but weak-growing varieties of pear, Quince A should be a strong enough stock; but weak growers ought to be on pear stock. Distances of planting for apple and pear espaliers vary from 6 to 8 feet between the rows, and from 15 to 20 feet between the trees in the row, according to conditions.

Espaliers are trained on walls, fences, or wires in two,

* "Espalier" is the French word for a paling or fence.

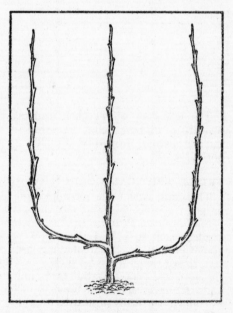

TRIPLE CORDON.

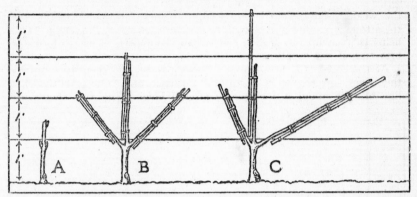

ESPALIER: SHAPING IN EARLY YEARS. FIG. I.

three, four, or five tiers according to the space available, the tiers being about one foot apart.

Shaping and Pruning in Early Years (Espaliers).—A maiden tree, preferably clean stemmed, without feathers, is cut back shortly after planting to a bud about 15 inches above ground level, at a point at which two well-developed buds are visible close together, a few inches below the terminal, one on each side of the stem (Fig. I.A above). During the first season, the central leader extension shoot developing from the terminal bud is trained vertically upwards by tying it to a cane fixed in that position on the wires. Meanwhile the shoots growing from the two buds below the terminal are trained out to right and left.

In order to encourage them to grow strongly, they are not trained horizontally during their first season, but are tied, as they grow, to canes fixed to the wires at an angle of about 45 degrees (Fig. I.B). If any other shoots grow out from the main stem, their tips are pinched out when they are about 5 inches long, and any secondary growths from these are pinched out when they are about an inch long. Should the two shoots to right and left of the central leader grow unevenly,

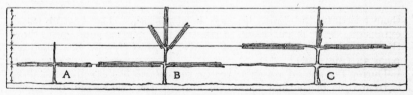

ESPALIER: SHAPING IN EARLY YEARS. FIG. 2.

the weaker shoot should be raised to a more vertical position, and the stronger one lowered to a more horizontal position (Fig. 1.C). This helps to even up the growth of the two shoots, which are to form the first tier of the espalier.

. At the end of the first season's growth, these two shoots are untied, the canes lowered to a horizontal position, and retied to the first line of wire about a foot above ground level. The two shoots are

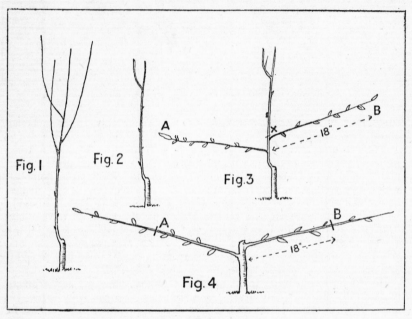

FAN.

FIG. 1.—Maiden Peach (1 year from bud or graft).
FIG. 2.—First winter pruning.
FIG. 3.—When (A and B) are 8–9 inches long in early summer cut out middle at x.
FIG. 4.—Second winter pruning cut at A and B.

then retied to the canes in their new position. The central leader extension shoot is cut back to an upward-pointing bud just above the second wire, about 2 feet above ground level. See diagram, page 59 (Fig. 2.A).

During the second season's growth, the central leader extension shoot is treated as in the first season, as also are the two second-tier shoots growing out just below it (Fig. 2.B, page 59). Any new laterals which

grow out from the first-
tier shoots are generally
summer-pruned (see sec-
tion on Summer Pruning,
page 42).

At the end of the
second season the second-
tier shoots are lowered to
a horizontal position, and
retied on their canes along
the second wire. The
central leader extension
shoot is again cut back as
in the previous winter

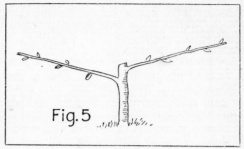

FAN.
After second winter pruning.

(Fig. 2.C, page 59). By this method the espalier can be trained to the
number of tiers required, taking one season to build each new tier.

FAN

This form is used mainly for the stone fruits trained on walls, at
distances of from 12 to 20 feet apart according to kind and variety
of fruit. The following is one of various methods used for shaping
and pruning in early years.

Shaping and Pruning in Early Years (Fan).—The maiden tree
as soon as it is
planted, should
be " tipped " by
cutting off the
top few inches to
a bud (see dia-
gram, page 60,
Fig. 2). As the
remaining buds
start to break in
the spring, they
are removed
until only two
strong buds are
left about 12
inches above the
"union." When
these two buds
have each made
about 18 inches
of shoot growth

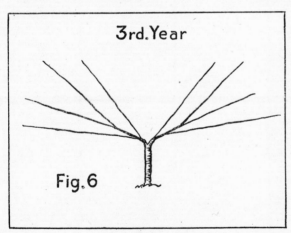

FAN.
At end of the third year : Four growths each side along
canes. (See also diagram of the Fan-trained tree at the
end of four years' growth, page 206.)

(Fig. 3, page 60), the main stem of the tree above them is carefully cut out. The two side branches are then tied out to canes, inclined at an angle of 45 degrees from the horizontal, one on each side of the main stem (Fig. 4, page 60).

In the winter these side branches are each cut back to a bud about 7 inches from the main stem (Fig. 5, page 61).

During the following summer four framework branches are allowed to grow from each of the two side branches (Fig. 6, page 61). These branches are cut back in the winter, each to a triple bud, to a length of from 2 to 2½ feet of well-ripened wood. The framework of the fan is thus completed in three seasons from the time of planting.

On page 206 will be found a diagram of the fan-trained tree at the end of four years' growth.

For pruning and disbudding of established fan trees, see page 206.

CHAPTER VII

FORMING AND TRAINING

THE " DELAYED OPEN-CENTRE " TREE

In recent years a form of tree that has come to be known as the " Delayed Open-Centre " or " D.O.C." has attracted the attention of our fruit-growers, and many acres, comprising apples, pears, plums, and cherries are now devoted to the system.

FORM OF TREE

As the term " Delayed Open-Centre " suggests, this form has something in common with the ordinary open centre. In the early stages of developing the D.O.C. a centre stem is purposely kept in, and from it shoots are formed that eventually become the main branches. These branches are spaced out over a length of centre stem which may be anything from 2 to 4 feet according to the size of tree required (see Fig. 1). Big trees may have a longer stem than dwarf trees, whereas in the open-

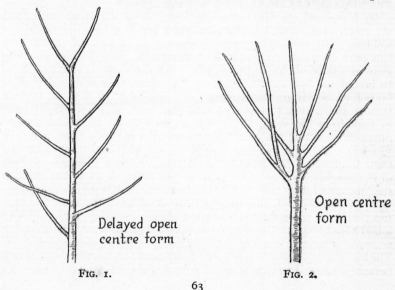

Delayed open centre form

Open centre form

FIG. 1.

FIG. 2.

centre tree all the branches have more or less a common point of origin
at the top of the stem (see Fig. 2, page 63). With D.O.C. trees, when
the grower decides that no further extension of the centre stem is needed,
all the young branches are directed outwards, away from the centre,
as in the open-centre system.

SPECIAL FEATURES

The special features of the D.O.C. that attract growers to the system
are as follows :

(1) The trees are strong. This is because all the shoots that are
chosen as branches come out at a wide angle to the main stem, and
these are strong by nature. Further, since the branches are spaced out
over a length of centre stem, it follows that the strain of carrying crops
is not concentrated at one point as is the case with open-centre trees.

(2) Big trees are formed quickly because little is pruned away in the
early years.

(3) A good supply of blossom buds is readily formed because the
branches lie almost flat, and are therefore well-supplied with light.

(4) Young growth is more evenly distributed over the entire surface
of flat branches than in branches that are vertically inclined.

(5) Low-lying branches may be removed without detriment to the
tree as a whole.

PRUNING TREATMENT FOR MAIDEN TREES

(a) *Non-Feathered Maidens.*—The lowest branches of all bush trees
are usually formed at a height of about 2 feet to 2 feet 6 inches above
soil level. In open-centre bush trees young shoots that are required for
this purpose are generally obtained as a result of shortening the single
stem of a maiden tree to this height. For D.O.C. trees it is preferable
to obtain the two lowest shoots by " notching " directly above those
buds from which growth is wanted. " Notching " is done at pruning
time in the dormant season by removing a small wedge-shaped piece
of bark from the stem, about half an inch above the selected buds.
Supposing one bud has been selected, and the notching done, it is wise
to select the second bud on the opposite side of the stem, at about the
same height from the ground (see Fig. 3). When a shoot on one side
of the tree has been matched by a corresponding shoot on the opposite
side, the initial steps have been taken to provide a balance in the arrangement of branches. Continuing with the pruning of the same tree, the
top portion of the stem should be completely cut away, directly above
a bud about 6 to 9 inches higher up the stem than where the notching
is done. This bud (see Fig. 4 (1)) is likely to grow more or less erect.
The bud directly below this (see Fig. 4 (2)) should be completely removed,
because if allowed to grow it would form a shoot that would be too erect

for a suitable branch. Supposing buds three and four come at right angles to the two notched buds (see Figs. 4 and 5), and they can easily do this if carefully selected, no further pruning need be done at this stage. But should either of these buds be found to occupy a position *directly above* either of the notched buds, it should be removed to prevent a shoot being formed where one is not wanted. Where one bud is removed for this reason, it is more than likely that the next bud to it will be found to occupy a position more or less at right angles to the notched buds, and a shoot will be formed where one is wanted. Thus provision is made for the development of five shoots, the top one to continue the extension of the centre stem, and the other four to form side shoots. These four side-shoots are spaced over a short stem and they are held roughly at right angles to each other.

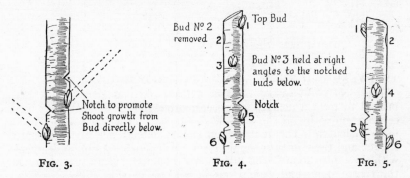

FIG. 3.   FIG. 4.   FIG. 5.

With half-standard and standard trees the lowest branches will be wanted at about 4 to 6 feet respectively above soil level, and no pruning will be done to the centre stem until it has reached the required height. The pruning will then be identical with that described for bush trees.

(*b*) *Feathered Maidens.*—Some maiden trees have, in addition to the erect centre stem, one or more side shoots ; such trees are spoken of as "feathered maidens," the side shoots being referred to as "feathers" (see Fig. 6, page 66). When two or more feathers occur at suitable positions they may be used to form principal branches. Such trees should be regarded as the equivalent of two-year-old trees, and should be pruned according to the description given on page 66. Feathers that occur too low down on the stem to serve as branches should be removed. Feathers on one side of the stem only and which, if retained, would give rise to unbalanced branch formation, should also be removed (see Fig. 7, page 66). Where all the feathers are removed from a tree, leaving a single erect stem, the tree should be pruned as already described for non-feathered maidens.

F.G.H.   E

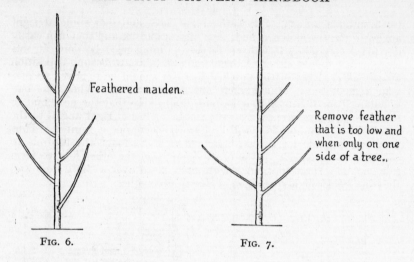

Feathered maiden.

Remove feather that is too low and when only on one side of a tree.

FIG. 6.　　　　　　　　FIG. 7.

TWO-YEAR-OLD TREES AND FEATHERED MAIDENS

The ideal two-year-old bush or a feathered maiden that has been pruned to form a delayed open-centre tree should consist of an erect centre stem with three to six side shoots, each of which is 18 inches or more in length. The centre stem should extend well above the side shoots, and these in turn should form a wide angle—45 to 60 degrees—with the centre stem. The side shoots should be evenly spaced around the centre stem, and should not be all on one side.

It is hardly to be expected that every two-year-old tree will be the ideal picture-book specimen; there will in fact be all kinds, from those with very poor growth to those with an excessive number of vigorous side shoots. And some may be two-year-old trees originally intended for open centres, but which are to be trained as D.O.C. trees.

PRUNING TREATMENT

(a) *Treatment of Side Shoots.*—When there are plenty of side shoots, any number of these up to six may be chosen to form branches. None of these should lie directly over, or point in identically the same direction as any of the others. Two shoots, one on one side, and one on the opposite side, should be chosen to form the lowest pair of branches; higher up the stem a second pair should be chosen, held between the first pair so that the four shoots are roughly at right angles to each other. The remaining pair should point in directions in between the right angles formed by the first two pairs (see Fig. 8). For preference, all the selected shoots should be held at a wide angle to the main stem.

All side shoots in excess of those selected to become branches should be removed. It is hardly likely that all the side shoots will be the same length, even on the same tree. When one shoot is shortened, the corresponding one on the opposite side of the main stem should be shortened to leave it the same length. When a pair of wide-angled shoots are more than 18 inches long they should be reduced to a length of from 12 to 15 inches by pruning them to buds pointing in the direction in which further extensional growth is required (see Fig. 9, page 68). Shoots that are less than 18 inches long will be left from 3 to 12 inches long after pruning. In general, the longer shoots are to begin with, the longer they should be left after pruning. The exception to this rule is when one shoot is much longer than its corresponding opposite one. In such cases the longer of the two shoots should be pruned more severely and left shorter than the weaker one.

As a rule, the more erect-growing side shoots should be completely removed, but there are occasions when one or more will be retained, for instance, when there are only erect ones to select from. This often happens in the case of the two-year-old " cut-back," that is a tree that has had its centre stem cut back at the end of its first growing season with a view to forming an ordinary open centre. These erect shoots will only form satisfactory branches provided that future extension

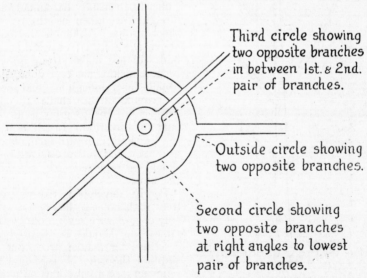

Third circle showing
two opposite branches
in between 1st. & 2nd.
pair of branches.

Outside circle showing
two opposite branches.

Second circle showing
two opposite branches
at right angles to lowest
pair of branches.

FIG. 8.—DIAGRAM SHOWING ARRANGEMENT OF SHOOTS.

shoots from them take a more outward direction. To effect this a suitable outward-facing bud on each erect shoot will be chosen, but the actual pruning will be done at a point one or two buds higher up the stem. All buds above the selected outward facing ones should be prevented from forming strong growths by "nicking." This is an old trick, long known to gardeners, and consists of pressing the edge of the pruning knife through the bark and well into the wood, below the base of the bud (see Fig. 10). It is well known that young shoots tend to grow in the direction from which they receive most light. When an

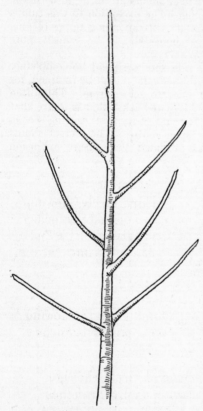

erect-growing shoot is pruned so that an outward-facing bud is left right at the top, it usually grows in an outward direction for the first inch or two, but after this it grows more vertically. The whole shoot would grow in an outward direction provided it derived most of its daylight from the side rather than from above. When the pruning is done so that one or two buds are left above an outward-facing bud, overhead shade is provided sufficient to ensure that an outward direction is taken as the young shoot grows. Although the buds above the selected outward-facing bud will not make strong growth because nicking has been done, they usually form enough leaf and shoot to provide further shade, thereby helping to ensure growth in the outward direction. In addition to the "nicking," inward-facing buds, near a selected outward-facing bud, should be removed—cut out with the knife.

Poorly developed two-year-old trees with no side shoots, or with only one, or with several, all on the same side, should be treated as described for maiden trees, but in addition the side shoots should be removed (see instructions on pages 64–66).

FIG. 9.—TWO-YEAR TREE AFTER PRUNING.

Three pairs of opposite shoots 12–18 inches long.

(*b*) *Treatment of Centre Stem.*—The centre stem should be from 6 to 12 inches taller than the tallest side shoot after pruning.   Normally, as a result of the pruning, three or four young shoots may be expected from buds directly below the point of pruning.   If side shoots are wanted from buds lower down than this, notching as suggested for maiden trees, should be practised (see Fig. 3, page 65). Some growers will prefer to have a tall centre stem over which the branches are formed, whereas others will prefer a short one.   If a tall centre stem is favoured, bud number one, at the top, will be left to continue its extension growth, and bud number two from the top will be removed as in the case of the maiden tree.

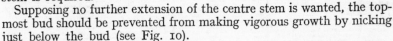

FIG. 10.—NICKING.

Edge of knife pressed beneath top of bud "nicking" to prevent extensional growth.
Bud required to make extensional growth in a more outward direction.

The same treatment will be applied whether a tree be two, three, four, or five years old, depending on how tall a centre stem is required.

Supposing no further extension of the centre stem is wanted, the topmost bud should be prevented from making vigorous growth by nicking just below the bud (see Fig. 10).

This treatment is advised so that most of the young growth will be made by lower buds in an outward direction, thus forming an open-centre head.   In the main a short centre stem should be preferred to a tall one.

YOUNG TREES OVER TWO YEARS OLD

A well-grown D.O.C. tree will consist of a centre stem with a number of newly formed wide-angle branches and branch-forming shoots.   The lower branches will be two or more years old, and these may have divided to produce further branches and young shoots.   The youngest branches will be at the top and at this stage they may only be wide-angled branch-forming shoots selected because they do not lie directly above neighbouring branches.

There will be no further extension of the centre stem, and all vigorous erect central shoots will have been removed as in an open-centre tree. Strong-growing trees will have made a good supply of young shoots, both principal and branch-forming ones, i.e., "leaders," and side shoots, i.e., "maiden laterals," whereas weak-growing trees will have a poor supply of young shoots.

PRUNING TREATMENT

General Treatment.—When a tree is three to five years old, young branches have been formed, and these have on them young shoots and spurs. A pruning treatment should be given that takes into account the varied functions and requirements of these branches, shoots and spurs. When branches are shaded they are usually unproductive, since plenty of light is required by the spur leaves for blossom bud formation. The main object of the pruning treatment is, therefore, to provide every branch with plenty of space and light in order to ensure blossom bud formation, and sufficient room for the production of young side shoots or "maiden laterals."

In practice, when one branch or shoot trespasses over another, so that rubbing or extreme shading occurs, one of them should be shortened or completely removed. Blossom buds are readily formed on young shoots when they are left unpruned, provided they are well supplied with light (see Figs. 11 to 16). One of the main points to remember is that *reliance for the supply of blossom bud should be placed upon side shoots that are left unpruned.* In view of this it is evident that the branches should be well spaced, first, to provide enough room for side shoots, and secondly, that these side shoots should be well supplied with light. Young shoots are readily formed when severe pruning is practised. It is well known that when existing shoots are severely pruned back during winter, the tree reacts by sending out more side shoots. It is not enough to shorten side shoots with the idea of making more room so that two branches may remain near together, since this would lead to even more crowding the next season ; the correct treatment would be to remove one of the branches. The general principle underlying the treatment of "maiden laterals" is to ensure ample space and light to each of them by restricting their number on any one main branch. Once this has been done, some will be shortened so that a further supply of young shoots is ensured for the next season, and the

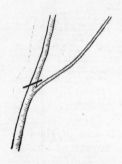

FIG. 11.—BRANCHES THAT ARE TOO TALL SHOULD BE SHORTENED TO A SUITABLE SIDE SHOOT.

FIG. 12.—BRANCHES THAT CROSS OVER OR RUB AGAINST OTHERS SHOULD BE SHORTENED OR REMOVED.

remainder will be left unpruned so that blossom buds can form on them. The detailed treatment of side shoots is dealt with later (see Treatment of Maiden Laterals). For strong-growing trees of the apple varieties *Bramley's Seedling, Blenheim Orange, Newton Wonder, Worcester Pearmain*, and others like them that are normally slow to yield much blossom bud, no further pruning is required once the branches and young shoots are well spaced and all tall erect-growing shoots near to the main stem have been removed. Trees that have made very little growth usually produce blossom buds in large numbers, and the pruning of such trees should consist mainly of removing blossom buds in the hope that better growth will result. It is doubtful, with trees so young, whether pruning alone will succeed ; improvements in manuring, cultivation, or drainage may be necessary first.

FIG. 13.—ALSO THOSE THAT LIE NEAR AND PARALLEL WITH OTHER BRANCHES.

TREATMENT FOR BRANCH FORMATION

In varieties such as *Cox's Orange Pippin* and *Fertility* pear, which produce whippy growth, leading shoots that are wanted for the extension of branches, or " leaders " as they are called, should be shortened every year. The pruning cuts should be made at positions where future new growth is wanted, and this usually involves removing from one-third to one-half of their " maiden " growth. Once the branches are long enough, i.e., when no further extension growth is required from them, the pruning or " tipping " of leaders at their extreme ends should cease.

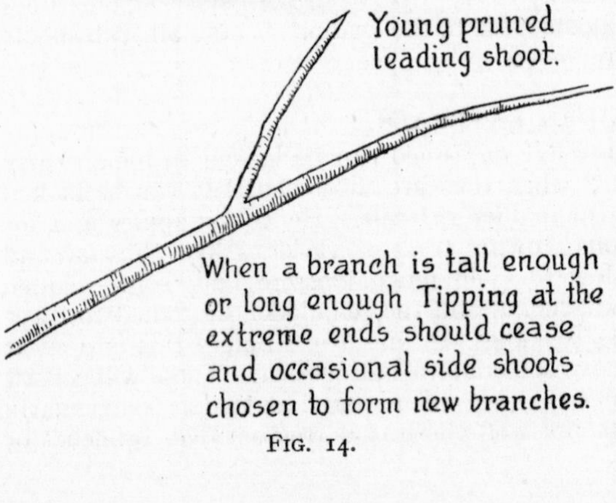

Young pruned leading shoot.

When a branch is tall enough or long enough Tipping at the extreme ends should cease and occasional side shoots chosen to form new branches.

FIG. 14.

As trees increase in size, and the branches are pulled lower by crops, occasional erect-growing side shoots may be selected to take on the rôle of leaders (see Fig. 14).

These new leaders should be shortened as suggested above, so that new branches are formed from the original branches. Thus although the pruning of leaders at the extreme end of branches that are sufficiently long ceases at this stage, it continues to be done where new branches are being formed. Care should be taken not to introduce too many branches at this stage of a tree's development ; this will be avoided if, when pruning, care is taken to ensure that the tips of the leaders are at least 12 inches apart. By the time the trees are five years old, it is wise to increase this distance to 18 inches. It is important that leading shoots should be evenly dispersed around a tree, and they should be so pruned that a balanced branch formation results. Stated another way, there should be as many leaders on one side of a tree as on the other, and although some will be taller than others, both taller and

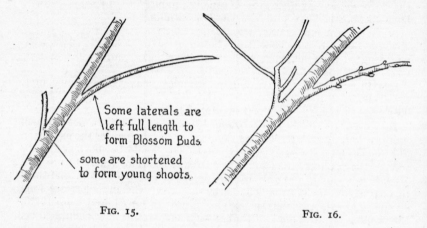

Some laterals are left full length to form Blossom Buds.

some are shortened to form young shoots.

Fig. 15.

Fig. 16.

shorter ones should be evenly divided between both sides. Sometimes there are tall vigorous shoots close to the leading shoots ; all such shoots should be completely removed.

TREATMENT OF MAIDEN LATERALS

Young laterals that are left unpruned can be looked to for an early supply of blossom buds ; when they are shortened they can be looked to for a further supply of maiden laterals. Hence for apples and for pears (excepting vigorous-growing trees of varieties like *Bramley* and *Worcester*, which are slow to yield much blossom bud) some maiden laterals should be left unpruned, and the remainder shortened to leave them 2 to 3 inches long (see Figs. 15 and 16). Before this is done it will be necessary to remove some laterals altogether. These will consist of the erect vigorous ones that are not required as leaders, particularly those close to leading shoots, and those that trespass over branches or

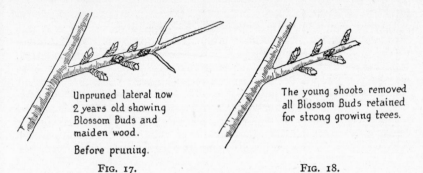

Unpruned lateral now
2 years old showing
Blossom Buds and
maiden wood.

Before pruning.

FIG. 17.

The young shoots removed
all Blossom Buds retained
for strong growing trees.

FIG. 18.

other shoots, thereby causing rubbing or extreme shading. Although
it is usual to remove shoots of the latter category, they may be shortened
provided there is reasonable expectation that subsequent shoot growth
from them will not give rise to a similar fault.

When trees are making a lot of growth, more laterals should be left
unpruned than for trees of moderate vigour.

In the former case two should be left unpruned for every one that
is shortened, and in the latter case every alternate lateral should be
shortened, and the intermediate ones should be left unpruned.

TREATMENT OF OLDER LATERALS

In the case of strong-growing trees, supposing blossom buds and young
shoots are formed on laterals that have been left unpruned (see Fig. 17),
the young shoots at the extreme end of each lateral should be removed
and the blossom buds retained (see Fig. 18). To trees of moderate
vigour a similar treatment should be given, retaining a smaller number
of blossom buds, say not more than three or four. All blossom buds
in excess of this number will be pruned away with the young shoots
(see Fig. 19).

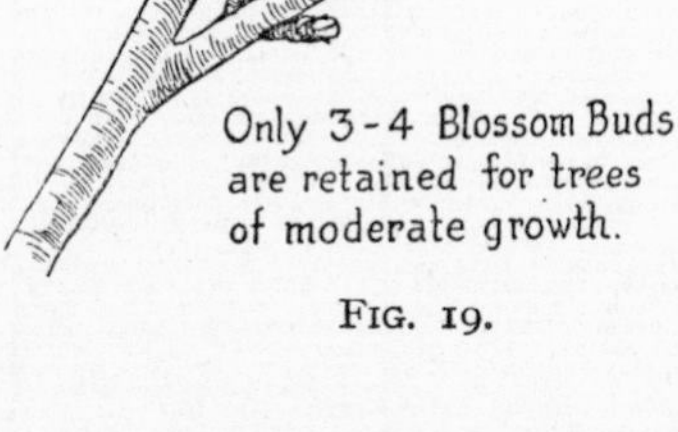

Only 3 - 4 Blossom Buds
are retained for trees
of moderate growth.

FIG. 19.

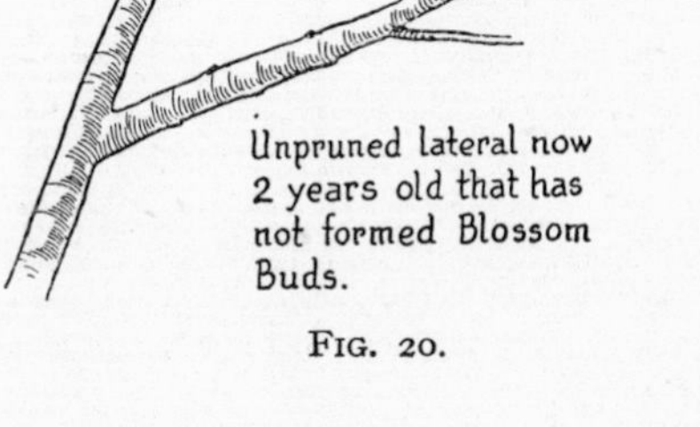

Unpruned lateral now
2 years old that has
not formed Blossom
Buds.

FIG. 20.

MATURE TREES

Having secured the principal branches, the main concern of the pruning technique is to obtain productive crops regularly. In order to do this branches should be suitably separated from neighbouring branches so that no one branch is unduly shaded. Furthermore, it is necessary to have an annual succession of blossom buds, and to make this possible a regular supply of young shoots is needed each season.

(a) *Treatment of Branches.*—Each branch should have a definite position on a tree, and because of this individual branches should be removed or shortened when they cross over, rub, or lie near, and parallel (i.e., within 1 foot) to other branches (see Figs. 11 to 13). Branches

FIG. 21.—FOR WEAK-GROWING TREES IT IS WISE TO SHORTEN DRASTICALLY BY SEVERAL FEET TWO OR THREE OF THE MAIN BRANCHES.

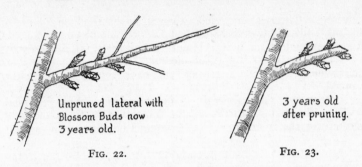

Unpruned lateral with
Blossom Buds now
3 years old.

FIG. 22.

3 years old
after pruning.

FIG. 23.

that are too low should be removed, and those that are too tall shortened
to a suitable side branch.   Once a branch begins to bend outwards, it is
usually wise to select an upward growing side shoot and shorten it so
that a new branch is being formed in readiness to take the place of the
older one.   Maiden shoots should also be chosen for the extension of the
main branches, and these should be shortened each season until they are
tall enough or long enough.   This applies particularly to varieties that
have slender and whippy shoots.   No leader pruning of this kind should
be practised on strong-growing trees of sorts that have sturdy shoots.
These, so long as they are vigorous, only require a bare minimum of
branch pruning.   For weak-growing trees it is wise drastically to shorten
by several feet two or three of the main branches, a practice spoken of
as " partial dehorning " (see Fig. 21).

(b) *Treatment of Maiden Laterals.*—The question as to whether some
of the side shoots should be shortened or not depends on vigour and
variety.   For most varieties it is necessary to provide for a regular
seasonal supply of young shoots, and to ensure this a certain number
of maiden laterals should be cut back every winter to within 2 or 3 inches
of their base.   Strong-growing trees of varieties that are normally slow
to yield blossom, and that produce a sturdy type of young shoot, such
as *Bramley's Seedling* apple, produce enough laterals of their own
accord, and on them no cutting back of maiden laterals is necessary.
Strong-growing trees of most varieties and weaker-growing trees of
varieties such as Bramley, should have one-third of their maiden
laterals cut back.   Most trees of medium and poor vigour should
have one-half of the maiden laterals shortened.   For trees in this
category the treatment of the spur systems (see page 76) is more
important since there is invariably a shortage of laterals.   On early
cooking apples such as *Early Victoria* (*Emneth Early*), from which very
large fruits are wanted early in the summer, making it necessary to
keep the vigorous state of growth, at least two-thirds of the maiden
laterals should be cut back.   On all trees strong maiden laterals close

to the selected leader, and erect-growing shoots near the main stem, commonly called "water shoots," should be completely removed by cutting them out at the base. Finally, on all trees, in order to provide for a regular seasonal supply of blossom bud, those maiden laterals which remain and have not been cut back should be left entirely unpruned.

(c) *Treatment of Older Laterals.*—Once blossom buds have formed on laterals, a shortening process should commence in the same way as suggested for the treatment of older laterals on three- to five-year-old

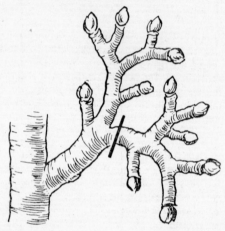

Fig. 24.—Spur Systems should not be left with more than 4–6 Blossom Buds on each.

trees. Once laterals are about four years old they should be drastically shortened to leave them 6 to 9 inches long for the purpose of stimulating a further supply of "maiden laterals."

(d) *Treatment of Spur Systems.*—Spurs that have become branched, forming two or more, are referred to as "spur systems." When large fruits are wanted early in the season, no spur system should be allowed to retain more than two blossom buds. This also applies to weak-growing trees when a restoration to more normal vigour is required. On no kind of apple or pear tree should the spur system be allowed to retain more than from four to six blossom buds (see Fig. 24).

Note.—For a full description of his modern pruning methods the reader should consult *The Pruning of Apples and Pears by Renewal Methods*, by C. R. Thompson, published by Faber and Faber.

CHAPTER VIII

PLANNING AND PLANTING

PLANNING

MANURIAL REQUIREMENTS OF DIFFERENT FRUITS

In planning the layout of a new piece of ground, whether for fruit-garden, plantation or orchard, consideration should be given in the first place to the broad distinction in the manurial requirements of different fruits to which attention has already been drawn in Chapter III.

The stone fruits and black currants, which are going to require a lot of nitrogenous manure and relatively small dressings of potash, should be planted in one part of the garden or orchard. Cooking apples, pears, strawberries, raspberries, loganberries, blackberries, red currants, gooseberries and cobnuts, all of which require regular dressings of both potash and nitrogen, should be planted in another part, whilst dessert apples, which will require heavy regular dressings of potash and very little nitrogen in the early years, ought to be planted by themselves in a place where, if necessary, grass can be sown to reduce the supply of nitrogen available to the tree roots.

SPRAYING REQUIREMENTS OF DIFFERENT FRUITS

Consideration should next be given to the spraying requirements of the fruit. Apart from the general importance of having an adequate supply of water for spraying in the immediate neighbourhood, there are particular factors to be considered in this connection.

Winter and Early Spring Sprays.—Any one of the tar-oils, petroleum-oils, or di-nitro-cresol sprays will burn the foliage of tender herbaceous plants, and if it comes into contact with such vegetables as cabbages and lettuces it will impart an unpleasant flavour to them. If fruit trees are planted to form the background for a herbaceous border or are interplanted with tender-leaved vegetables, they cannot be sprayed in the winter without injuring the under crop. Tar-oil wash discolours grass also for a time, but does no lasting injury to it.

Another point in connection with the use of tar-oil sprays is that there are a few fruits, such as the cherry-plum (Myrobolan), the strawberry, the cobnut and the filbert, which are susceptible to damage by these sprays when used at the strengths usually recommended for other fruits. This means that these fruits should be planted by themselves whenever possible.

Lime-sulphur.—This spray plays a very important part in protecting the trees and bushes from certain fungus diseases and insect pests, and although less injurious to tender-leaved plants than tar-oil, it does burn the foliage of flowers and vegetables to a certain extent. So far as possible, therefore, when planning the fruit layout, provision should be made for the use of these sprays under conditions which will not cause damage to other plants.

There are certain varieties of fruits, the leaves of which are specially susceptible to damage when sprayed with lime-sulphur, and care should be taken to plant " sulphur-shy " varieties of this kind in situations where they can receive special spray treatment.

When gooseberries are to be picked in the young tender stage, they should not be grown between tree fruits which are to be sprayed with lime-sulphur, because the deposit of lime-sulphur remains on the fruits, and although perfectly harmless, is likely to spoil their appearance.

POLLINATION

When planning the layout, it must be remembered that the flowers of some varieties of certain fruits are self-sterile and require the presence in the near neighbourhood of other varieties of the same fruit which flower at the same time, from which the pollen may be easily carried by insects to cross-pollinate the sterile flowers.

Notable examples of self-sterility in this sense are the *Doyenné du Comice* pear, the *Cox's Orange Pippin* apple, the *Coe's Golden Drop* plum and *Early Rivers* cherry. Moreover, many varieties, including these four, appear to set better with the pollen of some varieties than with that of others.

Obviously, such difficulties are best prevented by careful planning in the first place, but when the problem turns up in established trees it can best be got over by top-grafting one or two trees with a pollinating variety, or more locally still, by grafting one or two branches of each self-sterile tree with scions from a pollinator variety, by one of the methods described in Chapter IV.

TIME OF BLOSSOMING

In choosing pollinator varieties, time of flowering is important, but since most varieties overlap each other in their flowering periods, it is only in the case of very early blossomers planted with very late ones that difficulties of this kind are likely to arise.

It is, however, important when planning the layout to remember that cross-pollination has a two-fold aspect ; the flowering period of the pollinator must overlap and its pollen must be of a sort which will successfully cross-pollinate the self-sterile variety.

CHOICE OF ROOTSTOCK

Since the war of 1914–18, experiments in the research stations and demonstration centres of the country have given much information on the subject of rootstocks, with the result that fruit trees on known rootstocks are obtainable from all the best nurserymen. The question of which stocks are the best for different purposes, will be dealt with later in the sections dealing with each fruit, but it should be emphasized here that when planning the fruit-garden or orchard, the question of distance of planting is closely linked with the rootstocks on which the trees are to be grown.

SYSTEMS OF PLANTING

The position of the trees in the orchard or plantations may be arranged in various ways. The "Square plant," in which the trees are sited square and equidistant, is the most popu-

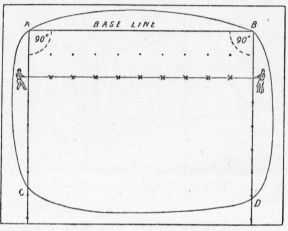

MARKING OUT THE GROUND FOR PLANTING.

lar because the easiest to thin. Other plants are the "quincunx," which merely adds one tree to the centre of each square formed by the "square" plant, and the "triangular," in which the trees are planted in rows to make a series of equal-sided triangles.

PLANTING

MARKING OUT THE GROUND

To mark out on the ground the position which the trees are to occupy, a long wire is often used on which pieces of string or coloured wool are tied tightly at intervals corresponding to the distances at which the trees are to be planted in the rows. A base line, AB, is first set out at one end of the field from which to square off the rest (see diagram). At each end of the base line a right angle is found by the most convenient method and the two side lines, AC and BD, are marked off. Supposing the distance between the tree rows to be 15 feet, short pegs are stuck into the ground 15 feet apart all down each of the side lines AC and BD. The wire then comes into play. One man takes hold of each end, and starting at A and B respectively, they walk down the side lines AC and BD. Stopping at the first peg, each one fastens down his end of the wire beside the peg. Then all they have to do is to walk towards each other along the wire, sticking a straight stick about 18 inches long into the ground at each point indicated by the pieces of string tied on to the wire.

In this way the whole field can quickly be marked out.

TIME TO PLANT

Fruit trees and bushes are planted in the dormant season between leaf fall in the autumn and bud burst in the spring.

The physical condition of the soil is of vital importance in deciding the best time for planting. If the ground is cold and wet and sticks in lumps, planting should not be contemplated. Should the trees arrive from the nursery at such a time, they must be heeled in by the roots in a sheltered position well secured from rabbits and other vermin, until the weather is suitable for planting. Should trees arrive for planting during frosty weather they should be kept in a frost-proof shed covered with several thicknesses of sacking.

When the trees are taken out to be planted in their permanent quarters, the roots should be covered with old sacks to prevent drying out.

NUMBER OF TREES PER FULL ACRE AT DIFFERENT DISTANCES APART

Distance in Feet	No. of Trees in Square Plant	No. of Trees in Triangular Plant
10	435	502
12	302	348
14	222	256
15	193	222
16	170	196
18	134	154
20	109	125
25	69	79
30	48	55
40	27	31

NOTE: 1. The numbers given above make no allowance for the fact that headland space of at least 15 feet should be allowed for all round the sides of each orchard or plantation. The best way to find out the number of trees that will be required for planting any given field is to draw the field to scale on squared paper and mark out the positions to be occupied by each tree.

ESPALIERS

Photos]   *[R. A. Malby.*
FAN-TRAINED TREES OF APRICOT AND GREENGAGE

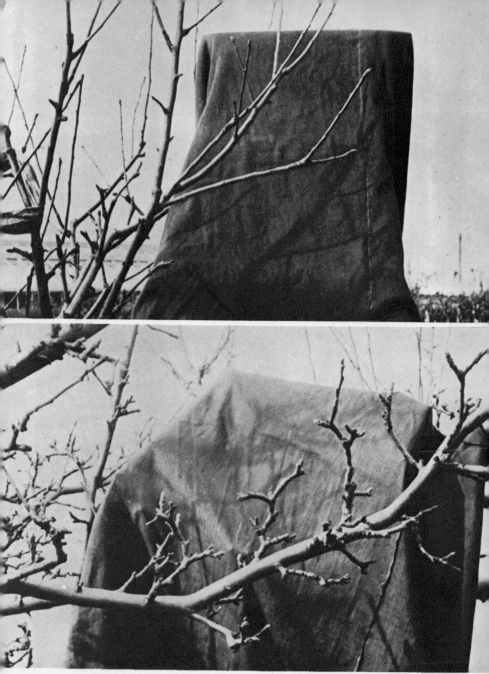

Top: Branch of a "Worcester Pearmain" Apple showing "tip-bearing" habit
Lower: Branch of a "Cox's Orange Pippin," showing close self-spurring habit

2. To find the number of trees or bushes per full acre at any given distance, multiply the distance between the rows by the distance between the trees or bushes in the row, and divide that into the number of square feet in an acre, namely 43,560.

DIGGING THE TREE HOLE

This operation is best done immediately before planting. The size of the hole will vary with the size of the root-system to be planted. It should be a few inches wider than the diameter of the root-system at its widest point.

When planting in heavy clay soils, the tree holes should be made very shallow, and the soil slightly mounded up in order to ensure surface drainage and aeration for the tree roots.

A PLANTING-BOARD TO SAVE SIGHTING WHEN PLANTING

When there are a large number of trees to be planted, it is a good plan to use a " planting-board." This is a plain wooden board about

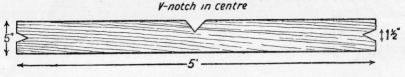

PLANTING BOARD.

5 feet long by 4 or 5 inches wide by $\frac{3}{4}$ inch thick, with a V-shaped notch cut in the centre and at each end as in the diagram. The central notch should be about $1\frac{1}{4}$ inches wide at the wide end.

When digging the holes in which to plant the trees, the planting-board is placed with the central V-shaped notch round the stick which marks the first position. Two thin, straight sticks, such as those that have been used for marking out, are then stuck in the ground in the two notches, one at each end of the planting-board (see diagram). The planting-board is taken away, the stick marking the site is removed, and the tree hole dug out to the required dimensions, care being taken to leave intact the two end sticks. When it comes to planting the tree, the planting-board is put across the hole with the central notch facing the same way as before, and the two end notches round the two end sticks.

PLANTING THE TREE

Before planting a tree, a long sloping cut is made with a knife on the underside of each root with a view to stimulating rapid callousing and the growth of new adventitious roots from the cut surface. The

F.G.H.   F tree is then held upright with its stem in the central notch of the planting-board by one man who lifts it gently up and down while a second man throws a few spadefuls of the finer soil over the roots. This soil is then stamped firmly down round the roots and more soil is thrown in. It is most necessary to make the soil really firm at each stage of the planting by treading and ramming in order to make sure that the soil particles are in close contact with the roots. In planting a tree against a wall, the roots should be as far from the wall as possible with the stem sloping slightly towards it.

TRANSPLANTING

It is possible to transplant fruit trees even when they are quite large, but the operation is expensive and rather risky. An extra large tree hole should be dug, *the soil must be rammed thoroughly after planting*, and a good mulch spread round the tree to keep the soil moist. For bush trees a 7-foot spile driven in at an angle, heading into the prevailing wind, and fastened to one of the main central branches, forms the best support. No pruning is usually done until the end of the first season after transplanting.

PROTECTION OF THE STEM

When fruit trees are planted with stock, some form of guard will be necessary to protect the stem of the tree from being eaten. Every fruit district has its own form of tree guard, and it is a good thing to consult the horticultural officer in regard to the best type to suit local conditions.

Wire netting curving outward away from enclosure

ERECTING WIRE-NETTING TO KEEP OUT RABBITS AND HARES.

The best way to keep out rabbits is to erect good wire-netting, 4 feet high from ground level, mesh 1¼ inch to 1½ inch, and gauge 18 or

19, all round the orchard or plantation, let well into the ground and laid outwards, in the furrow, with a line of strong hedging or barbed wire strung along about 6 inches above the top of the fence to which the wire-netting is attached at intervals with thin wire as shown in the diagram.

Another method of protecting the trunks of trees from being eaten is to paint them with one or other of the proprietary mixtures which are sold for this purpose as deterrents. These should be painted on the trees before the autumn frosts begin. They should be slightly warmed before being applied and should be painted on

STAKING : OBLIQUE.

fairly thinly. There are several mixtures containing such substances as linseed oil, sulphur and resin, which can be made at home and which will act as deterrents, but it should be noted that any mixtures containing paraffin oil are likely to damage the stem of young trees and should not be used.

TREE STAKES

For standard and half-standard trees one really strong Spanish chestnut, oak, or ash stake, driven well in close beside the tree, cut off just below the crotch (the point on the main stem from which the branches spring) and well pared over, will generally give sufficient support, provided the bottom two feet have been well treated under pressure with a good wood preservative, and that the tree has been fastened securely to the stake.

If stakes are plentiful, some people like to drive in two, one on either side of the tree, screwing on a crosspiece between the two stakes to which the tree is fastened.

If the crosspiece works loose, the tree wobbles about between the two stakes and is held less firmly than if it were fastened securely to a single stake, so that care must be taken to screw the crosspiece firmly on and not to trust to nails.

For low-headed bush trees, stakes from 4 to 5 feet long are generally used, driven well into the ground either vertically beside the stem, or obliquely as in the diagram, in which case they should point in the direction of the prevailing wind.

TYING THE TREE TO THE STAKE

There are many different ways of tying the tree to the stake. Some people wrap sacking or old cloth in a band about 6 inches wide round the stem of the tree, as in Fig. 1, to prevent chafing, and then tie with rope or string as in Figs. 2 and 3. Others use straw rope or strips of old rubber tyres, fastened either as in Fig. 4 or 5, but without any sacking.

Whichever method is used, all ties should be taken off yearly just before winter spraying, and renewed afterwards. If the old ties are left on, they harbour insects and may constrict the growth of the stem, especially in the case of young plum and cherry trees, which grow very quickly.

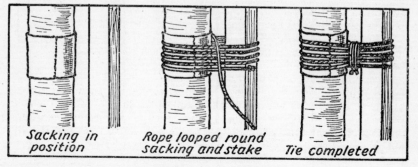

Sacking in position   *Rope looped round sacking and stake*   *Tie completed*

TYING THE TREE TO THE STAKE.

FIG. 1.   FIG. 2.   FIG. 3.

HOEING AND MULCHING NEWLY-PLANTED TREES

It is very important that the soil immediately surrounding the roots of newly-planted fruit trees or bushes should not be allowed to remain lumpy or to pan down so as to exclude the air from the roots. Hoeing round the young trees in the spring and early summer will prevent this and will also prevent the growth of weeds or grass. After the hoeing has been done, it is a good thing to cover the ground within a radius of about 3 feet from the stem with decaying organic material, such as spent hops, lawn mowings or the remains of old compost beds, with the idea of preventing evaporation of moisture from the soil.

If the young plant is vigorous, the soil conditions are normal, and the manuring right, the stirring of the soil with cultivators and hoes throughout the first few seasons is usually enough to keep the plant growing sufficiently vigorously.

But in gardens where material is readily available, mulching is a

very wise precaution to
take against an abnor-
mally dry season in clay
soils which are likely to
crack, or in sandy soils
which are liable to
drought.

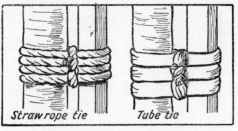

**PROTECTION FROM
FROST, WIND, BIRDS
AND WASPS**

TYING THE TREE TO THE STAKE.
FIG. 4.   FIG. 5.

Provided fruit trees are
not too much exposed to
the full force of east winds in the spring, or to south-west gales in the
late summer and autumn, no extra precautions should be necessary.

A walled or fenced garden gives the best shelter of all from wind,
but in a low-lying situation there is always a risk of damage from late
spring frosts.

Wall trees may be partially protected from frost by hanging double
thicknesses of fish-netting in front of the trees. If the situation is
known to be a frost pocket, orchard heaters may be used with advantage
(see also page 210).

One of the most satisfactory methods of protecting the buds of fruit
trees from the
attacks of birds in
winter and spring
is to wind black
cotton round the
trees or bushes by
means of bobbins
specially devised
for the purpose.
The only certain
way to protect
bush fruits from
birds or squirrels
is to enclose the
bushes in a fruit
cage. The cage
should be at least
6 feet high, the
sides being made
of strong half-inch
mesh galvanized

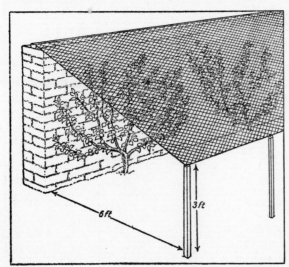

PROTECTION OF WALL FRUIT FROM HAIL. (Page 211.)

wire-netting nailed to posts let into the ground. The roof may be a permanent one of the same wire-netting, or a temporary roof of fish-netting may be stretched across the cage as soon as the first fruits begin to ripen. In either case a door of wire-netting will be necessary.

Protection from wasps can be secured only by enclosing each entire fruit in a muslin or strong transparent paper bag, just before it begins to ripen.

CHAPTER IX

GATHERING AND STORING FRUIT

GATHERING FRUIT

WHEN TO GATHER

Fruit which ripens in summer and autumn should invariably be gathered just a shade before it is absolutely ripe ; thus gathered, it is better in quality and higher flavoured than when picked absolutely ripe. But this must not be carried too far.

A single day before they are perfectly ripe suffices with peaches and similar delicate stone fruit, a week for apples and pears ; but cherries are gathered only when completely ripe.

Apples and pears which arrive at complete maturity in winter, are best gathered at the moment when the leaves begin to fall. Late-keeping fruit should be left on the trees as long as possible, so that it may increase in weight and improve in flavour. It is better to lose a few apples through falling from the trees than to gather late-keeping varieties too soon. In the latter case they will shrivel and lose their flavour when stored.

PICKING UTENSILS

The main requirements for picking utensils are adequate padding to protect bruising, and easy accessibility. For picking long-keeping apples and pears from high trees, a good form of picking bag that can be worn like a coat with large pockets behind, leaving both hands free to pick, can be made out of two clean sacks and some straps or webbing (see diagram).

For picking long-keeping cooking apples and pears from low trees the " orchard box " is to be recommended, because it

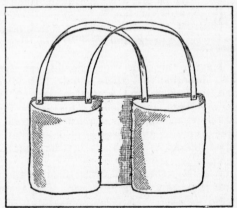

HOME-MADE FRUIT-PICKING BAG.

87

can also be used for storing the fruit. The orchard box is designed to hold one bushel (40 lb.) and is sufficiently well ventilated to allow one box to be stacked on top of another.

The boxes, if well wired, will last a long time.

For picking dessert pears and apples the shallow trays used for gas-storage are also to be recommended. They will take either one or two layers of all but the largest apples, but pears should always go in single layers.

Picking straight into orchard boxes and trays saves time and reduces the number of times the fruit has to be handled.

GATHERING FOR MARKET

The main thing to remember when gathering fruit, especially when it is intended for market, is to avoid damaging it by rough handling. The value of the crop at market depends largely on the care in picking, for if the fruit is roughly handled then its keeping qualities will be injured, and all the care in the world in packing cannot remedy the initial damage.

Fruit must never be gathered wet, and the earlier it is gathered in the morning, the better.

STORING FRUIT

THE STORE ROOM

A dark, well-aired cellar makes a good store room. Above ground, a room or substantial outhouse, preferably brick built, with a north aspect, is to be preferred, and if the room has a sloping roof this should slope towards the north.

The roof and walls must be substantial and frost and rain proof, preferably of brick, and the floor, too, should be of brick, tiles, concrete, or earth.

Though the fruit room should, for the most part, be kept dark, it is desirable that there should be one or two small windows in it, and some good and simple method of through ventilation, so that on dry days, and whenever necessary, the atmosphere may be completely changed. This is most important : for though it is not desirable to admit air unless needed, ventilation must never be neglected when the gases given off by the fruit have tainted the air of the room.

Whenever there is a strong smell in the fruit room, we may be quite sure that something is wrong. The atmosphere should be moist *but never stagnant*. An even temperature of about 40° F. in winter and 45° F. in summer is most suitable for storing apples and pears.

Ventilation during the first three weeks must be considerable, later it may be reduced. The store should be lined, the floor, sides and roof, with small-mesh wire-netting to keep out mice and rats.

Where long-keeping apples and pears are to be stored in orchard boxes or in trays, there is no need for any form of benching in the store. Where stacking is to take place, however, plenty of air space should be allowed between the stacks.

HOW TO STORE FRUIT

APPLES AND PEARS

Unless properly stored, apples and pears will shrivel and deteriorate in flavour. They must be kept in an even temperature and should be looked over periodically (once a fortnight) so that any decaying ones may be removed ; if these are allowed to remain, they will contaminate the whole.

Pears, especially, need constant inspection, as once they become over-ripe, decay is rapid and quickly spreads to all surrounding fruit. It is not always easy to tell when pears are beginning to ripen. With several varieties, however, the skin becomes a golden yellow or the tinge of red, if present, will become brighter. This may be taken as an indication that most of the fruit of these varieties is ready for eating.

Kinds that are only intended for immediate consumption, should not be stored at all, and long-keeping fruits should never be kept beyond their season.

There is evidence to show that long-keeping apples will last better in ordinary store if they are first stacked out of doors in orchard boxes or single layer trays, covered with a tarpaulin at night or if raining, for a week or ten days, to undergo the process known as " sweating." They should then be looked over carefully and fruits showing rots or cracks taken out before being put into store.

Oiled Wraps.—The use of oiled wraps for storing apples is to be recommended. The wraps are made in different sizes of tissue paper which has been treated with a flavourless mineral oil. Each fruit is folded in one of these wraps before being put in store. If oiled or plain tissue wraps are unobtainable, sheets of newspaper torn into squares are better than no wraps of any kind.

Another method is to store the fruit on the floor of the fruit room, spread out in heaps on straw, hay, dried ferns or bracken.

The heaps should not be more than 2 feet 6 inches high and should be covered with a good layer of the same material.

Such heaps require periodical inspection for rots and damage from mice or rats.

REFRIGERATED GAS STORAGE OF FRUIT

Owing to the relatively high cost of building and running these stores, they are mainly of interest at the present time to large commercial growers. The time may come, however, when small refrigerated gas-chambers for certain varieties of apples and pears will be worth considering even for comparatively small units.

Refrigerated gas-storage merely means the preservation of fruit in a gas-tight chamber to which oxygen can be admitted from the outer air by controlling the ventilation through an adjustable port-hole and in which the temperature can also be controlled. The living fruit in the store absorbs oxygen and gives off carbon dioxide and by keeping the proportions of these two gases at certain known concentrations, and the store at a known temperature for the variety, the ripening of the fruit in the store can be slowed down to about half the speed it would normally take to ripen in air at the same temperature.

CHAPTER X

GRADING AND PACKING FOR MARKET

SIZE GRADING

The simplest form of sizing is by eye only from specimen fruits of the required size for each grade, but unless this is done always by the same person the grade is likely to vary.

Where a comparatively small number of fruits have to be graded, the simplest method is to cut a number of circular holes out of a piece of three-ply wood, starting with a diameter of $2\frac{1}{4}$ inches and going up by quarter inches to $3\frac{1}{2}$ inches. This board is then nailed on to two standard or half-standard box ends as in the diagram, and the apple to be graded is simply passed eye downwards from above through each hole in turn until it exactly fits.

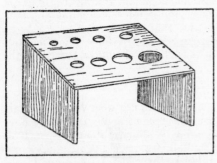

GRADING BOX FOR APPLES.

In size-grading, the smaller the package to be filled the greater the need for accuracy in size-grading. Thus for single-layer trays requiring from twelve to twenty-four fruits according to the variety, the sizing should be accurate to within less than a quarter of an inch, whereas with sieve baskets it is usually safe to allow a variation of nearly half an inch in diameter between the smallest and largest apple in each package.

The best commercial sizes for apples are as follows:

Apple	"Standard Box." Number in Box	"Standard Half-box." Number in Box	Half-sieves and Sieves. Diameter
Cox's Orange Pippin . . .	113–225	72–112	$2\frac{1}{4}$ in.–$2\frac{3}{4}$ in.
Other Dessert Varieties . . .	150–188	72–100	$2\frac{1}{2}$ in.–$2\frac{3}{4}$ in.
Cooking Sorts	80–120	—	$3\frac{1}{4}$ in. or over

Nothing is to be gained by packing fruits which are abnormally large for the variety. With *Bramley's Seedling*, for example, a diagonal

2–2 pack in four layers giving 112 apples to the box is one of the most popular packs. For sieve baskets, the larger sizes, 3½ inches upwards, can be used with advantage.

For trays, twenty-four apples 2¾ inches in diameter usually make the best pack, while with pears the number will vary from twelve to eighteen according to variety.

GRADING FRUIT FOR UNIFORMITY OF COLOUR, SKIN COLOUR AND FINISH

It is important to keep the fruit from different plantations separate before packing, since different manurial or cultural treatment may produce quite different colour and skin finish.

The fruit should be entirely free from blemishes. The skin must not be greasy. Apples in this country are never polished, but varieties such as *Rival* which have a natural bloom should retain it in the show package.

It is not always easy to know the best colour for any one variety. With *Cox's Orange Pippin* the specimens should not be too dark in colour, a mixture of red and yellow, and a limited amount of russet being popular at the present time for that variety.

Cooking apples need not necessarily be green, since some markets prefer them red, but whatever colour is chosen should be typical of the variety.

INTERNAL CONDITION

Two physiological troubles known as Bitter Pit and Water Core are apt to develop very quickly in some varieties of apple after they have been picked, especially after a season of climatic contrasts such as drought followed by very heavy rainfall (see page 136).

Apart from these particular troubles, the general condition of the apple or pear should be sound, not so immature as to be green where it should be coloured, nor so over-mature as to wrinkle when it is pressed with the fingers.

Pears are particularly treacherous in this respect, and should always be picked at an earlier stage in their development than would be advisable for apples.

PACKING POINTS

STANDARD BOXES

The packages are usually sent in the flat, each box consisting of two end pieces, two or four side pieces, two top pieces, two bottom pieces and four cleats. These constituent parts are in three different thicknesses, the ends being the strongest, then the sides, whilst the tops and bottoms are made of very thin wood which gives with the bulge of the pack and so forms a natural spring to keep the fruit in place. It is best to make a rough framework to hold the two ends upright while the sides are nailed on, touching each other in the centre. The bottom pieces are then nailed on, also touching in the centre, with two of the four cleats, the other two cleats being kept for nailing down the tops when the box has been packed.

A " liner " of corrugated paper is put first into the empty box, care being taken that the corrugated side is downwards, away from the fruit. The box is then lined with two strips of good quality lining paper of a kind specially made for the purpose, the dimensions of which are 23 inches long by 18 inches wide. These two lining papers should slightly overlap at the bottom of the box, and should cover the whole of the two sides, the remainder being folded outwards until the box has been packed, when they are folded back again over the fruit. Two more pieces of lining paper, 18 inches long by 11 inches wide, are used in the same way to line the ends of the box. In most commercial shows some form of label giving the entry number must be nailed on inside the box before packing begins. The end of the box farthest from the packer is then raised slightly for ease of packing. For exhibition work the first layer to be packed is left unwrapped, all the remaining layers being wrapped. When the box is packed the last layer of apples to be put in will bulge out slightly over the top of the box, and in order to get the top on without injuring the apples some form of press will be necessary.

The lining papers are folded inwards over the fruit, a second " liner " of corrugated paper is laid on these, with the corrugations upwards and the two top pieces are put in position. The box is then placed in the press, which grips the ends of the two pieces at either side while the cleats are nailed down. The box is next turned upside down and the word " TOP " is written or stencilled on what was originally the underside. Finally, a second label bearing the name of the con-signee, the variety, net weight and number of fruits and some indication of the quality, such as Extra Fancy, is tacked on to the end of the box.

Box packing is an exact process depending for its success on accurate size-grading and careful alignment of the fruit in the box. Full parti-culars of the various types of pack used for different sizes of apples are given in the special leaflets on the subject published by the Ministry of Agriculture and Fisheries.

Neat wrapping of the fruits in paper wraps of the correct size for the variety is an important item in box-packing. A good deal of practice both in wrapping and packing is advisable before undertaking packing for commercial shows.

The most popular "packs" for dessert apples in standard boxes are those known as the 3–2 diagonal in five layers.

When despatching boxes to market great care should be taken to see that they are stacked on their sides and are not allowed to rest on the thin, bulging boards which form the top and bottom of the boxes.

STANDARD HALF-BOXES

Whereas the standard box holds approximately 40 lb. net weight of fruit or one bushel, the standard half-box holds roughly 20 lb. or half a bushel. The standard box is used for cooking and for dessert apples and pears, but the half-box is used only for dessert apples and for small dessert pears. It is put together and prepared for packing in the same way as the box, but there is one big difference in packing which makes the half-box much easier to pack than the standard box. In the box there is an art in packing the apples, so that those in the centre of the box on the top layer project farther from the top than those at the end, thus making what is known as an even " bulge " or curve to the crown of the pack. The object of the bulge is to ensure that the apples are held firmly in position and do not rattle about in the box during transit.

In the half-box, a bulge is not considered strictly necessary, provided the whole of the top layer projects from $\frac{1}{4}$ to $\frac{1}{2}$ an inch above the level of the box after packing. This is to ensure that the fruit will not sink below the level of the box during transit. Not only does this make the packing of the half-box much easier, but it means that the top pieces can be nailed down under cleats without the aid of a box-press.

The most popular packs for the half-box are the 2–2 diagonal packs in four layers.

STANDARD No. 1 TRAYS

The tray is nailed together in the same way as described for boxes and half-boxes. There are several ways of preparing the tray for market, one of the most popular methods being as follows :

First put a thin layer of fine-grade woodwool in the bottom of the tray and cover it with a piece of good white lining paper cut to the required size. Next make narrow pads about $\frac{3}{4}$ of an inch thick of rolls of corrugated paper or woodwool wrapped in pure white tissue paper or in good lining paper. The pads should be the same length as the ends and sides of the tray, and are placed all round the inside to protect the fruit.

In packing trays for commercial shows the object is to fill the space with fruit without overcrowding. Particular attention should be paid to meticulous accuracy of size-grading and to the alignment of the fruit in their rows.

Another popular method of packing apples in trays is to put each apple in a small crinkly paper cup, and then to place the apples gently but firmly in straight lines across the tray. With *Cox's Orange Pippin*, a size-grade of 2¾ inches gives a good pack with six rows of apples, four apples in each row, making a total of 24 fruits in each tray.

Conical-shaped apples such as *Worcester Pearmain*, are usually placed in the cups on their sides, coloured side uppermost, with the eye pointing forwards in the direction of the end of the tray. Round apples, like *Cox's Orange Pippin*, are placed in the paper cups on their sides, coloured side uppermost, with eyes pointing sideways, towards one side of the tray. A sheet of lining paper is then placed on the top of the apples, and a layer of woodwool or a liner of corrugated paper, corrugation upwards, is laid over the whole. The tray can then be lidded in the ordinary way with or without cleats according to the type of tray provided, using cement-coated nails when possible.

SIEVES AND HALF-SIEVES

To prepare the sieve or half-sieve for packing, a circle of thick blue lining paper or of cardboard is put in the bottom of the basket, and a collar made of similar material is put round the whole of the inside. Three pieces of good white lining paper cut to the right size to allow a fair overlap at top and bottom, are then folded neatly down to line the sides of the basket, leaving sufficient outside to cover the fruit when packed. The apples are then " ringed in " in layers, usually with the stalk pointing outwards, and the eye pointing inwards towards the centre of the basket. The skill in " ringing in " consists in finding the best size of apple to give not less than the minimum net weight required, and at the same time to fill the basket and give it the right amount of " crown."

When the basket is packed, the white lining papers are folded neatly back over the fruit, another circle of blue lining paper or of cardboard is laid over the top, and a good thick pad of woodwool, clean straw or hay is fastened on with two or more pointed hazel wands crossing each other diagonally and stuck through the wicker-work.

The fruit should be well up to the rim of the baskets, and the " crown " should be well marked, but not excessively high.

PACKING CHERRIES AND SOFT FRUITS FOR EXHIBITION

Commercial show committees usually supply standard chips or punnets, but great care should be taken to conform in every particular with the rules given in the show schedule on the subject of lining materials and net weight of fruit. Exhibits are frequently disqualified before the judges see them, through neglect of one of these rules.

The packages may be prepared and lined the night before the show.

The fruit is best picked as early as possible on the morning of the show day, but must not be packed until it is dry. At least twice as much should be picked as will be needed to fill the packages. All the fruits in each package should be identical in size, shape, and colour, and completely free from blemish of any kind.

In commercial shows of these fruits there is sometimes a rule against any form of " fancy packing." By " fancy packing " is meant the placing of individual fruits in layers, with all the stalks facing the same way. Such packing is very attractive and where the rules allow, it should always be practised. Red currants always look best when the trusses are all laid in the same way, and in these fruits length of truss and size of individual berry score heavily.

Brightness of colour in the fruit is important in currants, raspberries, loganberries, blackberries and strawberries. In all these fruits and also in gooseberries, size of fruits is important, but it must be remembered that uniformity of size and colour is almost equally important, because of its effect on the general appearance of the fruit in each package. The package should be filled, but not too full to travel safely to market, and should be fastened down and carefully labelled with the special labels issued by the schedule committee.

Fruit shown on plates, either singly or in collections, requires smaller quantities to choose from, but just because the number of fruits is limited, there is all the more need for precision in sizing and in selecting fruits that are uniform in colour, skin quality, and freedom from blemish.

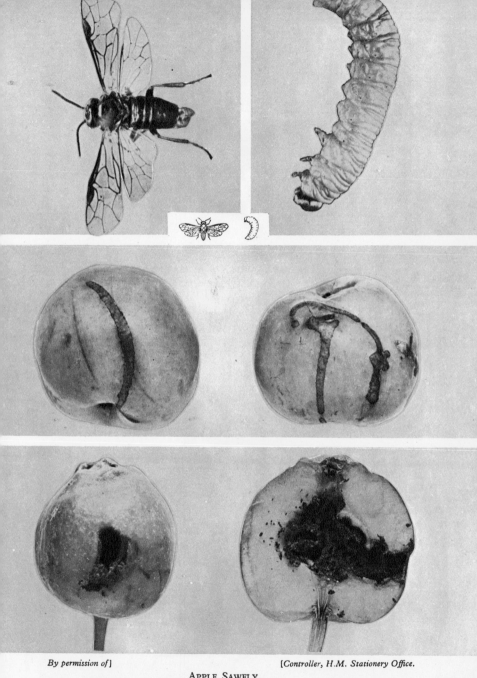

APPLE SAWFLY.

1. Adult Sawfly (inset, natural size).   2. Larva.   3. Apples scarred by larva.   4. Attacked fruitlets.

From the Ministry of Agriculture and Fisheries Advisory Leaflet No. 13.

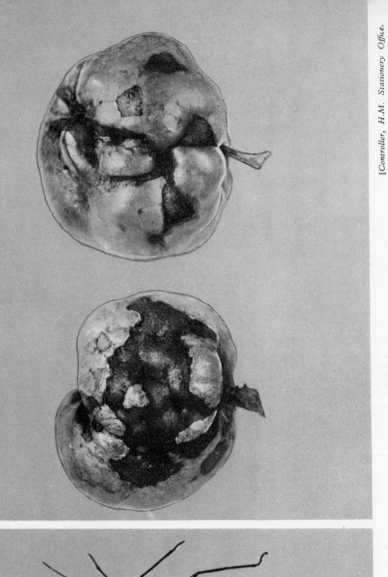

APPLE CAPSID

1. The Apple Capsid (*Plesiocoris rugicollis*) (inset, actual size).   2. Apples attacked by Apple Capsids.

CHAPTER XI

THE CONTROL OF PESTS AND DISEASES

ORCHARD HYGIENE

When planning the layout of a new plant of fruit, trees and bushes should be spaced wide enough apart to allow sun and air to reach them on all sides. Overcrowding of trees or branches leads to an unhealthy condition, predisposing the tree to attacks of pests and diseases. In old orchards, where the trees are so close that they cannot be properly sprayed, grub out some of the trees, remove dead and dying branches from others, trim up the hedges, and so let the sun and air into the orchard.

Mention has already been made (page 77) of the importance of planting different fruits separately. One of the chief reasons for this is the difficulty of spraying mixed plantings of fruit.

Thus, when strawberries, currants, or gooseberries are planted under pear trees or apple trees, the fruits on the undercrop may be spoilt in appearance by receiving the drip from the spray given to the top fruits. Again, apples and plums are a bad combination from the spraying point of view, the plums being in full bloom when the apples should be sprayed with fairly strong lime-sulphur.

The part played by manuring in preserving the growth-balance in a tree has already been referred to. Unsuitable manuring, in disturbing this balance, may make the tree more susceptible to attack by diseases or pests. In general it may be said that frequent and heavy applications of nitrogenous manures, without the right amount of potash to keep the balance, tend to promote sappy, unripened growth that seems to fall a ready prey to certain pests and diseases.

MECHANICAL METHODS OF PEST CONTROL

Trapping.—Trapping is one of the oldest methods of pest control, and for some pests it is very effective. For instance, the wingless females of the Winter Moths can be prevented from laying eggs on the twigs and branches by the application of a grease-band to the trunk of the tree. Similarly, the Clay-Coloured Weevil and other wingless weevils can be kept away from newly inserted grafts on which they like to feed, by putting a narrow band of a specially-prepared grease round the stem of the tree.

Pruning.—The removal of unwanted branches, and the cutting out of cankers on apple trees, or of dead wood bearing the silver-leaf fungus are important mechanical measures of pest and disease control.

Poultry.—Poultry has often been recommended as a means of controlling certain pests that pass part of their life-cycle in the soil. Poultry certainly do eat large quantities of insects, but can hardly be relied upon to exercise more than a partial control on any specific pest.

Natural Control.—Were it not for the combined influence of parasites, predacious insects, insectivorous animals and the vagaries of the weather, it is probable that man would never be able to hold his own in the struggle with insects. Owls, rooks and other birds eat insects, and among the predacious insects may be mentioned Ladybird beetles and their larvæ, feeding on greenfly, Wasps feeding almost entirely on flies and grubs, and a host of Ichneumon Flies, which are true parasites in the sense that they actually lay their eggs in the bodies of other insects.

SPRAYING—TYPES OF SPRAY

Winter Washes.—Before the advent of tar-oils, caustic winter washes were used largely as part of the orchard hygiene to remove moss and lichen. Tar-oils are now used almost exclusively to destroy the over-wintering eggs of Greenfly. They will also burn up moss and lichen, but have little or no effect on the eggs of Capsid Bugs or Red Spider. These can be killed with petroleum-oil sprays, which, however, are not harmful to the eggs of Greenfly. To avoid the need for two separate winter sprayings tar-petroleum mixtures, D.N.C.-oil and thiocyanate-oil washes have been developed. All winter washes should be applied as a drenching spray with sufficient force to ensure that every twig and bud is adequately covered.

Cover Washes.—Fungous diseases are carried about chiefly by spores which are wind-, water- or insect-borne. When a spore falls on a leaf, it must first germinate, sending out a small, delicate, root-like extension before the leaf can be infected with the disease. If the leaf has been previously coated with a protective covering of a fungicide such as sulphur or copper, the spores that fall on it are killed as soon as they start to germinate. Again, if the leaf is covered with a stomach-poison insecticide, e.g., lead arsenate, insects with biting or chewing mouth-parts, such as caterpillars or beetles that eat pieces out of the leaf or the fruit, will die before they can do much damage. Cover washes provide these protective coatings of fungicide or of stomach-poison insecticide.

Contact Insecticides.—Many insects, such as Capsids, Aphids, Scale Insects, Apple Sucker and Red Spider, are unable to chew but are provided with mouth-parts specially adapted for piercing and sucking.

These creatures bore through the surface layers of the leaf, to suck the sap from the inner tissues, and so remain unaffected by stomach poisons such as lead arsenate. For this type of insect it is necessary to use a poison like nicotine, which kills when it comes into *direct* contact with the body, or a residual contact insecticide such as D.D.T. (which can be regarded as either a contact or a cover wash). Contact washes, to be effective, must not only penetrate the hiding places of the insects, but must actually wet the skins of the insects themselves. To this end a drenching spray must be applied with plenty of pressure. Cover washes, on the other hand, should, in theory, be applied as a fine misty spray to ensure an even covering of the leaves. In practice, however, it is often necessary to effect a working compromise between these two extremes, and to combine stomach-poisons, contact insecticides and fungicides in one so-called " omnibus " wash. Moreover, economy and rapidity of spraying is further increased by applying this type of mixed wash at high pressure as a driving spray, and modern developments in spraying machinery are largely directed towards this end.

DUSTING

Dusting can be done much more quickly and easily than wet spraying and there are times in the best-regulated plantations when a quick dusting will make all the difference between success and failure in controlling a sudden outbreak of pest or disease. Yet dusting cannot be relied upon as the chief means of applying insecticides and fungicides, except possibly in a small garden where it can be done very frequently. Dust is more easily washed off by rain than a wet spray, and can be applied only when there is little or no wind. It is apt to drift a long way in a breeze, and may get on to plants for which it is not intended, and damage them.

In spite of these objections, the possession of a dusting machine is a valuable form of insurance for all fruit growers against some sudden outbreak of pest or disease.

DANGER TO BEES

Losses in stocks of bees have often occurred through careless use of lead arsenate and other poisons, and fears have been expressed that the widespread use of the newer " residual-contact " insecticides, such as D.D.T. and Benzene Hexachloride, might cause even greater losses. These fears have not been realized, and provided these insecticides are used with reasonable care, no trouble should arise. No spraying or dusting with any insecticide should be done whilst the blossoms are open and care should be taken to avoid leaving pools or open vessels of spray fluid, particularly lead arsenate, where bees may drink. If the bees are provided with an abundant supply of water near their hives they may be less inclined to drink promiscuously.

SPRAYING MACHINERY

If fruit trees are to be kept healthy and in a well-balanced condition, the selection of the very best spraying tackle is a matter deserving serious consideration.

The main points to look for are as follows :

Suitability of Type of Machine for the Purpose.—For small areas of young trees or bushes up to 2 or 3 acres in extent, one of the many types of hand-operated machines should meet the requirements. Larger trees will need a machine giving high pressure and a large output of spray, and this entails some form of power-driven machine.

A mobile, motor-driven outfit, drawn by horse or tractor, the men following behind and spraying as the machine goes up and down the rows of trees, may be ideal in flat grass orchards, with trees widely spaced, and water close at hand. But for a cultivated plantation on sloping ground or in sticky clay, a portable machine, operated at the headland in conjunction with overground steel mains, might be more economical.

Capacity of the Pump.—This means the output of spray-fluid in gallons per minute, or per hour. To be most effective, spraying should be done in the shortest possible time, and it is always wise to allow for a certain amount of reserve capacity in the pump.

Power to Drive the Pump.—In choosing a hand-operated machine, the available manual labour should be taken into account, having in view the desirability of working the pump to full capacity without undue strain on those who do the pumping.

Similarly, with a power outfit, it is unwise to get a machine which has a powerful set of pumps, with an engine incapable of sustaining the work over a long period.

Simplicity of Design.—A spraying machine of any kind needs constant attention and an occasional overhaul to maintain its efficiency. Accessibility of the various working parts is, therefore, an important point to be borne in mind, and rapid service in the replacement of spare parts should be guaranteed. The machine should be fitted with a reliable pressure gauge, and the tank should be made of well galvanized iron, or of wood.

TYPES OF SPRAYING MACHINE

Spraying machines vary in price according to size and design. The following brief notes should serve as a rough guide to intending purchasers of new machines.

HAND-OPERATED MACHINES

DOUBLE-ACTION SYRINGE TYPE

This is one of the most efficient forms of the syringe pump. A length of rubber piping is attached to the syringe, and is suspended in a bucket or tub containing the spray. The pump is operated by both hands and is of a double-action type, giving a continuous spray. The pump gives a pressure of about 60 lb. per square inch.

KNAPSACKS

(a) *Internal and External Pump Types.*—The usual tank capacity of this type of machine is about 3 gallons. No pressure gauges are fitted, but pressures up to about 70 lb. can be obtained.

(b) *Pneumatic Type.*—This type is cylindrical in shape, and fitted with an air pump for charging the container with compressed air. One of the chief advantages claimed for this type of machine is that pumping is done before spraying begins, leaving both hands free for working. The disadvantage is that the pressure is relatively low.

BUCKET PUMPS

The main advantage of this type over the knapsack is its larger tank-capacity of about 6 gallons, an advantage, however, which naturally detracts from its portability. The pumps vary a good deal, but only comparatively low pressures can be obtained. A double-action pump or a large air-chamber for single-action pumps seems to be desirable.

The types of spraying machines so far described can be used quite satisfactorily for small pieces of bush fruit, or for espaliers, cordons, and low-headed bushes in very early stages of their growth. But for established fruit trees, the pressures obtainable on these types of spraying machine, and the capacity of the tanks fall below the minimum requirements for really efficient spraying. For such trees a choice should be made from one of the more powerful machines.

BARREL PUMPS

In this class, the pump unit, including the agitator, can be clamped on to any spray-receptacle, barrel, tank, etc., thus saving the cost of a tank. The pump closely resembles those mounted on the wheeled types of spraying machine, and gives pressures of from 150–200 lb. Its advantage lies in its relative cheapness and portability.

HEADLAND PUMPS

In this class the pump is usually mounted on a platform with or without wheels for use in conjunction with rainwater tubs, galvanized tanks or other spray receptacles placed in suitable positions in the orchard. The mixed spray is poured into the receptacle, whence it is sucked up by the pump through a short length of hose, and delivered through a longer hose pipe to the lance. The twin pumps are usually designed to maintain an average pressure of from 150–200 lb., and are of the hand-lever type to be worked by one or two men.

WHEELED TYPE OF SPRAYING MACHINES

This class contains some of the most suitable types of hand-operated spraying machines for fruit tree spraying, where larger trees are concerned. Tank capacity varies from 12 to 40 gallons. Pressures of from 150 lb. up to 300 lb. are claimed, and on most of them a pressure of 200 lb. can be obtained with an output of from 1 to 2 gallons per minute. It should be realized, however, that to keep up the maximum pressure on these machines throughout a day's spraying involves hard physical labour, and to carry out the spraying properly, there should be one man on the pump, and one on the lance. Most types of hand-operated machines have a pump-handle action. This has the obvious disadvantage that the natural tendency to work with a short instead of a full stroke will ultimately result in uneven cylinder wear.

PORTABLE POWER-SPRAYING MACHINES

For orchard trees of any size, or where fruit is grown for market on any scale, there is no doubt that power-sprayers are more efficient, and in the long run more economical than any type of hand-operated machine. Portable power-sprayers can be used as stationary units in conjunction with overground steel mains, coupled together with flexible rubber joints, or they can be used as mobile units, to be drawn through the orchard.

(a) *Small Power Sprayers.*—The pumps on these small machines are operated by a 2- or a 3-h.p. engine, either air- or water-cooled, with two-throw high-pressure pump, giving pressures between 250 and 350 lb. for use with up to two nozzles. Their tank capacity varies from 50 to 100 gallons, and they can be drawn by horse or tractor.

(b) *Medium-sized Sprayers.*—These larger machines have a 4- or 5-h.p. engine with a three-throw high-pressure pump, giving 300 to 450 lb. pressure, and with an output of about 500 gallons an hour for use with up to six nozzles. Their tank capacity is 80 to 180 gallons, and they can be drawn by horse or by tractor.

(c) *Large Power Sprayers.*—These large machines usually have an 8- to 10-h.p. engine, giving up to 550 lb. pressure, and with an output of from 800 to 1,200 gallons an hour for use with up to twelve nozzles. Tank capacity is from 100 to 250 gallons, and they are tractor-drawn.

STATIONARY ENGINES

For large acreages of fruit it may be economical to put in a central spraying plant. For this purpose four-throw pumps are used, driven by petrol, diesel, or electric motor. Very high pressures up to 700 lb. are obtainable, with an output up to 3,000 gallons an hour, for use with up to sixteen leads. For these plants a system of underground pipes is necessary to take the spray-fluid from the mixing-tank at the central plant through the orchards. The cost of the pumps is proportional to those of the largest portable power-spraying machines, but allowance must be made, also, for the additional cost of laying down underground mains, and for a system of stand-pipes for hose attachment.

HOSES, LANCES, GUNS AND NOZZLES

Hoses.—Where tar-oils are to be used, it is advisable to buy rubber hoses guaranteed suitable for this purpose. The hoses get very muddy in wet weather, and this adds to their weight, so that, within reason, the shorter the hose, the easier the work.

Lances and Guns.—For efficient spraying, the lance should be light and not too long, a good average length being about 4 feet 6 inches.

Nozzles.—The chief requirement is a nozzle that can easily be stripped for cleaning, since a blocked nozzle is one of the bugbears of spraying. Moreover, the nozzle should have the minimum of adjustable components. When ordering spray accessories, spare discs and washers should not be forgotten.

TYPES OF DUSTING MACHINE

There are many types of dust-blowers, from the small hand-bellows to the large motor-driven outfit. The main points to look for are convenience of manipulation and uniform distribution of the dust.

KNAPSACKS

These machines are carried on the back, and are worked by a handle at the side in the ordinary way, the outlet pipe being held in the other hand. A double-action bellows is a useful refinement, ensuring more even distribution of dust. A double-outlet lance can be fitted.

SMALL HAND-OPERATED ROTARY BLOWERS

These are carried in front of the body, one hand turning a handle at the side, while the other hand guides the delivery tube. A uniform distribution of dust is secured by a fan-operated dust feed. A Y-piece can be fitted on the delivery tube for dusting two rows at once.

HAND-OPERATED ROTARY BLOWERS ON WHEELS

This is the same kind of machine as the small rotary blower just described, but with a larger capacity. Being on wheels, it can be moved about by one man while another turns the handle.

GEARED-DRIVE DUSTING OUTFITS

(a) *Horse-drawn.*—In these machines the fan is geared to the road-wheels, and blows the dust through flexible delivery tubes, each of which can be arranged to point in any direction. The dust " hopper " holds about 1 cwt. of dust. The road wheels are usually adjustable for width, and the machine is drawn by a horse or pony. Some makes are fitted with a freewheel clutch. The main criticism of this type of duster is that it cannot be geared sufficiently high. The price varies with size and type.

(b) *Motor-driven.*—These machines are capable of dusting large acreages very rapidly, but their purchase involves considerable capital outlay in addition to what is being spent on wet-spraying machinery. They can be recommended only for large farms where special circumstances, such as scarcity of water, would seem to indicate a real need for such an outfit.

SOME SPRAYING HINTS

Before the winter washing season begins in December, all spraying tackle should be thoroughly overhauled. The machine should be stripped to see whether any repairs are needed, and the hoses, lances and nozzles cleaned, repaired or renewed. A day or two before spraying begins, the tank should be partly filled with water, and the machine given a trial run to see that the engine, pump and agitator are all in working order. Washers may have to be renewed, or there may be some leaks to be mended in the rubber hoses. The strainer is one of the most important parts of the spraying machine, and since imperfect straining means repeated blocking of the nozzles, it must be kept in good repair.

After each day's work it is a wise plan to empty the tank and pump clean water through to wash out the pipes.

At the end of the winter spraying season the tank should be scrubbed out with weak caustic soda in readiness for the spring. Spraying should be started in good time on account of the number of unforeseen hitches that usually occur. If a mixed spray has to be left standing in the tank for any length of time during the day, the pump should be worked for a few minutes before spraying begins again, to allow the agitator to mix up the spray. The liquid already in the hoses should be sprayed on to the ground.

CHIEF SPRAY MATERIALS EMPLOYED

In buying a proprietary insecticide or fungicide it is advisable to choose one of the brands that are officially approved by the Ministry of Agriculture and Department of Agriculture for Scotland. Most types of spray material are covered by this scheme and the official list is the purchaser's best safeguard.

TAR-OIL WASHES

These are emulsions (usually of the " miscible " type) containing certain selected grades and fractions of tar-distillate as the chief ingredients. They are used, normally, at 5 per cent. dilution, during the dormant season only. They are toxic to eggs of the Apple Sucker, Aphides, and, at higher concentrations, to those of the Winter Moth. They will remove Scale and Lichen and help to control Blossom Wilt.

PETROLEUM-OIL WASHES

These are emulsions of selected grades of petroleum-oils of the light lubricating type. They are used at 5 per cent. to 8 per cent. dilution at bud-break or even later to kill the winter eggs of Capsid Bugs and Red Spider.

Both the " miscible " oil and the " stock " or " mayonnaise " type of emulsion are obtainable. The former mixes more readily with water and is somewhat more convenient to use. Emulsions of special grades of highly-refined "water-white" oil are sometimes used at 1 per cent. dilution as summer sprays for Red Spider.

TAR-PETROLEUM MIXTURES

These are emulsions containing tar-distillate and petroleum-oils, and are intended to do the work of both a tar-oil and a petroleum-oil wash in one operation.

D.N.C. WASHES

Sometimes referred to as D.N.O.C. washes, these are petroleum-oil emulsions incorporating a small amount of a nitro-cresol, usually a dinitro-ortho-cresol, the function of which is to kill the eggs of Apple Sucker and Aphis. They can be used as dual-purpose washes, replacing both petroleum- and tar-oil winter washes, and applied any time up to bud-break. Their wetting power is often indifferent and this must be borne in mind when using them.

THIOCYANATE-OIL WASHES

Like the D.N.C., these are dual-purpose washes and have the same uses. They are more expensive, but can be used later with safety.

These and some of the previously-mentioned winter washes can be obtained with D.D.T. as an added ingredient.

LEAD ARSENATE (Poison)

This is obtainable as a powder, as a paste, and in a semi-liquid (so-called " colloidal ") form. The paste is generally used at a dilution of 4 lb. and the powder, which is the most popular and convenient form, at 2 lb. per 100 gallons. It may be used alone or in combination with any spray-material other than soap or soap-containing preparations. Being heavy, it needs to be constantly agitated.

NICOTINE (Poison)

This is an alkaloid manufactured from tobacco, and is sold with a guaranteed purity of 95 to 98 per cent. Used as a contact insecticide at the rate of 8 oz. per 100 gallons of spray (6 oz. when used against Greenfly only) for Capsid Bugs, small Caterpillars, Apple Sawfly eggs, Apple Sucker, and all kinds of Greenfly. It can be mixed with any other spray-material. When used as a dust the nicotine content does not, as a rule, exceed 4 per cent.

DERRIS PREPARATIONS

These are insecticides composed of finely-ground derris root, or containing the powdered root or an extract of it as the active ingredient. Toxic to many classes of insects, e.g., Aphides, Capsids, Caterpillar, derris is of especial value where a non-poisonous insecticide is required. The pure ground root can be mixed with any other spray.

D.D.T. PREPARATIONS

D.D.T. (dichloro-diphenyl-trichlorethane) is a powerful insecticide with a very wide range of usefulness and has partly taken the place of lead arsenate, nicotine and derris. It is especially useful in the control of various Caterpillars, Beetles and Capsid Bugs but is not particularly effective against Greenfly, and seems quite harmless to Red Spider. On fruit it is generally used as a spray powder, which can be mixed with water or with any other spray fluid to form a suspension. Such wettable powders contain a stated proportion of D.D.T., and for most purposes they should be diluted to contain 0·05 per cent. of the active material. Thus a 50 per cent. powder would be used at 1 lb. and a 20 per cent. powder at 2½ lb. per 100 gallons. Emulsions also are available but, if admixture with lime sulphur is intended, the purchaser should obtain a brand that is suitable for that purpose. Where dusting is practicable or advisable a 5 per cent. D.D.T. dust will meet the case.

LIME-SULPHUR

Lime-sulphur is a clear, amber-coloured solution, manufactured by boiling lime and sulphur together. It is most conveniently purchased ready-made in concentrated form. It is used as a fungicide for Scab, Mildew, etc., and as a contact insecticide for Red Spider and Big-Bud Mite. Lime-sulphur can be mixed with any of the commonly-used insecticides but not with soap.

"COLLOIDAL" SULPHUR

This is a suspension of sulphur of very fine particle-size. It usually contains approximately 40–50 per cent. elementary sulphur. Sometimes it is used as an alternative to lime-sulphur, because, at the dilutions recommended, it is generally non-injurious to fruit trees and bushes, and leaves no visible deposit on fruits. It is not as fungicidally powerful as lime-sulphur at normal dilutions.

"COLLOIDAL" COPPER

This is similar in type to colloidal sulphur but has copper as the fungicidally-active ingredient. It is not as generally " safe " on fruit as the sulphur form, but is increasingly popular because easier to prepare than Bordeaux Mixture.

BORDEAUX MIXTURE

Bordeaux Mixture is a fungicide prepared by pouring a solution of copper sulphate ("bluestone") into milk of lime. Milk of lime is obtained when already-hydrated lime powder is stirred up with water. When the lime has been diluted with the bulk of water, the bluestone, dissolved in a little water, is added slowly, the mixture being stirred during the process. The proportions generally used in fruit-tree spraying are : 1 part bluestone to 1½ parts hydrated lime, e.g., 4 lb. bluestone, 6 lb. hydrated lime to 100 gallons water.* In making Bordeaux Mixture, the use of galvanized-iron vessels should be avoided when the bluestone is being dissolved. Wooden buckets or tubs are best. Any commonly used spray-material, other than soap, can safely be added to Bordeaux Mixture.

SOFT SOAP

This must be dissolved in hot water before use. It is the best wetting agent known for fruit trees. Used with an insecticide such as nicotine, it enables the insecticide to penetrate the foliage, and thus to wet the surface of the insects. It should not be used with lime-sulphur, Bordeaux Mixture or lead arsenate, or shortly before or after such sprays, especially lead arsenate, are applied.

* It has been found that the addition of Cotton-seed oil at 6 pints per 100 gallons prevents much of the injury commonly associated with Bordeaux Mixture, but it makes the spray rather more expensive to use. The oil should be stirred into the dissolved copper sulphate before this is added to the milk of lime.

PROPRIETARY WETTING PREPARATIONS

There is a wide choice of these preparations, known as " wetters," most of which can, unlike soft soap, be used with lime-sulphur, Bordeaux Mixture or lead arsenate, and which are intended to improve the wetting and spreading properties of the sprays with which they are used. Such preparations should be used according to the makers' instructions.

GROUND SULPHUR DUSTS

These yellow powders should contain 90 to 95 per cent. sulphur, the rest being a " carrier," often of the china-clay type. Fineness of particle-size is important. The use of these dusts is an excellent adjunct to wet spraying, especially for late-summer applications against Apple Scab ; their chief advantage lies in the ease and rapidity with which they can be applied. They are not safe on sulphur-shy varieties.

COPPER-LIME DUST

A form of copper sometimes used in dusting for Scab and other fungous diseases. Fineness of particle-size is important here also ; the finer the dust, the more effective it will be. It is risky to use on many varieties of apples.

MATERIALS LESS COMMONLY USED

Benzene hexachloride.—This is even more toxic than D.D.T. to many insects whilst being effective against just as wide a range of pests. It has an unpleasant odour and, unless carefully used, may taint the fruit of trees and bushes to which it is applied. It has a rather shorter residual effect than D.D.T. and does not appear to be quite as safe to tender shoots and foliage. Of the preparations available, most have hitherto been dusts.

Dinitrocyclohexylphenol.—Preparations of this and of closely related compounds are available in proprietary form and are reported to give a good control of Red Spider during the summer.

Mercury preparations.—These are obtainable in proprietary form only ; one, based on phenyl mercuric chloride, has given good results against Apple Scab and is available also as a combined insecticide-fungicide, compounded with, e.g., lead arsenate.

New products for plant protection.—Many new insecticides have arisen in the wake of D.D.T. and benzene hexachloride and more and more such synthetic materials can be expected as time goes on. Some may be found to serve a useful purpose, but the fruit grower is well advised to be cautious in his use of them. It is unwise to try out a new material on a large scale until, not only its effectiveness, but its safety to growing plants and to personnel has been satisfactorily proved.

A GUIDE TO SPRAYING

See footnote, page 112.

APPLE

Time of Application	Treatment	To Control
October **December–February**	Apply grease bands **Tar-oil emulsion at 5 per cent.**	Caterpillar Greenfly, Apple Sucker, Scale Insects
February–March	D.N.C. wash at 8 per cent. may be used in place of both tar- and petroleum-oil sprays	Greenfly, Apple Sucker, Scale Insects, Capsid Bugs, Red Spider, Winter Moth
February–Early April	Petroleum-oil emulsion at 8 per cent. (6½ per cent. if put on late March or early April)	Capsid Bugs, Red Spider, Winter Moth
Late March–Early April **April (at "green-cluster" stage)**	D.D.T. alone or in a late winter wash **Lime-sulphur at 2½ per cent.** D.D.T.	Apple Blossom Weevil Scab Capsid Bugs, Cater-pillars
Late April–Early May (at "pink-bud" stage)	Lime-sulphur at 2 per cent. Nicotine at 8 oz. per 100 gallons	Scab Capsid Bugs, Greenfly
Late May (at "petal-fall" stage) **Mid-June (at "fruitlet" stage)**	Lime-sulphur at 1 per cent. Nicotine at 8 oz. per 100 gallons Lime-sulphur at 1 per cent.	Scab and Red Spider Sawfly Scab and Red Spider

Note.—Leave *Stirling Castle, Beauty of Bath,* and *Lane's Prince Albert* unsprayed with fungicide after blossoming.

For *Newton Wonder,* apply lime-sulphur ¾ per cent. after blossoming. This dilution, or alternatively colloidal or other appropriate sulphur preparation should be used at "fruitlet" stage for other varieties where experience shows 1 per cent. lime-sulphur to be unsafe.

BLACKBERRY

Time of Application	Treatment	To Control
Early May Early and Mid-July	D.D.T. dust Derris at 2 lb. per 100 gallons or D.D.T.	Rhynchites Weevils Raspberry Beetle

COBNUT AND FILBERT

Time of Application	Treatment	To Control
April–May Early June	Lead-arsenate or D.D.T. D.D.T. spray or dust	Caterpillar, Nut Weevil Nut Weevil

A GUIDE TO SPRAYING—*continued*

CURRANT, RED

Same programme as for Blackcurrant (see below), but omitting lime-sulphur and Bordeaux Mixture.

BLACKCURRANT

Time of Application	Treatment	To Control
December–February	**Tar-oil emulsion at 5 per cent.**	Greenfly and Winter Moth
February–March	Petroleum-oil emulsion at 8 per cent.	Capsid Bugs and Winter Moth
February	D.N.C. at 8 per cent. or a tar-petroleum-oil emulsion at a concentration recommended by the makers may be used in place of above two sprays	Capsid, Winter Moth, Greenfly
April (just before flowers open)	**Lime-sulphur at 2–8 per cent. (To this add lead, Derris or D.D.T. if Caterpillars present)**	Big-Bud Mite
June–July	Roguing	Reversion
July (after crop is picked)	Bordeaux Mixture 4–6–100	Leaf Spot and Rust

CHERRY

Time of Application	Treatment	To Control
October	**Apply grease bands**	Caterpillar
December–January	Tar-oil emulsion at 5 per cent. Spray very thoroughly and as late as possible if Blossom Wilt is bad	Blackfly and Blossom Wilt
April–May (not during blossoming)	Lead-arsenate or D.D.T. Bordeaux Mixture 6–9–100 pre-blossom and 4–6–100 post-blossom	Caterpillar Bacterial Canker

DAMSON (see Plum)

GOOSEBERRY

Time of Application	Treatment	To Control
December–February	**Tar-oil emulsion at 5 per cent.**	Greenfly, Red Spider
February–March	Petroleum-oil emulsion at 8 per cent.	Capsid Bugs, Winter Moth, Red Spider
April (before flowering)	**Lime-sulphur at 2½ per cent.**	Mildew, Red Spider
April (after flowering)	Lime-sulphur at 1 per cent. (omitting " sulphur-shy " varieties)	Mildew, Red Spider
April–May (as required)	Derris or D.D.T. Note : May be added to lime-sulphur	Sawfly, Caterpillar

LOGANBERRY

Time of Application	Treatment	To Control
May	Bordeaux Mixture 4–6–100	Cane Spot
Mid-June	Derris or D.D.T.	Raspberry Beetle
	Colloidal Copper at makers' recommendations	Cane Spot
Late June	Derris or D.D.T.	Raspberry Beetle

PEACH AND NECTARINE

Time of Application	Treatment	To Control
December	Tar-oil emulsion at 5 per cent.	Greenfly
February–March (at bud-burst)	**Lime-sulphur at 3 per cent.**	Leaf Curl and Red Spider

PEAR

Time of Application	Treatment	To Control
October	Apply grease bands	Caterpillars
December–January	Tar-oil emulsion at 5 per cent.	Greenfly
Early April (at " green-cluster " stage)	**Lime-sulphur at 2½ per cent.**	Scab and Blister Mite
	D.D.T.	Caterpillars
April (at " white-bud " stage)	**Lime-sulphur at 2 per cent.**	Scab and Blister Mite
Mid-May (at " petal-fall " stage)	Bordeaux Mixture at 4–6–100 or a colloidal-copper wash used at makers' directions	Scab
June	{ Lead arsenate at 2 lb. per 100 gallons	Codling and Slugworm
July	{ Derris, D.D.T. or Nicotine (dust or spray)	Slugworm

PLUM (INCLUDING DAMSON, QUETSCHE AND BULLACE)

Time of Application	Treatment	To Control
October	Apply grease bands	Caterpillars
December–January	**Tar-oil emulsion at 4 per cent.**	Greenfly
February	Petroleum-oil emulsion at 5 per cent.	Red Spider
Early April	Lead arsenate or D.D.T.	Caterpillars
May	Derris	Sawfly and Red Spider
May	Lime-sulphur at 1 per cent.	Red Spider
Before Mid-July	**Cut out and burn all dead and dying branches and shoots**	Silver Leaf

A GUIDE TO SPRAYING—*continued*

RASPBERRY

Time of Application	Treatment	To Control
Mid-March	Lime-sulphur at 5 per cent. or Bordeaux Mixture at 10–15–100	Cane Spot
Late June	**Derris or D.D.T.**	Raspberry Beetle

STRAWBERRY (see page 270)

Note.—In the foregoing tables, the operations shown in heavy type are those which should always be carried out.   The particulars given here are purposely brief, but further information is given in the sections dealing with the diseases and pests of each fruit.   The nature of the actual sprays and dusts, and the precautions to be taken in using them, are dealt with in the early part of this section.

THE CULTURE OF PARTICULAR FRUITS

CHAPTER XII

THE APPLE

SOIL, SITUATION AND ASPECT

Apple trees can be grown successfully on a wide range of soils. Those that are badly drained and liable to waterlogging should be avoided, as also should those which are excessively drained and liable to dry out in a hot summer. Soils with a high nitrogen content such as are to be found in old hop gardens or in heavily-manured kitchen gardens, should not be used for planting dessert apples until means has been found to reduce the amount of nitrogen that is available to the young trees.

Shelter from the south-west and from the east winds, and protection from spring frosts are necessary. Although the apple can be grown under conditions of moderately high rainfall and low sunshine, these are by no means ideal conditions.

Dessert apples are grown most economically in districts with a yearly rainfall of from 20 to 25 inches, and with a correspondingly high rate of sunshine, these being conditions which impose a natural check on excessive growth, and ensure good skin colour and texture in the fruit.

In districts of more than 40 inches of rainfall in the year, dessert apples must be regarded as difficult to grow successfully, and preference should be given to cooking apples.

FORM OF TREE

The form of tree to be adopted must be considered in relation to the type of apple culture required.

Grass Orchards.—For grass orchards where stock is grazing, the standard, three-quarter-standard and half-standard forms may be used according to the height above the ground at which it is necessary to keep the branches out of reach of grazing stock.

Plantations.—For plantations the bush form is the most popular and is used in all sizes from the very large " permanent " to the very small " filler."

The oblique cordon form has been largely used for intensive apple culture, and in more recent years the dwarf pyramid and the double cordon forms have been planted.

F.G.H. 113 H

The Fruit Garden.—For the fruit garden there are several forms of tree to suit the space available. Where there is very little headroom and hardly any lateral space in more than two directions, the horizontal cordon may be used, the trees being planted at intervals of from 10 to 20 feet for subsequent inarch grafting of one into the other. Where there is headroom but only limited lateral space in more than two directions, the vertical cordon, either single or double, the oblique cordon, and the espalier forms all have their merits. Where both headroom and lateral space in all directions are available but limited, the dwarf pyramid and small bush forms may be useful, and where there are no restrictions of space, the large bush and even the half-standard may be used.

ROOTSTOCKS FOR APPLES

Apple trees are raised by budding or grafting the scion variety on to a rootstock raised either vegetatively by stooling and layering or from seed (see pages 26–38).

Before raising a tree, or when ordering trees ready-worked, careful consideration should be given to the selection of the most suitable rootstock. Research has shown that the size of the tree when fully grown and, to a certain extent, the quality of the fruit are influenced by the rootstock. Local conditions, particularly the nature of the soil, should also be borne in mind when selecting the rootstock. If the conditions are conducive to excessive growth, the stock chosen should be of a more dwarfing nature than would normally be required for the purpose, and vice versa. In the light of present knowledge the most useful standardized apple rootstocks for different sizes of tree are:

Rootstocks for Dwarf Trees

Malling Number Nine (Jaune de Metz).—Under favourable growth conditions this stock makes a small but healthy tree which begins to come into bearing in from two to three years' time, and which throughout its life remains smaller than on any other commercial rootstock. Its roots are brittle and the trees must be carefully staked.

The early cropping of trees on this stock, combined with the high colour and large size of fruit which it tends to produce in trees worked upon it, make Number Nine the ideal rootstock for all varieties of apples grown under garden conditions. Here the natural shelter and the artificial support afforded by wall, fence, or wire can be relied upon to prevent the trees from being blown over.

Rootstocks for Larger Trees

Malling Number Two (Doucin) and Malling Number One (Broadleaf).— At the present time the stock which appears to be most widely used

by English nurserymen for bush trees, and which is also used for
cordons in many commercial plantations, is Malling Number Two. In
early years this is a semi-dwarfing stock with all varieties, but with
Cox's Orange Pippin and many other sorts it becomes more vigorous
as the trees grow older. Malling Number One is a stock which appears
to be more vigorous with some varieties than with others. *Cox's
Orange Pippin* on Number One starts off fairly strongly and then settles
down into a tree of medium size, whereas with *Worcester Pearmain*
and *Bramley's Seedling* there appears to be little to choose in size in later
years between trees on Numbers One and Two.

Rootstocks for Very Large Trees

Malling Number Twelve and Number Sixteen.—Of the standardized
rootstocks for very large trees, whether standard, three-quarter-standard,
half-standard or bush, Malling Number Twelve and Sixteen are to be
recommended, trees on Number Twelve taking rather longer to come
into bearing than those on Number Sixteen. Failing this, the trees
should be on selected free or crab stocks, such as Malling Crab C., or one
of the Long Ashton selections.

PRUNING OF APPLES

Nothing is more fatal to quick cropping than the old-fashioned
method of pruning the leading shoots and all laterals hard back every
winter before the tree has come into bearing. If the leaders are only
lightly tipped or even left entirely unpruned after say the third or
fourth year from planting, and all the laterals of medium growth on
the outside of the tree are left full length for one or two seasons, the
trees will come into bearing reasonably quickly. If this is not done,
strong growers like *Bramley's Seedling* and varieties like *Allington
Pippin* and *Cox's Orange*, which make much lateral growth, may go on
growing vigorously without cropping for years after they should have
come into bearing.

Another varietal habit which is important in determining the degree
of winter pruning for apples is the way in which the tree naturally
carries its fruit-buds. Some varieties, such as *Worcester Pearmain*, are
"tip-bearers," carrying their fruit-buds, especially in early years, at the
end of rather thin, twiggy lateral shoots.

To be fruitful most of such laterals must be left full length. (See
illustration facing page 81.)

Other varieties, such as *Cox's Orange Pippin*, carry a large proportion
of their fruit-buds on naturally-formed fruit-spurs and are known as
"self-spurrers." Such varieties are naturally much easier to spur-
prune than tip-bearers, and can be made to look tidy without ruining
their prospect of cropping, provided always the leaders are not pruned

too hard during the critical period in which the trees are coming into bearing. (See illustration facing page 81.)

The three most popular methods of winter pruning apples are known as the "renewal" system, the "established spur" system and the "regulated," respectively.

The renewal system is to be recommended for most varieties when grown in the forms of open centre and delayed open centre.

The established spur-system, combined with summer pruning, is to be recommended for most of the artificial forms, including cordon, espalier and double U.

The regulated system is recommended for large standard trees in orchards.

The Renewal System.—The leading shoots or leaders are treated according to age, habit and vigour of tree. Under this system it is seldom that more than one-half or two-thirds of the leaders are tipped in any one season. Tipping of the leaders tends to keep the tree small and to delay cropping, so that it should be done as seldom as possible and only to selected leader branches. Importance is attached to keeping leader branches well spaced to at least one foot apart at the tips to give room for leaving laterals full length without overcrowding the tree.

The side shoots or maiden laterals are treated in one of two ways. They are either cut back to within 2 or 3 inches of their base or they are left unpruned. The proportion of shoots in any one tree to undergo each of these treatments depends on the age, varietal habit and vigour of the tree and is a matter which can only be determined by the grower's own experience.

The shoots that are left unpruned for one year are generally cut back at the end of the next season, removing from one-half to two-thirds of each shoot according to circumstances. It is important to see that a replacement shoot is trained in to preserve the upward and outward growing habit of each main branch as it begins to come down with the weight of the crop.

The Established Spur System.—In early years all the leaders on all but the most vigorous varieties are tipped regularly to ensure strong framework branches. When the trees are being brought into cropping, tipping of the leaders becomes much lighter and may cease altogether for a time.

When the trees are in full cropping, tipping of the leaders varies in severity with the growth and cropping.

The pruning treatment of the maiden laterals varies with the strength and position of each. Until the tree is in full cropping, as many laterals as possible on the outside of the tree should be left unpruned to develop axillary fruit-buds. Very strong laterals are best cut clean out at the base. Medium and weak laterals are cut back to within about 3 or 4 inches of their base to form the beginning of the established spur system. Any shoots that grow out on the young spur during the season are cut back to within an inch or two of their base the following winter, with a view to stimulating the development of a fruit bud and fruit on the original spur. After some years these artificially induced spur systems may become overcrowded and too large, and must then be reduced both in number and in size.

When this system of pruning is used on cordons, espaliers and other artificial forms it may be advisable to combine it with summer pruning. This operation is performed in July or August, when most of the young shoots are stiffening, and consists of cutting or breaking the shoots about 4 to 5 inches from the base. In some seasons secondary growth may follow this pruning and should be cut off in the course of the routine winter spurring.

The Regulated System.—No attempt is made to tip leaders or to spur laterals, but ingrowing and crossing branches are cut out or cut back to prevent the tree from becoming lop-sided or thick in the middle.

The more artificial the form of the tree, the more difficult it is to lay down hard and fast rules for successful pruning. With the standard and the bush forms the vegetative vigour of the tree can be distributed in lateral shoots over a large number of main branches, but when it comes to limiting the main branches to one, two, three or even to ten main branches as in cordons, pyramids, fuseaux and espaliers, there will always be the problem of how to deal with the dense crop of closely-growing new laterals which in the more natural forms of tree have room to spread themselves without overcrowding. With such trees the first essential is to leave the leaders as long as possible in order to counteract the tendency to throw out strong new shoots immediately behind them. Late spring pruning of the leader, when about one inch of new growth has already been made, will prove an additional check to this unwanted vegetative vigour, but probably the most certain method for all these artificial forms of tree is to adopt one or other of the summer pruning treatments already described in Chapter V.

Apples of Upright Habit of Growth.	*Apples of Spreading Habit of Growth.*	*Varieties that Need to be Pruned lightly.*
Adam's Pearmain	Belle de Boskoop	Blenheim Orange
Annie Elizabeth	Blenheim Orange	Bramley's Seedling
Christmas Pearmain	Bramley's Seedling	Belle de Boskoop
Edward VII	Gladstone	
Egremont Russet	Lane's Prince Albert	
Heusgen's Golden Reinette	Langley Pippin	
John Standish		
King of the Pippins		
Lord Derby		
Orleans Reinette		
Worcester Pearmain		

MANURING OF APPLES

Potassium.—When there is reason to suspect a deficiency of potassium available to the tree, and " scorch " is prevalent on the margins of the leaf, the " immediate action " is to apply potash. Experiments have shown that sulphate of potash is the most satisfactory form in which to apply potassium to the soil for apple trees, in amounts varying from 1 to 4 cwt. per acre ($\frac{1}{2}$ to 2 oz. per square yard), but at present Muriate of Potash is easier to get, and should be applied at the same rate.

Nitrogen.—Young apple trees are usually better without nitrogenous manures. For trees in bearing the quantity required depends on the kind, variety and growth-conditions of the tree. For instance, cooking apples will take more nitrogen than dessert apples, and among dessert apples *Cox's Orange Pippin* will take more than *Worcester Pearmain.*

Symptoms of Excess Nitrogen.—Much vigorous shoot growth, very large, dark green leaves, badly-coloured fruit of greasy texture and poor keeping quality, and susceptibility to attack by the canker fungus, all these are symptoms of excess nitrogen in the apple tree. Trees showing such symptoms should receive no nitrogenous manures, and cultivations should be stopped altogether or limited to the first half of the growing season. Other alternatives are to leave the trees entirely unpruned, and in extreme cases to ring-bark or even to root-prune.

Symptoms of Nitrogen Deficiency.—Small weak shoots, small pale green leaves, small, sweet, highly-coloured fruit of good texture and good keeping quality, these are the symptoms of nitrogen shortage in the apple tree. The high colour of the fruit and the good keeping quality are both desirable conditions in dessert apples, and where these are required the less nitrogen the trees get the better, so long as the leaf does not get too small and yellow and provided the trees are not allowed to stop growing altogether. When this happens, it is often better, before applying nitrogen, to try the effect of thorough cultivations or hard pruning. Trees on weak stocks may be invigorated by planting one or more vigorous rootstocks close beside the tree and inarching them into the stem below the bottom branches. Trees which are deficient both in nitrogen and in potassium will require heavy feeding with potash before they can benefit from applications of nitrogenous manures.

Forms and Amounts of Nitrogen for Apple Trees.—Of the organic forms of manure, farmyard dung, up to 25 tons per acre, high-grade shoddy, at 20 to 30 cwt. per acre, and meat and bonemeal, at 5 to 6 cwt. per acre, are most widely used by commercial growers for supplying nitrogen to apple trees. The organic forms are generally used on light soils to keep the moisture in the ground during the summer months.

Of the inorganic forms of nitrogenous fertilizer, sulphate of ammonia, nitrate of soda, and nitro-chalk are the most popular and are given usually in two half-dressings, say in February and May. Strong-growing varieties of cooking apples, such as *Bramley's Seedling* when in full bearing, may require up to 5 cwt. per acre, or even more, to give healthy foliage and large-sized fruits, provided the potash applications are being well-maintained. Dessert apples like *Cox's Orange Pippin*, on the other hand, even when in full bearing, should not usually require more than half this amount.

Phosphorus.—Field experiments have so far failed to show exactly in what way, if any, phosphorus is necessary for an apple tree in this country. At the same time, many successful fruit growers emphasize the importance of this element, and until experiments prove it to be unnecessary, experts are agreed in recommending the application of some form of phosphatic manure to apple trees. Steamed bone flour is, perhaps, the most popular of the organic forms, and superphosphates and basic slag are both used as inorganic forms. Rates of application vary, 5 cwt. per acre being about the average dressing, applied in winter or very early spring.

GUIDE TO THE MANURING OF APPLE TREES

The following table indicates the conditions under which the requirements of the trees for Potassium (K) and Nitrogen (N) are likely to be either more or less than normal.

	Subsoil Sandy, Gravelly or Badly-drained	Hard Pruned	Light Pruned	Cooking Apple	Dessert Apple	Unculti-vated (Grass or Weeds)	Cultivated (No weeds or grass)
Potassium (K)	More	More	Less	Less	More	Less	More
Nitrogen (N) .	More	Less	More	More	Less	More	Less

INDICATIONS OF MANURIAL REQUIREMENTS

Symptoms	Probable Cause
Leaves, marginal browning, " Leaf-scorch "	Potash deficiency
Leaves, large and dark green, vigorous shoot growth; badly-coloured fruit of greasy texture and poor keeping quality	Excess of Nitrogen
Leaves, small and pale green, weak shoots; small, highly-coloured, sweet fruit of good texture and good keeping quality	Nitrogen deficiency

FRUIT THINNING

The three main objects in fruit thinning are to increase the ultimate size of the fruits which remain, to give a uniform sample, and to induce regular bearing in the tree. There is no doubt that with the codling types of apple, such as *Early Victoria* (*Emneth Early*), thinning the fruits to 8 or 10 inches apart when they are the size of walnuts is the best way to get large fruit. The same is true of varieties like *Miller's Seedling*, which normally produce rather small-sized apples.

It is becoming a widespread practice among commercial fruit-growers to thin dessert apples such as *Worcester Pearmain* and *Cox's Orange Pippin*, leaving not more than two, and often only one fruit to a truss, with a view to getting uniformity of size in the fruit. When thinning, the centre fruit of each truss, the " King " apple, is removed, because it is usually an abnormal fruit, which is often misshapen, and does not always keep well in store.

The best way to thin apples is to take the stalk between the first and second fingers of the right hand and to push the apple gently but firmly off its stalk with the thumb of the same hand.

GATHERING OF FRUIT

Different varieties of apples ripen in different months. Early ripening varieties should be picked over more than once, and cannot be kept for more than a few weeks except in low-temperature stores. Keeping varieties of apple develop more slowly, and late colouring varieties, if they are to be really well coloured, ought to be left on the tree as long as possible. One of the best tests of whether an apple is ready for picking is to lift it gently on its stalk. If the apple comes away without an effort, the fruit is usually sufficiently ripe to finish the rest of the ripening process off the tree. If it is picked at a stage when the stalk has to be torn off, there is a likelihood that the apple may not keep well in ordinary storage. It should be emphasized, however, that for low-temperature storage of any kind, the fruit is best picked rather sooner than it would be for ordinary storage.

For selections of *Early, Mid-season* and *Late* varieties, see page 149.

Weather for Gathering.—Apples should be gathered when they are quite dry and should not be exposed unnecessarily to the sun after being picked.

For *Storing* and *Marketing*, see pages 87–91.

INSECT PESTS OF THE APPLE

Apples are liable to attack by more pests than any other fruit crop, and this accounts for the large Spray Schedule for apples given on page 109.

WINTER MOTHS

In the spring the opening buds are attacked by caterpillars of the Winter Moth. These are at first very small and dark coloured, but eventually become an inch or more in length, green in colour, and with a characteristic " looping " method of walking. When small they feed in the buds and blossom trusses, but when foliage becomes more plentiful, they feed on the leaves and fruits. In very large numbers they can defoliate the trees, with serious consequences. In June they drop to the ground and turn to pupæ (chrysalids) in the soil. Here they remain till winter comes, when the moths emerge and make their way to the branches and twigs. There they lay their small, oval, at first green but later reddish-brown eggs from which the destructive caterpillars ultimately develop.

The March Moth is the latest of the several species of winter moth to emerge in the spring. It differs from the others in its habit of laying its full complement of eggs not singly but in a band around a twig.

Control.—Although the male moths can fly readily, the females have no proper wings, and are therefore obliged to crawl up the trunks of the trees. Attack by caterpillars of this type of moth can therefore be prevented by applying grease-bands to the tree trunks in October, and by ensuring that the " tackiness " of the grease is maintained till the spring. If grease-banding is not practised, the trees should be sprayed with lead arsenate or D.D.T., when the caterpillars start to appear in April and May.

TORTRIX MOTHS

Tortrix caterpillars can always be recognized by their habit of wriggling backwards when disturbed, and by the way in which they spin the leaves together. Some kinds hibernate as tiny caterpillars encased in cocoons of silk and rubbish, which they construct in crevices and under loose bark. They come to life in the spring and eat their way into the buds, which then wilt or shrivel and turn brown. Later, they feed on the leaves, which they spin together for protection, and, in May or June, turn to chrysalids and then to moths. These lay minute, pale green, almost colourless eggs on the leaves, either singly or in clusters. About the middle of July more caterpillars hatch out and feed on the leaves and frequently on the fruit too. Small portions of the skin of the apple are eaten but the damage often passes unnoticed when the fruit is picked. Consequently the caterpillars may be introduced into the fruit store, where they continue their feeding. Rotting follows and soon spreads to neighbouring sound apples.

Control.—No one remedy as yet seems adequate for the control of these destructive caterpillars, but they can be kept within reasonable limits by the various spray mixtures used for other pests (see page 109).

Tar-oil winter washes destroy the more accessible of the hibernating larvæ, but lead arsenate or D.D.T. at the green cluster stage is more effective. For the fruit-eating generation mid-July sprays of non-poisonous materials such as derris or D.D.T. should be used.

GREENFLY

Several species of aphides (green- or blackfly) occur on apple trees, and when plentiful can cripple the growth and reduce the crop. The Permanent Green Apple Aphis (*Aphis pomi*) and the Rosy Aphis, or Blue Bug (*Anuraphis roseus*) both spend the winter on the trees as small, black, shiny eggs. The eggs of the former are laid thickly clustered together on the young sappy shoots, whilst those of the Rosy Aphis are laid singly, mainly on the spurs.

The *Green Aphis* hatches at bud-break, but does little damage until June, when it becomes abundant on the younger growths. These become stunted and malformed and often die back from the tip.

The *Rosy Aphis* is a larger insect and can be distinguished by its bluish or purple colour and mealy appearance. It causes more damage than any other apple aphis, feeding not only on the leaves and shoots, but on the newly-formed fruits also. Badly-affected fruits may drop off altogether ; those that remain are stunted and deformed, especially at the eye end, which becomes " knobbly." In July this insect migrates to certain weeds, such as plantain, but returns to the apple in the autumn.

Owing to their habit of curling the leaves on which they feed, aphides are not always reached by spring or summer spraying with nicotine, but the eggs are easily destroyed by winter tar-oil washes.

WOOLLY APHIS OR AMERICAN BLIGHT (*Eriosoma lanigerum*)

This is a severe pest in the nursery and is often troublesome, though of less economic importance, on established trees. The insect itself is reddish in colour, but produces masses of waxy wool which hangs in festoons from the branches. A few aphides spend the winter on the trunk or main branches, in the shelter of cracks or crevices, and further protected by their covering of wool. In the spring they reproduce rapidly and so give rise to the heavy infestations often experienced in early summer. The insects are spread from tree to tree by the wind, or partly by the wind and partly by crawling over the ground.

The feeding of Woolly Aphis causes gall-like swellings on the twigs and branches. Badly attacked twigs often die ; in any case the galls enlarge and split and become cankerous or provide a ready entrance for the troublesome fungous disease " Apple Canker."

Control.—If Woolly Aphis is present when the trees are lifted from the nursery they should be dipped in a 10 per cent. solution of tar-oil wash. In the nursery the pest can be kept within bounds by painting the larger colonies with methylated spirit, and by spraying thoroughly with nicotine and soap. Larger trees should, if necessary, also be sprayed with nicotine, preferably at petal-fall but thorough winter spraying with tar-oil may keep the pest in check. Should it become troublesome in summer it can be dealt with by means of nicotine, used in conjunction with plenty of soap or with a summer-oil emulsion.

APPLE BLOSSOM WEEVIL *(Anthonomus pomorum)*

Very soon after the Winter Moth and Tortrix caterpillars start their damage, the Apple Blossom Weevil emerges from the litter, loose bark or other rubbish in which it has sheltered during the winter, and begins to feed on the buds. This insect is about an eighth of an inch or more in length, grey or black in colour, with a silvery V-shaped mark on its back. It is more or less oval in shape and possesses a long, slightly curved snout or rostrum, the apex of which is furnished with small, powerful jaws. It feeds on the sides of the buds, making small, round holes in the still folded leaves. The chief damage, however, is caused by the grub, which hatches in April from an egg laid within the flower-bud. On hatching it feeds on the stamens and style, sticking the petals down to form a kind of tent above it. Affected blossoms never open but remain " capped " until the petals turn brown and drop off. Such blossoms cannot be pollinated and so are usually unable to set fruit. The grub, which is white and legless and has a black head, develops into a yellow chrysalis and, subsequently, into an adult beetle. In this form it leaves the capped blossom and, after feeding for a while on the leaves and fruits, seeks out suitable sleeping quarters in which to remain till the following spring.

Control.—Egg-laying should be prevented by applying D.D.T. when the buds are bursting. The D.D.T. can be used alone or mixed with a late winter wash, for which purpose a wettable powder is very suitable.

APPLE SUCKER *(Psylla mali)*

Since the advent of tar-oil winter washes, this pest has practically disappeared and is now found chiefly in gardens and neglected plantations. The young insects hatch out, as soon as the buds break, from tiny, yellow, cigar-shaped eggs, which are laid on the spurs and smaller branches in the autumn. They somewhat resemble greenfly but are flatter and have prominent eyes. The young suckers, which are at first minute and yellow and may occur in large numbers, creep into the opening buds and suck the sap. Buds turn brown and fail to grow out, or the blossom may appear and then shrivel and drop off. Sucker damage has often been attributed to frost, but can always be recognized from the drops of white, sticky wax which exude from the suckers. The adult insect is rather more than a tenth of an inch long and possesses transparent wings, which are held roof-like over its back when not in use.

Control.—Sucker eggs can be easily destroyed in winter by means of a tar-oil wash. If this is not done and Sucker appears in the spring, recourse must be had to nicotine, which may be added to one of the pre-blossom scab sprays. (See Guide to Spraying, page 109.)

APPLE CAPSID BUG *(Plesiocoris rugicollis)*

When the leaves of the blossom trusses have unfolded, and the green flower buds are visible, the young of the Apple Capsid begin to hatch out. They are very small and green and somewhat resemble greenfly, but are very active. They feed on both leaves and fruits, first piercing the tissue with their needle-like-stylets, and then pumping in salivary juices to enable them to suck up partially-digested sap. Certain toxic materials contained in the salivary juices cause the death of the punctured cells and surrounding tissue.

The first signs of Capsid damage are small black marks, later becoming brown and turning into holes, on the young leaves. Soon after the fruits are set, the bugs feed upon them, the ultimate result frequently being small, deformed fruits disfigured with corky scars. As the bugs grow in size, they acquire wing pads, fully-developed wings appearing only at the final moult. The winged, adult insects fly from tree to tree, laying their small, elongated eggs beneath the rind of the twigs and branches. Some damage is done by these adult bugs, which feed on the succulent new shoots, producing corky scars and sometimes distorting or even killing the shoots.

Control.—The eggs can be killed by winter spraying with petroleum or D.N.C. emulsions. This is generally but not always effective and may cause some bud injury. Nicotine, applied just before the blossom opens, can be effective but demands favourable weather and good timing.

APPLE SAWFLY *(Hoplocampa testudinea)*

This insect makes its appearance when the trees are in bloom, and feeds on the pollen. The adult is rather more than a quarter of an inch in length, with transparent wings, a conspicuous head and a pair of short, thick antennæ. The under belly is yellow, but the upper surface is black. The female drills a hole just below the sepals with her saw-like ovipositor, and deposits an egg in the calyx tissue at the base of the stamens. The "sting" mark below the calyx can readily be detected as a minute brown spot, and after practice the egg also can easily be found. After a week or more a small, white, black-headed larva or caterpillar hatches from the egg and enters the side of the fruitlet. At first it tunnels just below the skin but ultimately reaches and eats out the centre. The infected fruit drops, but not before the larva has deserted it and entered a sound one, this time by boring a round hole in the side. A wet black mass or a yellow fluid dripping from the side of a fruit is a symptom of sawfly attack.

When fully fed, the larva drops to the soil and spins a tough, parchment-like cocoon an inch or two below the surface. Here it remains till the spring, when it pupates, finally turning to an adult and emerging from the soil when the apples are in bloom.

Control.—The egg can be killed by an application of nicotine at petal-fall. Care should be taken to drench the trees so that the spray reaches the eye of the fruitlets within a few days of the fall of the petals. If this spray is neglected, all that can be done is to apply a dust of derris or D.D.T. when migration and the secondary attack by the young larvæ begin (late in May), in the hope of arresting some of this secondary attack.

CODLING MOTH *(Cydia pomonella)*

This insect also is responsible for maggoty apples, but its damage may easily be distinguished from that of Apple Sawfly. The damage occurs much later—sawfly larvæ having left the trees and most of the damaged fruits having dropped by the end of June, when the first small Codling larvæ begin to attack the fruits. Moreover, Codling-damaged apples, if they drop at all, do not do so until shortly before picking time. If an apple is picked for eating and found to be maggoty, it is almost certainly attacked by Codling and not by Sawfly.

The moth itself does not appear until after petal-fall. It is grey in colour, with dark markings towards the tips of the wings, which have an expanse of about half an inch. It is shy and seldom seen, since it flies chiefly at dusk and at sunrise and then only when the air is calm. The eggs are no bigger than a pin's head and are laid on the skin of the fruit or on the leaves. They are inconspicuous and almost transparent.

After hatching, the little white caterpillar eats its way into the fruit either at the eye or through the side, and feeds in the neighbourhood of the core. Often it reveals its presence by the heap of brown excrement which it pushes out of the entrance hole. When it leaves the fruit it spins a cocoon in any convenient crevice. It is usually a pale pink colour by this time and spends the autumn and winter as a larva in the cocoon, turning to a chrysalis in the spring or early summer.

In some seasons a few manage to pupate almost immediately, and a second generation of moths is the result. These give rise to more maggoty apples in September and October.

Control.—Codling is more difficult to contend with than Sawfly. Lead arsenate should be applied late in June. As the egg-laying period is a long one, extending well into July, further applications may have to be made. For all but late-picked varieties these later sprayings should be of derris or D.D.T. and not of lead arsenate. D.D.T. is very effective against Codling but must be used with circumspection since much summer spraying may lead to an increase of Red Spider.

RED SPIDER (*Metatetranychus ulmi*)

This pest has increased since the advent of tar-oil washes which destroy some of the enemies of the Red Spider, but which are ineffective against the pest itself. The small, round, red winter eggs are laid in the autumn on the older twigs. These hatch out when the trees are in bloom, and the young spiders, or "mites," feed on the undersides of the leaves till they are fully grown. Summer eggs are laid throughout the summer from petal-fall onwards and vast numbers of the mites are sometimes produced, which by their feeding turn the leaves a brownish colour and absorb sap which would normally go into growth or fruit.

Control.—The lime-sulphur sprays applied for Apple Scab (particularly at petal-fall) are valuable in destroying the active stages of this pest. Sulphur-shy varieties, such as *Lane's Prince Albert*, cannot receive this treatment and for them derris or a special summer petroleum-oil emulsion is recommended. The most satisfactory control, however, is obtained by the use of a winter petroleum spray in February or March, and this will control Capsid too.

It is necessary to add a word of warning. It sometimes happens that the mites migrate, given suitable weather conditions, and drift through the air. From these migrants late summer attacks can arise, in spite of all previous spray treatment, and require further spraying with lime-sulphur or summer oil. Materials, such as derivatives of dinitrocyclohexylphenol, have been developed specially for summer use against Red Spider but have not yet found wide acceptance.

MINOR PESTS

The foregoing are the commonest and most important insect pests of the apple. There are many others which can be very troublesome at times, such as the Fruit Rhynchites (*Rhynchites æquatus*), which drills holes in the sides of the fruit, the Twig Cutter (*Rhynchites cæruleus*), which cuts off the growing shoots in June, and the Apple Fruit Miner (*Argyresthia conjugella*), which makes holes in the side, and tunnels in the flesh of the fruit.

Mention should also be made of the Clay-coloured Weevil (*Otiorhynchus singularis*), which destroys grafts, and of the Pith Moth (*Blastodacna hellerella*), the larvæ of which destroy the opening buds.

Other minor pests are the Wood Leopard, the Goat Moth, Clear-wing Moth, Lackey Moth, Case-bearers, Shot Hole Beetles, Scale Insects, and Chafer Beetle Grubs.

DISEASES OF THE APPLE

SCAB *(Venturia inæqualis)*

Often known as Black Spot, this is by far the most prevalent and most destructive disease of apples in this country. It attacks the leaves and fruits of all susceptible varieties and the bud-scales and shoots of some, particularly the shoots of *Cox's Orange Pippin* and *Worcester Pearmain.* On these it forms blister-like pads ("pustules") of fungous tissue that are exposed in spring when the bark covering them splits, and the spores formed on the surface of the pustule are dispersed, probably by wind-blown rain. On the leaves and fruits the disease appears as more or less circular, olive-green spots. These are velvety in texture at first because they are rapidly producing spores, but later they become rather dry and corky in the centre, when they more nearly resemble " scabs."

Scab-infection is also responsible for indirect adverse effects. The pustules on the young shoots are a source of entry for the canker fungus, while fruits that are infected early and subsequently crack are victims of fruit-rotting organisms, such as brown rots and moulds, in storage. The crop can be greatly reduced by an early infection of the tiny fruitlets which causes them to drop.

Infection occurs in spring (primary) and throughout the summer months (secondary). As the host-tissues get older they become less susceptible to attack. Infection may arise from spores dispersed from (a) dead, over-wintered leaves on the ground, (b) pustules on the one-year-old shoots of susceptible varieties, (c) pustules on the bud-scales of susceptible varieties, e.g., *Worcester Pearmain.*

The prevalence of the disease greatly depends on the weather conditions in April and May. If, in general, this period is wet and cool, infection is encouraged, for these conditions are very suitable for the growth of the fungus and they tend also to hold the trees for a long period in a very susceptible condition. The converse is equally true. The soil, cultivation, manurial programme and the rootstock can each influence the susceptibility of the host-variety. Excessive nitrogenous manuring, which delays the ripening or "hardening" of the growth, and promotes luxuriant foliage that keeps the tree moist after rain, tends to increase susceptibility to Scab while potash manuring tends to correct this, although the manurial problem is certainly not as simple as would appear from this generalization.

Control.—There are two chief methods : (a) general sanitation which includes collecting and burning, or burying fallen leaves in autumn, and pruning that opens up the head of the tree to light and air, and removes scabbed shoots. (b) spraying to protect all new growth as it develops.

Lime-sulphur should be used at the following periods :

(1) *Green-cluster* or *green-bud*, when the short-stalked flower-buds are still tightly clustered, the sepals are mostly covering the petals, and the truss is surrounded by a rosette of half-expanded leaves. Use $2\frac{1}{2}$ per cent.

(2) *Pink-bud*, immediately pre-blossom, when individual flower-buds are well separated, the " cap " of petals not covered by the sepals and showing bold pink, and the truss is surrounded by fully-expanded leaves. Use 2 per cent.

(3) *Petal-fall.* When about three-quarters of the petals have fallen. Use 1 per cent. This spray can cause leaf-burn, leaf-drop, and fruit-drop on certain varieties such as *Stirling Castle, Lane's Prince Albert, St. Cecilia,* and *Belle de Boskoop,* and these should have no lime-sulphur after blossoming. In dry, warm summers, *Cox's Orange Pippin, Newton Wonder, Rival, Beauty of Bath, Duchess's Favourite,* and some others, are liable to show leaf- and fruit-drop from this spray. Where previous experience has shown this to be so, the strength may be reduced to $\frac{3}{4}$ per cent. or even to $\frac{2}{3}$ per cent., or alternatively, a colloidal or other sulphur preparation, or one of the more recently introduced mercurial sprays, used at maker's directions, can be tried, though poor control of Red Spider must then be expected. A mixture of weak lime-sulphur with one of these other sulphur preparations may also be used.

(4) *Fruitlet*, two weeks after petal-fall. Repeat petal-fall spray.

These four sprayings should suffice, but later ones can be given if necessary. It is always best to spray before infection occurs so that the fungicide can act protectively. D.D.T. or lead arsenate may be mixed with lime-sulphur *before* blossom for the control of caterpillars ; indeed, the combined spray is more effective against Scab than lime-sulphur alone. Lead arsenate must not be used with weak lime-sulphur of 1 per cent. or less because of the risk of arsenical spray damage, but there is no such risk in using it with colloidal or similar sulphur preparations. Dusting, either with ground sulphur or with copper-lime dust, is a useful adjunct to spraying, for application can be rapidly made. It should be borne in mind, however, that dust can drift over a wide area, and with sulphur, interplanted sulphur-shy varieties are liable to be adversely affected, while with copper-lime dust, the onset of prolonged, showery weather after application is likely to lead to copper injury on the fruits. This is usually seen as small, purplish-brown, circular, " peppering " of the skin, and its effects can be as severe as those of Scab itself. Copper sprays and dusts are not generally safe on apples, and they are not widely recommended.

The type of soil, the weather conditions, the rootstock and the manurial treatment each and all influence the trees' susceptibility not only to Scab but also to spray damage. Differing experiences in this connection are thus commonly met with, and no hard and fast ruling is possible.

In general, *Charles Ross, Stirling Castle, Egremont Russet, Belle de Boskoop*, and *King Edward VII* are highly resistant to Scab ; *Beauty of Bath, Gladstone, Lord Derby, Early Victoria, Grenadier, Rival, Lane's Prince Albert, John Standish* and *Duchess's Favourite* are not very susceptible ; *Cox's Orange Pippin, Worcester Pearmain, Allington Pippin, Newton Wonder, Bramley's Seedling, Annie Elizabeth, Bismarck, James Grieve, Laxton's Superb* and *Wellington* are usually very susceptible.

Scab sometimes develops on stored apples, but inadequate spraying early in the season is usually to blame. Spores from older infections are washed over the skin of the fruit in splashing rain just before picking, and they give rise to Scab in the store, particularly when the fruit is stored in a moist condition.

CANKER *(Nectria galligena)*

This disease is very prevalent in some places, and is commonly said to be associated with poor drainage. At the same time it must be admitted that severe Canker is occasionally found on soils that are well drained though lacking perhaps some other desirable character, and in several instances heavy nitrogenous manuring has been suspect. Infection is most commonly centred around buds or fruit spurs, and not usually in wounds made by pruning until these have healed, when the fungus may become established on the calloused surface. Cankers can also occur where Woolly Aphis or Apple Scab has first attacked the shoots.

The cankers often develop elliptically around the centre of infection, making more progress along the length of an affected branch than across the breadth. The cankered area is usually concentrically sunken and discoloured, and fringed, particularly in persistent wet weather, with a ridge of disintegrating stem tissue from which the covering bark flakes irregularly.

Sometimes the canker girdles an affected branch, resulting in its death above the canker.

This fungus bears two kinds of fruit-body, each of which occurs on cankered areas : (*a*) Small, whitish pustules burst through the bark, often in rings around the centre of infection. They produce spores plentifully in spring and autumn and following wet periods in summer, and these are capable of causing fresh infections through wounds. (*b*) Crimson, spherical bodies densely clustered together in groups. Superficially, these resemble the eggs of the Fruit Tree Red Spider, but the latter are a brighter red, and are found on healthy as well as on diseased areas. These fruit-bodies produce spores in large quantities in winter and early spring, and are a very real source of danger in the plantation. Apple Canker can also cause an " Eye Rot " of the fruits, but there is a similar disease, " Dry Eye Rot," caused by another fungus, *Botrytis cinerea*, with which it can easily be confused.

Control.—The best method is to cut out the cankers as soon as they are seen, and before the fruit-bodies have been produced. A sharp gouge, or hollow-ground chisel, is very useful for this work with older cankers where the wood is affected. All diseased tissue, and dead or dying branches, should be removed and burnt. Though it is commonly held that the wounds should be dressed with a white-lead paint to prevent reinfection, experience shows that if the cankers are thoroughly cleaned out painting is unnecessary, except on varieties prone to Silver Leaf infection (see page 133). The normal programme of sprays for Scab control has little direct effect on the incidence of Canker, but the control of Scab and Woolly Aphis is indirectly helpful. Badly-drained soil should be aerated by some system of drainage.

Many commercial and garden varieties are susceptible, notably : *Worcester Pearmain, James Grieve, Laxton's Superb, Ellison's Orange, Warner's King, Beauty of Bath, Orleans Reinette* and *Cox's Orange Pippin.* This last is more susceptible on No. XII and No. XVI than on most other stocks in the Malling series. *Bramley's Seedling, Grenadier, Early Victoria, Gladstone* and *Newton Wonder* are amongst the most resistant.

BROWN ROTS (see also Plum, page 240)
Blossom Wilt and Spur Canker (*Sclerotinia laxa, forma mali*).

The flowers become infected by spores from pustules on dead twigs and withered flowers infected during the previous year. Sometimes the whole flower-truss withers and dies when the fungus grows down the flower-stalks and into the spur, forming a canker there which sometimes extends into the branch and kills it.

The variety *Lord Derby* is very susceptible, trees being sometimes so badly infected that the branch system is almost completely destroyed by the disease.

Control.—Cankered branches and spurs should be promptly cut out and burnt, for *grey-coloured* pustules of spores arise on them in the following spring, and these can, in their turn, infect the flower-trusses and so continue the disease-cycle. Spraying late in the dormant period with 5 per cent. tar-distillate wash, very thoroughly applied, burns up the fungus pustules on any dead spurs that may have been overlooked in the cutting out.

It is thought that this fungus is distinct from that which causes Blossom Wilt of plums and cherries, hence, that apples are not likely to be infected from plums and cherries.

Brown Rot (Sclerotinia fructigena).

This disease causes heavy loss of picked fruits every year. The fungus produces a brown, soft rot of the fruits on the trees, usually within a few weeks of picking-time, and also after they are picked and stored. Spore-pustules are very readily produced on an infected fruit, often in concentric rings around the point of infection. Under certain storage conditions, however, a fruit may turn black and may bear few or no pustules.

The fungus gains entry through a blemish where the skin has been pierced ; this may happen in many ways—bird pecks, insect punctures, cracking following Scab or spray-injury, hail or spur damage, rough handling during picking operations, etc. A diseased fruit is capable of infecting a healthy one by persistent contact on the tree or in the orchard box.

It is wise, therefore, to discard blemished apples at picking-time and during the preliminary sorting before the fruits are graded.

A *spur-canker* similar to that caused by the Blossom-Wilt fungus sometimes occurs on soft-wooded varieties such as *Lord Derby* and *James Grieve*. This arises when the fungus grows along the fruit-stalk and into the spur.

Control.—Dead spurs, which early in the following summer bear relatively large, *buff-coloured* pustules of spores (by which this fungus can be distinguished from that causing Blossom Wilt and Spur Canker) should be cut out and burnt.

If infected fruits are permitted to remain on the tree, they become mummified, and, in late spring and summer, are covered with the familiar buff-coloured spore-pustules. Mummied fruits should be removed and burnt where they persist for they are a common source of infection. The spores are light and powdery when dry, and are easily blown about in the wind. They are also carried from fruit to fruit by insects. Spraying for Scab and Insect control is helpful.

APPLE MILDEW *(Podosphaera leucotricha)*

Affected shoots and leaves are white and mealy ; flower-trusses present a similar appearance, and the flowers are small and distorted and often fail to open. The buds become infected in summer and remain all winter with the fungus spawn alive between the bud-scales. Such buds grow out into mildewed shoots in spring or they may be killed and fail to start into growth. The powdery spores produced on affected shoots and leaves carry infection to healthy tissues throughout the summer ; the spores are mainly wind-borne. A winter stage in the form of tiny, black fruit-bodies, produced mainly on the shoots, is thought to have little influence in this country on the annual cycle of the fungus.

Occasionally the fruits are affected. *Lane's Prince Albert* is a susceptible variety to this form of attack. Affected fruits bear the whitish, mealy fungus-tissue on the surface of the skin.

Control.—Cut out and burn infected shoots and flower-trusses, and spray as for Apple Scab.

Among susceptible varieties are *Lane's Prince Albert, Cox's Orange Pippin, Bismarck, Bramley's Seedling, Allington Pippin. Worcester Pearmain* is resistant.

ARMILLARIA ROOT ROT (Honey Fungus—*Armillaria mellea*)

This fungus is commonly found in woodlands, and it frequently causes a serious disease of conifers and of broad-leaved trees. It spreads underground by means of strands of fungous tissue that look rather like black boot-laces ; indeed the disease is often said to be caused by the " Bootlace Fungus." When these " boot-laces " come into contact with the roots of fruit trees, they are able to attack them, causing infection which spreads back along the infected roots to the collar of the tree. Eventually all the feeding roots may be affected and the tree dies. This may happen suddenly if the collar of the tree is soon girdled by the fungal strands. The fungus produces sporing fructifications, usually in autumn, on the dead stump and on the surface of the soil immediately surrounding it. These fructifications are like toadstools and are usually densely clustered together. The " umbrella " of each " toadstool " may be from 2 to 4 inches across ; it is honey-coloured and, when young, often bears dark scales on its upper surface. The bark of a dead tree can readily be peeled off, and underneath, between it and the wood, fan-like layers of white fungous tissue, sometimes flecked with black lines, will be found. These layers have a distinct fungous odour.

The fungus attacks not only apples but pears, plums, cherries, gooseberries, and even strawberries. The leaves usually show the first symptoms ; they are yellow, sickly, and may be wilting, often over the whole tree, but since there are other possible causes (see Waterlogging) an accurate diagnosis must depend on the presence or absence of the fungus.

Control.—It is most important that trees dying from attack by Armillaria Root Rot should be promptly removed and burnt. The digging-out of broken roots must be thorough and the sites of affected trees should be kept cultivated and, if planted up at all, used for annual crops such as potatoes for several years before being replanted with fruit. Frequent stirring of the soil breaks up any " boot-laces " or bits of affected root that remain, helps to dry them out and prevents the fungus from becoming re-established on the roots of weeds, which help to keep it going. Close watch must be kept on adjoining trees for the first symptoms of attack, and any that show these should also be promptly removed and destroyed, for only in this way can an outbreak be checked. Cleared woodland is best put down to arable crops for at least three or four years before fruit is planted up, otherwise there is considerable risk of infection.

Since the fungus can also attack fencing poles, these should be well creosoted before setting up.

When thinning out overcrowded plantations, it is bad practice to leave tree-stumps in the ground, for the fungus can become established on them by means of spores dispersed from the toadstools.

CROWN GALL *(Bacterium tumefaciens)*

This bacterium occurs in the soil and infects the roots of apple stocks and many other plants including raspberries, loganberries, and blackberries. Wounds are a common source of entry. The bacterium produces galls or tumours of up to several inches in diameter on the roots and on the stems near soil level. East Malling, No. VII rootstock is particularly susceptible.

The galls probably have very little adverse effect on the tree in most cases.

Control.—Affected stocks should not be planted in nurseries and precautions should be taken to protect wounds from infection, e.g., by covering with grafting-wax, or by dipping the roots in a mercurial preparation.

SILVER LEAF

This disease is described under Plum, page 242. In apple the most susceptible variety is *Newton Wonder*, infection often being associated with a condition popularly known as " Papery Bark." The danger to *Newton Wonder* is in *top*-grafting it to another variety, when large wounds must be made on established trees.

These wounds provide a ready place of entry for the fungus, and they are therefore best avoided by using one of the modern methods of framework grafting (see page 35).

FUNCTIONAL DISEASES

These are non-parasitic diseases due to some disorder in the life-processes of the plant. They are not caused by a fungus or by any other organism of that nature.

WATERLOGGING

The leaf symptoms are similar in some respects to those caused by Armillaria Root Rot in that the foliage wilts and looks sickly. Where Waterlogging, also popularly known as " The Death," is the cause, the wilting usually occurs fairly suddenly and within a few weeks after growth starts in the spring, and it may affect only certain branches or parts of them. An affected tree may have looked quite healthy during the previous year, whereas with Armillaria Root Rot the chronic stage is frequently preceded by symptoms of steady decline. The signs of fungus attack present with Armillaria—toadstools in autumn, " boot-laces " in the soil, a mat of fungus under the bark near the soil—are absent with Waterlogging, and the clue to the cause of the trouble will be found in the root-system. Some of the larger roots show internal, and possibly external, discoloration, and they often have an alcoholic smell when freshly cut. This is due to their having been asphyxiated in a soil where the air has been excluded by excessive moisture, especially in badly-drained soils or pockets of soil during very wet weather in autumn and winter. In severe cases the affected tree dies, though in mild cases only certain branches, or even flower-trusses here and there, may wilt and die.

Another form of the disease is sometimes found when inefficiently staked trees that have been rocked by autumn gales and have then been subjected to heavy rains show a rotting and discoloration of the bark of the collar at ground level, even in an apparently well-drained soil. Here, the soil surrounding the collar has been " puddled " by the intermittent pressure of the swaying trunk and by frequent rain, it becomes impervious, and the excess water collects in the crater so formed, eventually resulting in rotting at the collar and the death of the tree.

Symptoms superficially similar to those of a mild attack of Water-logging are caused by excessive spraying with tar- or petroleum-oil, but in this case, though the bark may be blackened, the roots usually show no sign of disease, and the buds either fail to break, or fail to develop leaves after starting into growth. Severe potash-deficiency occasionally results in the wilting and death in spring of flower-trusses on individual branches of trees, though here, as in Armillaria Root Rot, the appearance of sickliness is a gradual, and not a sudden, process. It can be identified in earlier stages by general debility and a scorching of the margins of the leaves in summer. (See Leaf-Scorch on page 135.)

Control.—Some system of drainage must be adopted for inefficiently drained and very retentive soils. Shallower planting on such soils also is recommended. Very badly drained soils should not be planted with fruit. Efficient staking of trees, especially where they are exposed to gales, will do much to prevent the " collar-rot " form. As no organism is responsible for this disease, an affected tree is not a source of infection to its neighbours.

Some form of this disorder has been found on almost every type of fruit that is grown in this country (e.g., see Root Rot in Straw-berries).

LEAF-SCORCH

The symptoms are best seen in summer when the leaves (especially the older ones) of an affected tree have a reddish-brown margin, sometimes, in bad cases, $\frac{1}{2}$ inch deep. Towards the end of summer, these margins become dark-brown, dry and crisp, and the leaves are " hard " and usually up-curled. The fruits on such a tree are often smaller than normal, lack colour and flavour, and do not store well. Trees on certain rootstocks, e.g., East Malling No. V, are particularly susceptible, and *Cox's Orange Pippin* and *Bramley's Seedling* are susceptible varieties.

Control.—This form of Leaf-Scorch can be controlled by regular applications of a potassic manure (e.g., sulphate or muriate of potash at 3 to 4 cwt. per acre) to restore the nutritional balance.

The symptoms should not be confused with those of lime-sulphur injury, which are superficially similar but are seen usually within a week of a spray-application. Furthermore, the *young* leaves, as well as the older ones, are affected, the spray-burn being present in reddish patches, often, but not always, concentrated around the leaf-margins, which later turn dark brown and die.

A different form of Leaf-Scorch from that caused by shortage of available potash is sometimes found on apples, and it is due to a shortage of available magnesium in the soil. The chief symptom is a thin " feel " with discoloration between the veins, and later in the season these areas die and become brown, thus giving rise to the usual descriptive phrase " interveinal scorch," as opposed to the " marginal scorch " of potash deficiency. The fruits are poor and lack flavour in severe cases. Magnesium deficiency is most usually found on light soils deficient in lime, and is most pronounced in wet seasons. An interesting practical point is that symptoms of magnesium deficiency can be induced on some soils by the too liberal use of potassic manure to correct potash deficiency.

Control.—Magnesian limestone should be substituted for ordinary lime in the normal process of liming acid soils. Trees on neutral or alkaline soil suffering from magnesium deficiency should be sprayed with 2 per cent. magnesium sulphate. It is advisable to consult the local Advisory Officer when magnesium deficiency is suspected.

CHLOROSIS

This disease can affect pears, plums, cherries, and soft fruits as well as apples, the typical symptoms being pronounced loss of green colour and consequent yellowing or even bleaching of the leaves, especially those on the young growths. It is caused by deficiency of available iron, which, though necessary for healthy plant growth in only very small quantities—it is a so-called " trace element "—is nevertheless essential to the proper functioning of the leaves. Without iron the leaves are unable to form the green colouring matter (chlorophyll) on which the nutrition of the plant depends.

Chlorosis is commonly associated with fruit trees growing in soils rich in lime, and is thus frequently referred to as " lime-induced " Chlorosis.*

Control.—Since Chlorosis is due more usually to lack of availability of iron than to its absence, the disease is not likely to be curable by the application of iron salts to the soil, especially where the Chlorosis is " lime-induced." Spraying the leaves with ferrous sulphate at 4 lb. per 100 gallons as a constituent of the 1 per cent. post-blossom lime-sulphur spray for Scab is effective, or solid compounds of iron can be injected into holes bored in the trunk or branches. Grassing-down, too, tends to cure Chlorosis.

BITTER PIT

Within a few weeks before picking time, affected fruits show scattered, slightly sunken, circular areas, in the skin, often on only one side of the fruit. The spots vary in colour from dark green to brownish-green. If the skin covering an affected area of the fruit be peeled off, the flesh immediately underneath each sunken area will be seen to be collapsed and brown in little pockets of up to a quarter of an inch in diameter. The pockets are not usually very deep-seated in the flesh, but are more often near, or at the surface. This disease is known as " tree pit." " Storage pit," another form with the same, or similar, underlying causes, occurs in apples after a period of storage, though the fruits may have seemed quite normal when picked. In storage pit, especially in the early stages, the skin is often not sunken but merely mottled, though when the flesh of the fruit is exposed, numerous, scattered pockets, pinkish-brown in colour, will be seen sometimes extending nearly to the core. These pockets tend to be smaller individually than those of tree-pit, and are often concentrated at the calyx end.

The cause of these troubles is very complex and rather obscure. Hard pruning ; hot, dry weather (particularly when accompanied by hot winds) ; and, with storage pit, too-early picking, are all said to predispose the fruit to the disorder. Bitter Pit is often met with on fruit from young trees just coming into bearing and on those from older trees with only a light crop. Heavy nitrogenous manuring also is suspect.

Control.—The grower is able to control some of these factors, and his general line of attack is to do all he can to promote steady, balanced growth throughout the season, to check biennial bearing as much as possible by judicious pruning and crop regulation, and to avoid any practice likely to cause violent fluctuations in the reaction of the trees. To some extent, however, he must be at the mercy of the weather.

---

* Chlorosis can in some stages be confused with nitrogen or other deficiency symptoms (see *The Diagnosis of Mineral Deficiencies in Plants*, by Dr. T. Wallace).

Bitter Pit has been observed in many varieties. Most of the better-known ones are liable to show symptoms under appropriate conditions, but among these, *Allington Pippin, Newton Wonder, Edward VII, Bramley's Seedling, Lane's Prince Albert*, and *Cox's Orange Pippin* are perhaps the worst offenders.

" GLASSINESS " OR WATER-CORE

Affected apples show yellowish areas, which appear to be water-soaked or " glassy," in the flesh and often around the core. Natural recovery sometimes occurs, but apples prone to Glassiness are liable eventually to develop Bitter Pit. In severe cases, affected fruits appear to have been badly bruised, and in advanced cases, an extensive, discoloured " crinkle " may appear on the surface.

The underlying causes are rather obscure but are known to be similar to those of tree pit. (See page 136.) The varieties *Rival, St. Everard*, and *Lord Lambourne* are prone to Glassiness.

LENTICEL SPOT

Certain varieties, *Allington Pippin* prominent among them, are specially prone to develop small, brown, often sunken spots centred around the lenticels or breathing pores of the fruit. Again, the main cause is functional, though soft fungal rots may eventually set in at some of the affected places. The trouble is much worse in some seasons than others and affected fruits store badly. Soil and weather conditions are thought to be largely responsible. Fruits that develop Lenticel Spot also frequently show symptoms of other functional disorders.

Control.—As with Bitter Pit and Glassiness, the grower can do little apart from striving to maintain steady growth conditions.

SUN SCALD

Following a period of very high temperature in summer, apples and other fruits may show signs of burning on the exposed sunny side. Such conditions occurred at the end of August, 1942, when Sun Scald was very prevalent on apples. Severely affected fruits showed circular, brown, flattened areas sometimes surrounded by a bright, reddish halo, while those only slightly affected showed roughly circular, pale areas or deeper flushes of colour, depending on the variety. Occasionally, and especially on *Allington*, the affected area resembled a bruise, and was arc-like and sunken, and of a deep red or purplish-red colour.

Control.—There is no means of control under commercial conditions where shading would clearly be impracticable, but in gardens it might be feasible to shade the fruits by some simple means in the hottest part of the day during heat-wave conditions.

PESTS : DIAGNOSIS TABLE

THE APPLE

DAMAGE	PROBABLE CAUSE
Branches and Twigs	
Patches of "woolly" white substance gall-like swellings	American Blight (Woolly Aphis)
Branches tunnelled	Goat Moth or Wood Leopard Moth
Shoots and Foliage (Including Blossom)	
Leaves, opening buds and blossom attacked by small "looping," green caterpillars	Winter Moths
Leaves and buds eaten and spun together by small brown, green or yellowish caterpillars which wriggle quickly backwards when disturbed. Eaten buds wilt or shrivel and turn brown. Leaves again attacked in mid-July	Tortrix Moths
Leaves curled and attacked by masses of small, green or bluish-purple aphides. Young shoots twisted, stunted and deformed	Greenfly or Rosy Apple Aphis
Flower buds eaten from within in April by black-headed white grub ; blossoms remain capped, turn brown, and drop	Apple Blossom Weevil
Buds attacked by yellow to pale green, flattish, aphis-like creature; buds turn brown and drop after opening. Drops of white, sticky wax proclaim nature of trouble	Apple Sucker
Small black marks turning brown and then into holes on young leaves—quickly moving aphis-like creatures. Young shoots distorted and with corky scars	Capsid Bug
Leaves turn brownish	Red Spider
Growing shoots cut off in June	Twig Cutter
Fruit	
Small fruits eaten by green, "looping" caterpillars	Winter Moths
Small patches of skin on developed fruit eaten by tiny larvæ	Tortrix Moths
Small deformed and disfigured fruits, corky scars	Apple Capsid Bug
Fruits drop off in June and July—hole in side with wet mass of black frass exuding ; long, corky lines on fruits may be present	Apple Sawfly
Maggoty apples ; may drop just before picking-time	Codling Moth
Holes drilled in sides of fruits	Fruit Rhynchites
Holes drilled in sides of fruits and tunnels in flesh	Apple Fruit Miner

DISEASES : DIAGNOSIS TABLE

THE APPLE

DAMAGE	PROBABLE CAUSE
Branches and Twigs	
Cankerous formations—patches of small, whitish pustules or crimson spherical bodies grouped together	Canker
Sheets of fungous tissue under bark at base of trunk. Long black strands like "boot-laces" on roots and in adjacent soil ; tree dies	Armillaria
Galls on roots	Crown Gall
Shoots and Foliage (Including Blossom)	
Leaves and shoots white and mealy ; flowers small and distorted ,may fail to open, trusses white and mealy	Apple Mildew

Diagnosis Table (*continued*)

DAMAGE	PROBABLE CAUSE
Shoots and Foliage (Including Blossom)	
Blister-like " pustules " on shoots and possibly on bud scales in Spring. Circular, olive-green spots, turning corky and scab-like later	Scab
Silvery sheen foliage on affected branch—brown stain in wood	" Silver Leaf "
Flowers wither, turn brown and die ; subsequently spurs cankered with grey pustules	Brown Rot, Blossom Wilt
Apparently healthy tree wilts or fails to grow soon after bud burst ; blossom trusses and surrounding leaves only may be affected above ground	Waterlogging
Reddish-brown margins to leaves in summer, becoming dark-brown, " hard " and usually up-curled	Potash-deficiency. Leaf Scorch
Brownish, scorched areas between veins, leaves feel thin	Magnesium-deficiency. Leaf Scorch
Leaves yellow or bleached particularly on young growths	Chlorosis
Fruit	
Eye-rot of ripening fruit	Canker
Brown, soft rot of fruit on tree (usually within few weeks of picking), also while stored ; buff spore pustules often in rings. Stored fruit may turn black ; fruit left on tree becomes mummified	Brown Rot
Brownish, roughly circular, indefinite smudges on skin (usually near picking time)	Sooty Blotch
Skin white and mealy	Apple Mildew
Circular olive-green spots, velvety at first, turning corky and scab-like in summer	Scab
Slightly sunken, small, dark green to brownish-green spots within a few weeks before picking ; brownish pockets in flesh after picking	Bitter Pit
Brown, often sunken areas around lenticels	Lenticel Spot
Spherical, discoloured areas on sunny side of fruit, may be pale, flushed, or brown	Sun Scald

Once the trouble has been diagnosed, the reader should refer to the paragraph dealing with the particular disease and pest, and also to the Guide to Spraying, see page 109.

VARIETIES OF APPLES

A comparison of nurserymen's catalogues of to-day with those of ten years ago gives a measure of the reduction the war has brought about in the number of varieties that can be easily bought for planting. The lists that follow include some of the old favourites and some promising new varieties ; they are not intended to be a complete list, nor do they attempt any detailed descriptions, since these can be found set out in full in reference books such as W. Hogg, *The Apple*, E. A. Bunyard, *Handbook of Fruits, Apples and Pears*, and H. V. Taylor, *The Apples of England*.

When sending apples or other fruits to experts for identification, it is very important to send at least two typical specimens of the fruit, together with specimens of the current year's shoot and leaf growth and as full a description as possible of the age and growth habit of the tree and of the conditions under which it is being grown.

DESCRIPTIVE NOTES ON VARIETIES

DESSERT APPLES

Adam's Pearmain. A medium-sized conical apple, red and yellow with russet. Fine flavour. Season, December to March. Upright habit. Makes thin branches. An excellent late apple for the garden.

Advance. See Laxton's Advance.

American Mother. A medium-sized, conical-shaped fruit, rich yellow, flushed and striped deep red. Yellow flesh. Sweet and aromatic. Season October. Uncertain cropper.

Beauty of Bath. A small, round, flat apple, brilliant dappled scarlet, widely grown for market as a first early. Season, early August. Strong growth, untidy habit and rather tip-bearing. Slow bearer. Very difficult to train in any artificial form. Fruit drops easily. Flavour fair and crisp but not first-rate.

Belle de Boskoop. Medium to large round apple, rather like a Blenheim Orange. Season, December to April. Very strong grower, useful for top-grafting on to standard trees. A very good flavour when ripe, but unattractive in appearance. Triploid variety, see page 147, and needs cross-pollinator diploid variety. (See coloured frontispiece.)

Blenheim Orange. A medium to large-sized, flattish, round apple, rich golden-yellow, tinged and striped red and russeted. Fine flavour, firm yellow flesh. Season, November to January. Dessert or cooking. Good cropper when established but usually takes some years to come into full bearing. Does well on medium loam and heavy soils, and in grass orchards. Forms strong and spreading standard or bush and needs maximum space. Does well as bush on East Malling No. IX. Prune hard to form tree and then lightly. Susceptible to scab and canker. Triploid variety, see page 147, and needs cross-pollinator diploid variety.

Brownlees Russet. A medium-sized, flattish and irregular-shaped apple, a reddish-brown and green russet. Excellent flavour, tender, greenish-white flesh, sharp but sweet and juicy. Season, January to April. A fine garden fruit, usually grown in bush form. Self-sterile.

Charles Ross. A large-sized, beautiful round apple, very similar in appearance to Peasgood Nonsuch, highly-coloured, a greenish-yellow, streaked with red and patched with russet. Fair flavour, brisk, sweet and juicy. Season, September to November. Thrives in chalky soils and in any locality. Best grown as pyramid or bush. The fruit is too large for cordon culture. Recommended for pot culture. A fine exhibition fruit but not recommended for standard trees. Self-sterile. Resistant to scab but susceptible to canker and capsid bug.

Christmas Pearmain. A medium-sized, round to conical apple, rosy cheek and russeted. Fine flavour, crisp flesh, slightly sub-acid. Season, December to January. Good bearer. Upright and neat in growth and recommended for inclusion in small private gardens in bush, or cordon form. Said to be partially self-fertile.

Claygate Pearmain. A medium-sized, round to conical apple, somewhat similar to Ribston Pippin, dull green, flushed reddish-brown and russeted. Fine flavour, tender greenish-white flesh, luscious and aromatic. Season, December to February. A good cropper and stores well if gathered when perfectly ripe. Recommended for garden culture. One of the best late dessert apples. Self-sterile.

Cornish Gillyflower. A medium-sized, oval and conical apple, ribbed at top, yellowish-green and red and thinly russeted. Excellent flavour, crisp yellowish-white flesh. Season, December to February. Of somewhat straggly growth. Good cropper in mild districts. Tip-bearer. Self-sterile.

Cox's Orange Pippin. A medium-sized, round apple, a golden to orange and red russet skin. Delicious flavour, tender yellowish-white flesh, luscious and aromatic. A good cropper. Season, November to January. Does well only in well-, but not excessively-drained soils. In the colder districts the shelter of a wall should be provided. Medium vigour but twiggy in growth. It makes a fair orchard tree on loamy soil. Also grown as bush, espalier and cordon. Recommended for private garden culture. Also suitable for pot culture. Needs regular pruning and heavy potash supplies. Self-sterile, but cross-pollinates well with Worcester Pearmain and James Grieve.

Crimson Cox's Orange Pippin. This is merely a coloured bud-sport of the above—a deep claret-coloured apple otherwise possessing all the characteristics of Cox's Orange Pippin.

D'Arcy Spice. A medium-sized, roundish, flattened and ribbed apple, a brownish russet over dull yellow. Excellent flavour, firm greenish flesh, sweet, juicy and aromatic. Season, March to May. A fair cropper but needs very careful handling and storing. Comes from Essex, where it is much prized but considered difficult to grow. Self-sterile.

Duke of Devonshire. A small to medium-sized, round apple, a dull yellow, tinged with russet. Excellent flavour, crisp flesh, juicy, sweet and aromatic. Season, March to April. A good cropper and storing well. Gather in October. Makes a good standard or may be grown as espalier, bush or cordon. Suitable for garden culture. One of the best of the late dessert apples. *Highly resistant to scab.* Said to be partially self-fertile.

Egremont Russet. A medium-sized, round and flattish apple, golden yellow and russeted. Very good flavour, firm greenish flesh, crisp and sweet. Season, October to November. A good cropper for immediate use. A good garden variety, forming a neat standard, pyramid or bush. One of the most attractive and best of the russets. Said to be partially self-fertile. Resistant to scab.

Ellison's Orange. A fairly large-sized, round to conical apple, said to be a cross between Cox and Calville Blanche, somewhat similar to Cox's Orange Pippin in shape and colour. Greenish-yellow, streaked with red. Of tender yellowish flesh, luscious and aromatic. Flavour not universally popular. Season, September to October. A good cropper for immediate use. Does well on almost any soil, thriving in the Midlands and Northern counties. Forms an upright, neat standard or bush and is recommended for garden culture. Also grown as cordon. Said to be partially self-fertile. Good for top grafting.

Exquisite. See Laxton's Exquisite.

Fortune. See Laxton's Fortune.

Gladstone. See Mr. Gladstone.

Golden Reinette. See Heusgen's Golden Reinette.

Heusgen's Golden Reinette. A medium-sized, round and flattened apple, bright scarlet and russeted over. Good flavour, crisp yellowish flesh. Season, March. A good cropper and keeps well. Grown as standard, bush or espalier. Makes a small tree. Recommended for garden culture. One of the best of the late dessert apples. Self-sterile.

James Grieve. A medium-sized, round to conical apple, greenish-yellow, striped and tinged with red. Fine flavour, soft, yellowish flesh, juicy and sweet. Season, September to October. Good cropper but does not keep in store. For market it should be picked in August and September while still hard and green, and to obtain large fruit, heavy thinning is necessary. Makes a compact neat bush excellent for private gardens or for growing in pots. Does well in the Midlands and the colder Northern counties. Susceptible to canker and brown rot. Said to be partly self-fertile.

King's Acre Pippin. A medium-sized, round to conical apple, somewhat similar in appearance to Ribston Pippin, dull yellowish-orange, warmly flushed and russeted. Excellent flavour, firm, yellowish flesh, juicy and highly flavoured. Season, January to March. A medium cropper and stores well. Forms a moderately robust standard, bush or trained tree. Suitable for garden culture. Needs a warm sunny situation to colour well. A good late dessert apple. Said to be partially self-fertile.

Laxton's Advance. A small to medium-sized, round to conical apple, a bright crimson in colour. A cross between Cox's Orange Pippin and Mr. Gladstone, recently introduced. Good flavour, with crisp and juicy flesh. Season, early August. Does not keep and is best eaten as soon as possible after picking. Recommended for garden culture. Self-sterile.

Laxton's Epicure. A medium-sized, flattened, round apple, a pale yellow, flushed and striped bright crimson. Good flavour, tender, yellowish flesh, juicy and sweet. Season, September. Best eaten as soon after picking as possible. Grown in all forms. Suitable for garden culture. Said to be self-fertile.

Laxton's Exquisite. A fairly large-sized, round to oval apple, yellow flaked and streaked red. Fine flavour, tender and juicy, similar to Cox's Orange Pippin. Season, September to October. A good cropper for immediate use. The fruit should be picked as soon as ready. A very good second-early dessert apple. Said to be self-fertile. Susceptible to scab.

Laxton's Fortune. Medium round to conical apple, rosy red when ripe. Very juicy and sweet. Season, October to November. One of the most promising of new varieties. Tree of medium vigour. Suitable for garden culture. Flowers with Cox.

Laxton's Pearmain. A medium to large, round to conical and flattened apple, yellowish, tinted ruddy brown and rosy cheek. Fine flavour, firm, yellowish flesh, sweet and juicy. Season, December to April. Keeps well. Recommended for private garden culture. Said to be self-fertile.

Laxton's Superb. A large to medium-sized, round to conical and flattened apple, green to yellow, flushed red and rosy cheek. Fine flavour, crisp, white flesh, juicy, sweet and aromatic. Season, November to March. A good cropper and keeps well. Makes a strong and spreading standard or bush. Also grown as espalier or cordon. Recommended for private garden culture. Has been widely planted in recent years.

Lord Lambourne. A medium-sized, round to conical apple, a rich red flushed over yellow. Good flavour, firm, yellowish flesh, juicy and sweet but greasy. Season, October to December. A good cropper but does not keep long. Makes a strong standard or bush, espalier or cordon. Subject to an obscure trouble known as " rubbery wood."

Mr. Gladstone. A medium-sized, round to conical and ribbed apple, yellow flushed and striped dark red. Fair flavour, soft, greenish flesh, juicy and aromatic. Season, July to August. A good cropper for immediate use, preferably eaten as picked. Does well in the Midlands and in Northern localities. Somewhat weak grower and a tip-bearer. Best grown as a bush. One of the earliest dessert apples. Unsuitable for artificial forms of culture. Does not respond well to spur pruning. Said to be partially self-fertile.

Miller's Seedling. A small to medium-sized oval apple, yellow with primrose flush. Season, August to September only. One of the juiciest apples. Much in demand on the London market in some seasons. Neat and upright in habit. *Fruit must be thinned.* Suitable for small bush, fuseau or cordon. Recommended for garden culture. Unsuitable for standard. A biennial bearer.

Orleans Reinette. A medium-sized, flattened round-shaped apple, somewhat similar to a Blenheim Orange but smaller. A golden russet, flushed deep red. Superb flavour, sweet, crisp and juicy. Some experts maintain this to be the best flavoured of all dessert apples. Season, December to February. A fair cropper and storing well. Makes a strong-growing standard or bush, espalier or cordon. Said to be partially self-fertile. Somewhat susceptible to canker. Apt to shrivel in store if picked too soon.

Pitmaston Pine Apple. Small conical golden russet with yellow flesh. Of exceptional flavour. Described by Bunyard as " honeyed." Now seldom grown, but should do well as cordon, fuseau or bush in small garden.

Ribston Pippin. A medium to fairly large-sized, round to conical, apple, a dull greenish-yellow and brownish-red russet. Superb flavour, firm yellowish-white flesh, crisp, slightly dry and aromatic. Season, November to January. A moderately good cropper and stores well. Does best in sheltered situations and warm soil where ample moisture is available. Makes a moderate-sized standard, espalier, or bush, or may be grown as cordon ; also useful for pot culture. One of the best desserts. Somewhat liable to canker and scab. Needs hard pruning. Self-sterile. (See Triploid varieties, page 147.) Needs diploid pollinator.

Rival. A medium to fairly large-sized, round, flattened and somewhat uneven-shaped apple, a beautiful salmon-carmine and rich yellow. Fair flavour, firm white flesh, crisp and juicy. Season, October to December. A fairly good cropper, keeping well into December- Makes a medium-sized, neat-growing standard or bush, pyramid or cordon. Of decorative value in the garden, recommended for pot culture, good for dessert, or cooking and also grown for market. The bad shape makes it difficult to pack in boxes. Said to be partially self-fertile. " Sulphur shy "—i.e., the leaf is susceptible to scorch when sprayed with lime-sulphur.

Rosemary Russet. A medium-sized, flattened, conical apple, yellow, flushed brick-red and russeted, with a very long, thin stalk. Good flavour, crisp yellowish flesh, juicy and aromatic. Season, December to March. A good cropper and stores well. Makes a moderate-sized standard or bush or may be grown as espalier or cordon. Suitable for garden culture. One of the best late russets. Self-sterile.

St. Cecilia. A medium-sized, oval apple, a beautiful golden-yellow, striped and flushed crimson. Fine flavour, sweet, juicy and rich. Season, January to March. A good cropper and stores well. Makes a weak, drooping bush. Not suitable for espalier or cordon. Recommended for private garden culture. Self-sterile. The leaf is susceptible to sulphur damage when sprayed.

St. Edmund's Russet. A small to medium-sized, round and flattened apple, an even, light golden russet all over. Excellent flavour, tender flesh, juicy and aromatic. Season, September to October. A good cropper but does not store and should be eaten as soon as possible after picking. Makes a moderately robust standard or bush. Too much of a tip-bearer for artificial forms. Said to be partially self-fertile. Much recommended as a small garden bush on Number Nine stock.

St. Everard. A medium-sized, round-shaped apple, yellow and heavily striped with crimson. " Cox " flavour, tender, yellowish flesh, sweet and luscious. Season, August to September. A good cropper for *immediate* use and best eaten as soon as gathered. Forms a moderate-sized standard, or compact and sturdy bush and is one of the best early dessert apples and a good garden fruit, although a shy cropper. May also be grown as espalier or cordon. Said to be self-fertile. Susceptible to glassiness.

Sturmer Pippin. A small to medium-sized apple, a greenish-yellow with dull russet and rosy cheek. Good flavour, firm, greenish white flesh, crisp, sweet and luscious. Season, March to May. A heavy cropper and stores well, provided it is not gathered too soon. Forms a compact standard or bush in almost any soil, or may be grown as espalier or cordon. A fine dessert apple. Said to be partially self-fertile. *Must have a warm, sunny situation to finish properly.*

Sunset. Medium-sized, round, flattish apple ; golden yellow with bright crimson flush. Stem long in a deep russeted cavity. Flesh, yellowish, crisp and juicy, of very good flavour. Season, October to February. Tree vigorous and fertile. Leaves deep green. Mid-season flowering. A promising new introduction.

Winter Queening. Medium size, conical, yellow background almost covered with dark crimson. Handsome, good flavour, yellow flesh. Season December to March. Rather uncertain cropper.

Woolbrook Pippin. A new seedling of promise from Devonshire. A medium-sized round apple, red and yellow with some russet and a wide open eye. Season, after Christmas.

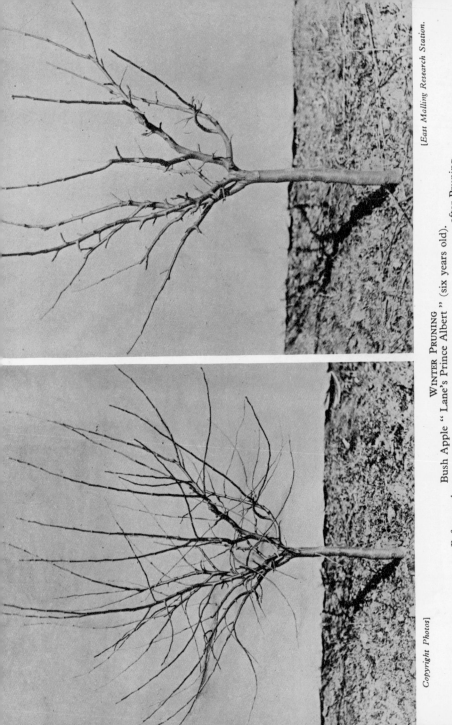

Copyright Photos]

[East Malling Research Station.

WINTER PRUNING

Bush Apple " Lane's Prince Albert " (six years old).
Before and— —after Pruning.

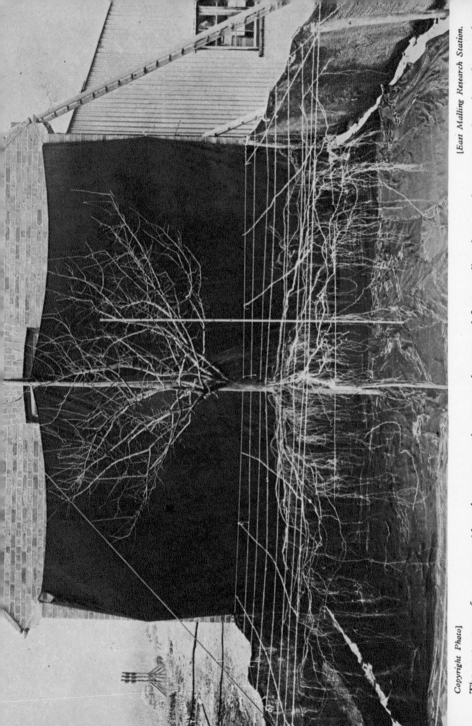

[*East Malling Research Station.*

The rootsystem of a ten-year-old apple tree on a vigorous stock excavated from medium loam, and reconstructed to show the actual

Worcester Pearmain. A medium-sized, round to conical apple, bright crimson all over. Fair flavour, firm white flesh, crisp, luscious and aromatic. Season, September to early October. A good cropper and cold-stores well. Should not be gathered until well-coloured and ripe. Does equally well in the colder districts and forms a medium-sized standard or bush. A good market apple and recommended for private garden culture. Said to be partially self-fertile. A tip-bearer and not suitable for artificial forms. Susceptible to scab and canker but one of the most regular cropping of all apples.

COOKING APPLES

Arthur Turner. A new large-sized, round, green apple in season in August and September. Strong growing.

Bramley's Seedling. A large, flattened, round-shaped apple, green and sometimes tinted or flushed dull red. Fine flavour ; firm, yellowish flesh, juicy and sharp. Season, November to March. A heavy cropper and stores well. Does well even in the colder Northern districts and on almost any soil, including heavy and dry soils, and forms a strong standard or bush. One of the best cooking apples. Too strong growing for small gardens or for cordon culture. Susceptible to scab, resistant to canker. Triploid variety, see page 147, and needs cross-pollinating diploid variety.

Crawley Beauty. A beautiful, large, even, round apple, green with red stripes. Good flavour, crisp, white flesh, juicy and tart. Season, March to April. A heavy cropper and stores well. Makes a fine standard or bush for garden culture. *Very late flowering.* Suitable for frosty situations. Self-sterile.

Crimson Bramley. Similar in shape, size and other characteristics to the well-known Bramley's Seedling, which see, but coloured a bright crimson all over.

Early Victoria (Emneth Early). A medium-sized, conical apple, light green in colour. Good flavour, soft, white flesh, juicy and tart. Season, July to August. A heavy cropper but does not store and should be used as soon as possible. Market fruit should be picked before it is fully grown. Forms a fairly strong standard or bush and is one of the best early codlings for garden culture and market, thriving even in the colder localities. Needs severe fruit thinning. Said to be partially self-fertile. Responds well to spur-pruning. Susceptible to Silver Leaf.

Edward VII. A large, round to oblong apple, pale yellow with slight reddish-brown flush. Good flavour, firm flesh, juicy and sharp. Season, January to April. A shy cropper, storing well. Forms a strong-growing standard, bush or trained tree and is especially recommended for pyramid form. Good orchard or garden fruit. Late flowerer. Plant with Royal Jubilee, Crawley Beauty, or Court Pendu Plat for cross-pollination.

Emneth Early. See Early Victoria.

Grenadier. A large, flattened, round to conical apple, light green to

F.G.H.   K pale yellow in colour. Good flavour, crisp, juicy and sharp. Season, end of July to October. A good cropper but does not store and should be used as soon after picking as possible. Makes a moderately strong-growing standard or bush and does well even in cold districts and on heavy soils. A popular market apple. A tip-bearer unsuitable for artificial forms. Prune lightly. Said to be partially self-fertile.

Lane's Prince Albert. A beautiful large, round to oval apple, light greenish-yellow, flushed and striped red. Good cooker, tender, white flesh, juicy and sharp. Season, November to April. A heavy cropper and storing well up to six months. A dwarf grower of pendulous habit best grown in bush or cordon form. Hardy even in the colder localities. This is one of the very best of all cooking apples for garden culture in any form. " Sulphur-shy."

Lord Derby. A very large, round to conical and irregular-shaped apple, dark green turning golden-yellow. Firm, yellowish flesh, juicy and sub-acid. Season, November to December. A good cropper and storing well to December. Does well in almost any soil, including heavy and cold land, and in the Midlands and Northern districts. Grown in all forms, standard, bush, espalier, or cordon. Recommended for private garden culture. Said to be partially self-fertile. Susceptible to brown rot.

Monarch (Seabrook's). A large, beautiful, roundish apple, light green with rosy flush. Good flavour, firm, white flesh, juicy and sub-acid. Season, October to April. A heavy cropper and storing well. Forms a vigorous and spreading standard or bush, or may be grown as espalier. Self-sterile.

Newton Wonder. A medium to large-sized, even and round-shaped apple, green to golden and beautifully tinged with red. Good flavour, crisp, yellowish-white flesh, juicy and acid. Season, October to April. A splendid cropper and stores well. A very strong grower. Does well almost anywhere, including the colder Northern districts, and forms a strong, spreading standard or bush. Late flowerer and slow to come into bearing. Too strong growing for cordon or small garden culture. One of the best late cookers and valuable for market or exhibition. Prune lightly. Said to be self-fertile.

Rev. W. Wilks. A very large, flattened and ribbed, round-shaped apple, a pale yellow with red spots and slashes. Good flavour, tender, white flesh, juicy and sub-acid. Season, October to November. A good cropper but does not keep and should be used as soon as possible after picking. Of dwarf habit but hardy and usually grown as a bush in gardens. Useful for exhibition. Subject to scab and brown rot. Said to be self-fertile.

Royal Jubilee. A large, beautiful, round to conical apple, of clear golden hue. Good flavour, firm, yellowish flesh, juicy and sharp. Season, October to December. A good cropper and stores well. Does well even in the colder localities, forming a sturdy, flat-headed standard, bush or espalier. Recommended for garden culture. *Very late flowerer.* Suitable for frosty situations. Self-sterile.

Seabrook's Monarch. See Monarch.

EARLY-BLOSSOMING VARIETIES OF APPLE

Beauty of Bath	(D)	Oslin	(C)
Belle de Boskoop	(D)	Rev. W. Wilks	(C)
Egremont Russet	(D)	Ribston Pippin	(D)
Gravenstein	(D)	St. Edmund's Russet	(D)
Mr. Gladstone	(D)		

LATE BLOSSOMING VARIETIES

American Mother	(D)	Edward VII	(C)
Christmas Pearmain	(D)	Heusgen's Golden Reinette	(D)

VERY LATE BLOSSOMING VARIETIES

Court Pendu Plat	(D)	Royal Jubilee	(C)
Crawley Beauty	(C)		

C = Cooking ; D = Dessert.

A certain limited number of apple varieties will set a fair to good percentage of their blossom in most seasons when planted entirely alone. In spite of this the wisest course is never to plant a single variety in any quantity without making sure that some other variety with a similar blossoming period is planted within easy flying distance of bees and other insects as a " pollinator."

When planting any of the varieties given in the above lists of early and late blossomers, care should be taken to see that the pollinator variety belongs to the same group of blossoming period.

TRIPLOID VARIETIES OF APPLE

Belle de Boskoop	(D)	Gravenstein	(D)
Blenheim Orange	(D)	Ribston Pippin	(D)
Bramley's Seedling	(C)	Warner's King	(C)

C = Cooking ; D = Dessert.

Research into the cytology of the apple by M. B. Crane and his fellow workers at the John Innes Horticultural Institution has revealed an important difference in the genetical make-up of a small group of apple varieties, a difference in the number of chromosomes or " carriers of the hereditary factors." The majority of apple varieties are " diploids " and have 34 chromosomes, but small groups of " triploids " have 51 chromosomes.[*]

Crane's experiments in cross-pollinating varieties of these two groups showed that the triploid varieties would not cross-pollinate each other at all well, and were not very good cross-pollinators even for the vast majority of diploid varieties.

In the light of present knowledge, therefore, it would be clearly un-wise to plant up an orchard of triploid varieties only or to use them as pollinators for each other. For the commercial grower it would

---

[*] This work is lucidly dealt with in *The Apple*, by Sir Daniel Hall and M. B. Crane, published in 1933. See also " The Fertility Rules in Fruit Planting," John Innes Leaflet No. 4, published by the John Innes Horticultural Institution.

also seem important, when planting *Bramley's Seedling*, to include at least two other varieties, both diploids, to ensure efficient cross-pollination of the *Bramley's Seedling* and of each other.

APPLES SPECIALLY RECOMMENDED FOR GARDEN PLANTING

Dessert

Adam's Pearmain
American Mother
Claygate Pearmain
Christmas Pearmain
Cornish Gillyflower
Cox's Orange Pippin
D'Arcy Spice
Duke of Devonshire
Egremont Russet

Heusgen's Golden
  Reinette
James Grieve
King's Acre Pippin
Laxton's Advance
Laxton's Epicure
Laxton's Exquisite
Laxton's Fortune

Laxton's Superb
Miller's Seedling
Orleans Reinette
Pitmaston Pine Apple
Rosemary Russet
St. Edmund's Russet
St. Everard
Sturmer Pippin

Cookers

Arthur Turner
Bramley's Seedling
Crawley Beauty
Early Victoria

Edward VII
Grenadier
Lane's Prince Albert
Lord Derby

Monarch
Rev. W. Wilks
Royal Jubilee

DESSERT APPLES FOR GROWING ON WEST WALLS

Claygate Pearmain
Cox's Orange Pippin
King's Acre Pippin

Orleans Reinette
Pitmaston Pine Apple
Ribston Pippin

Rosemary Russet
Sturmer Pippin

ESPALIERS

Plant about 15 to 20 feet apart

Variety	Stock	Dessert or Cooking
American Mother	East Malling IX, II or I	Dessert
Belle de Boskoop	East Malling IX	Dessert
Blenheim Orange	East Malling IX	Dessert
Brownlees Russet	East Malling IX, II or I	Dessert
Cox's Orange Pippin	East Malling IX, II or I	Dessert
Crawley Beauty	East Malling II or I	Cooking
Early Victoria	East Malling II or I	Cooking
Edward VII	East Malling IX, II or I	Cooking
Egremont Russet	East Malling II or I	Dessert
James Grieve	East Malling II, I or XVI	Dessert
King's Acre Pippin	East Malling II, I or XVI	Dessert
Lane's Prince Albert	East Malling II, I or XVI	Cooking
Laxton's Superb	East Malling IX	Dessert
Lord Lambourne	East Malling IX, II or I	Dessert
Ribston Pippin	East Malling IX, II or I	Dessert

ORDER OF RIPENING OF SOME GOOD VARIETIES

Early (July–September)

Variety	Garden or Orchard	Dessert or Cooking
Arthur Turner	Garden	Cooking (*Immediate use*)
Early Victoria	Garden or Orchard	Cooking (*Immediate use*)
Grenadier	Garden or Orchard	Cooking (*Immediate use*)
Miller's Seedling	Garden	Dessert (*Immediate use*)
Lady Sudeley	Garden or Orchard	Dessert (*Immediate use*)
Laxton's Advance	Garden	Dessert (*Immediate use*)
Laxton's Epicure	Garden	Dessert (*Immediate use*)
Mr. Gladstone	Garden or Orchard	Dessert (*Immediate use*)

Mid-Season (September–November)

Variety	Garden or Orchard	Dessert or Cooking
American Mother	Garden or Orchard	Dessert
Charles Ross	Garden	Dessert and Cooking
Egremont Russet	Garden	Dessert
Ellison's Orange	Garden or Orchard	Dessert (*Immediate use*)
Golden Noble	Garden	Cooking (*Stores well*)
James Grieve	Garden	Dessert (*Immediate use*)
Laxton's Exquisite	Garden	Dessert (*Immediate use*)
Laxton's Fortune	Garden or Orchard	Dessert (*Immediate use*)
Lord Derby	Garden or Orchard	Cooking (*Keeps to December*)
Rev. W. Wilks	Garden	Cooking (*Immediate use*)
Rival	Garden or Orchard	Dessert (*Stores well*)
Worcester Pearmain	Garden or Orchard	Dessert (*Immediate use*)

Ripening Late (November–March)

Variety	Garden or Orchard	Dessert or Cooking
Adam's Pearmain	Garden	Dessert
Belle de Boskoop	Orchard	Dessert and Cooking
Blenheim Orange	Orchard	Dessert and Cooking
Bramley's Seedling	Orchard	Cooking
Cox's Orange Pippin	Garden or Orchard	Dessert
Lane's Prince Albert	Garden or Orchard	Cooking
Laxton's Superb	Garden or Orchard	Dessert
Monarch	Garden or Orchard	Cooking
Newton Wonder	Orchard	Cooking
King's Acre Pippin	Garden or Orchard	Dessert
Orleans Reinette	Garden or Orchard	Dessert
Ribston Pippin	Garden or Orchard	Dessert
St. Cecilia	Garden	Dessert
Sturmer Pippin	Garden	Dessert

BEST-FLAVOURED APPLES
Dessert

Variety	Garden or Orchard	Season of Best Flavour
Adam's Pearmain	Garden	December–March
Blenheim Orange	Orchard	December
Brownlees Russet	Garden	December–March
Claygate Pearmain	Garden	December–March
Cornish Gillyflower	Orchard	December–March
Cox's Orange Pippin	Garden	December
D'Arcy Spice	Garden or Orchard	February–May
Egremont Russet	Garden	October
James Grieve	Garden or Orchard	September
King's Acre Pippin	Garden	February
Laxton's Exquisite	Garden	September
Laxton's Superb	Garden or Orchard	January–March
Mother (American)	Garden or Orchard	End of October
Orleans Reinette	Garden or Orchard	December–March
Pitmaston Pine Apple	Garden	March
Ribston Pippin	Garden or Orchard	November
Rosemary Russet	Garden	February
St. Edmund's Russet	Garden	September
St. Everard	Garden	September

Cookers

Annie Elizabeth	Grenadier	Newton Wonder
Bramley's Seedling	Lane's Prince Albert	Wellington

VARIETIES SUITABLE FOR GROWING AS DWARF PYRAMID AND CORDON

Plant Single-vertical or oblique cordon 2 to 3 feet apart,
Single-horizontal cordon 10 to 12 feet apart,
Double-U cordon 5 to 6 feet apart, and
Dwarf Pyramid 3 to 6 feet apart.

Variety	Stock	Dessert or Cooking
Cox's Orange Pippin	East Malling IX, II or I	Dessert
Early Victoria	East Malling IX, II or I	Cooking
Edward VII	East Malling IX, II or I	Cooking
Egremont Russet	East Malling IX, II or I	Dessert
Ellison's Orange	East Malling IX, II or I	Dessert
James Grieve	East Malling II or I	Dessert
Lane's Prince Albert	East Malling IX, II or I	Cooking
Laxton's Fortune	East Malling IX, II or I	Dessert
Laxton's Superb	East Malling IX	Dessert
Lord Lambourne	East Malling IX, II or I	Dessert
Miller's Seedling	East Malling II or I	Dessert
Ribston Pippin	East Malling IX, II or I	Dessert
St. Cecilia	East Malling IX, II or I	Dessert

BEST ORCHARD VARIETIES

Variety	Season	Dessert or Cooking
Belle de Boskoop	Late (Dec.–March)	Dessert or Cooking
Blenheim Orange	Late (Nov.–January)	Dessert or Cooking
Bramley's Seedling	Late (Nov.–March)	Cooking
Duke of Devonshire	Late (March–April)	Dessert
Laxton's Superb	Late (Nov.–February)	Dessert
Lord Derby	Late (Nov.–December)	Cooking
Monarch	Late (Dec.–March)	Cooking
Newton Wonder	Late (Feb.–March)	Cooking
Ribston Pippin	Late (Nov.–January)	Dessert

THE APRICOT (*Prunus armeniaca*)

SOIL AND SITUATION

Apricots grow well in soils with a high water table, and tradition credits them with a preference for a fairly high lime content and a sunny sheltered wall. They will grow out of doors as far north as Ayrshire.

FORM OF TREE

The apricot being highly susceptible to a branch die-back generally attributed to the Brown Rot fungus—*Sclerotinia laxa* (*Monilia cinerea*) —the low headed fan would appear to be the most suitable as allowing the best means of remaking the fan should any of its ribs be killed back by the fungus.

PROPAGATION

The apricot is budded or grafted on to plum rootstocks, those at present recommended being the Common Mussel and Brompton.

PLANTING

To minimize the risk of infection by fungus a maiden tree should be planted in autumn and cut hard back the following spring as suggested for peaches on page 206. Planting distances should be from 15 to 25 feet apart according to the vigour of the rootstock.

POLLINATION

The apricot is one of the earliest of the stone fruits to blossom, and recent trials have shown that going over the tree two or three times as the blossoms open, hand pollinating each with pollen by means of a small brush or pad of cottonwool improves fruit setting. The pollen appears to be self-fertile and may therefore be taken from the tree on which the blossoms are situated.

PRUNING

The apricot likes to fruit on short natural spurs and these should not be cut out. The ribs of the fan are encouraged to extend without branching as far as wall space allows. Side shoots are pinched out in summer at one inch, and the same treatment is given to all secondary growths. Replacement is practised as for peaches (page 208).

FRUIT THINNING

Fruit thinning is done in two stages. When the fruitlets have set they are reduced to 2 or 3 per cluster, and after stoning is finished, the fruits are thinned out to distances varying from 4 inches to 9 inches according to crop.

GATHERING AND MARKETING

The fruit should be allowed to ripen before picking and should always be picked dry. Packing for market is as for peaches, and no pains should be spared to provide adequate protection for the fruit in well-padded rigid containers.

DISEASES AND PESTS

As already mentioned, the apricot is subject to attack by the Brown Rot fungus, and unless this disease can be controlled it is not easy to keep the walls fully furnished for any length of time.

Apricots are also liable to shed an excessive number of fruits at the stoning period. The cause of this is not known but is probably connected in some cases with lack of pollination and in others with some sudden check to growth as in the case of " running off " of blackcurrants.

Apricots are also subject to gumming. In young trees the branch may recover, but when old trees start gumming the branch often dies back later. How far gumming is due to disease or to growth disturbance is not known at the present time.

Silver leaf is another disease that may attack the apricot.

Aphis is the most serious insect pest and other pests include Bark or Trunk Borers, Scale, Red Spider, Leaf-roller Moth and Magpie Moth.

For diagnosis table, see Peaches and Nectarines, and Plums.

DESCRIPTIVE NOTES ON VARIETIES

APRICOTS FOR GROWING OUT OF DOORS

The following is a selection of the most satisfactory varieties. Any one of these may be grown alone, as all varieties are self-fertile.

Blenheim. See Shipley's Blenheim.

Breda. Small to medium-sized round fruit, orange-yellow, flushed brownish-red. Ready in mid-August. Nice flavour and particularly hardy. May be grown as a standard in the open in the milder districts.

Early Moorpark. Large, roundish oval, pale apricot with dark flush. In season mid-July.

*Hemskerk. Large and round to conical fruit, orange-yellow, blotched with red. Ripe from the end of July to early in August. Delicious greengage flavour. Hardy and a good cropper. Also suitable for pot culture.

*Moorpark. Large, round fruit, orange-yellow, flushed red in colour. Ready in August and September. Excellent flavour. A strong and vigorous grower and a good bearer. Useful for pot culture.

*New Large Early. Large, oval fruit, orange-yellow and red in colour. Ready from the end of July to early August. Fine flavour, hardy and prolific. Has taken the place of Large Early.

Powell's Late. Large, round fruit, deep yellow, flushed red in colour. Ready in August and September. Nice flavour. A vigorous grower and a good bearer.

Shipley's Blenheim. Medium-sized, oval fruit, rich orange with crimson spots. Ready early in August. Good flavour. Hardy and a prolific cropper. Also useful for pot culture.

SELECTION IN ORDER OF RIPENING

Early (Mid-July till Early August)

Early Moorpark
Hemskerk

New Large Early
Shipley's Blenheim

Mid-season (Mid-August)

Breda

Late (End of August–September)

Moorpark

Powell's Late

THE BLACKBERRY *(Rubus fruticosus)* AND ITS HYBRIDS

The blackberry grows wild in great profusion in this country, where it is a feature of many hedgerows. When cultivated, it yields very large crops, which are used mainly for canning, bottling or culinary purposes. Some of the hybrid berries are much appreciated for dessert.

SOIL AND SITUATION

The blackberry prefers a really deep, rich, well-drained soil, but it will do fairly well in any soil that is moist and well-drained, and sunny.

PROPAGATION

Blackberries may be propagated from " tips " in the manner described for loganberries (page 198), or they may be raised from suckers dug up from round the base of an established plant.

* Recommended by the Royal Horticultural Society for cultivation in private gardens.

DISTANCE OF PLANTING

The plants should be from 12 to 16 feet apart, according to the variety, in rows 6 to 8 feet apart. Blackberries will generally continue to carry good crops for periods up to about 15 years.

TRAINING AND PRUNING

There are various ways of training the blackberry, one of the most practical being that known as the Rope Method. Three strands of galvanized straining wire, gauge 10, are stretched on uprights at 2, 3 and 5 feet above ground level, and the canes are tied to the two top wires in autumn as shown in the diagram. As the new canes grow out from the base of each plant the following summer, they are looped together and tied loosely to the bottom wire, shown in the diagram.

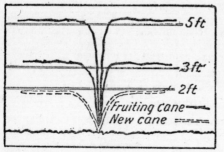

ROPE METHOD OF TRAINING BLACKBERRIES.

With the most vigorous sorts of cultivated blackberry, such as *Himalaya Giant*, it may be advisable to put the top two wires at 4 and 6 feet respectively above ground level, but this will make picking rather more difficult.

Most cultivated varieties of blackberries make very strong, prickly canes and are very awkward plants to train, requiring strong leather gauntlet gloves to protect the hands.

MANURING

It is not unusual for cultivated blackberries to carry crops up to 5 or 6 tons per acre, and at the same time each individual plant may put out several new canes up to 16 feet in length. It requires generous manurial treatment with plenty of nitrogen and regular dressings of potash. Farmyard dung, 20 to 30 tons per acre, dug in, in winter, is the best form of manure if obtainable, but shoddy, poultry manure, meat and bonemeal are all suitable, provided they are supplemented by sulphate of potash at 2 cwt. per acre. Steamed boneflour at the rate of 5 cwt. per acre, is one of the best forms of organic phosphatic manures to apply to blackberries in the spring.

GATHERING AND MARKETING

These berries are usually treated in similar manner to loganberries. (See page 200.)

INSECT PESTS

Raspberry and Loganberry Beetle (*Byturus tomentosus*). (See Loganberry, page 201.) Bramble Shoot-Webber (*Notocelin uddmanniana*). (See Loganberry, page 201.)

Greenfly. Of the various species of greenfly which attack Loganberries (page 201), *Macrosiphum rubiellum* is the most important on Blackberries.

The aphides cluster and feed on the growing tips of the cane, but can easily be killed with nicotine. Common Green Capsid (*Lygus pabulinus*). (See Black Currant, page 179.)

Both generations of this insect feed on the Blackberry and Loganberry, splitting and deforming the leaves and stunting the canes. Nicotine or D.D.T. should be applied soon after the damage first appears.

PESTS : DIAGNOSIS TABLE

THE BLACKBERRY

DAMAGE	PROBABLE CAUSE
Shoots and Foliage	
Leaves at tips of new canes spun together	Bramble Shoot-Webber
Leaves or young tips of shoots attacked by clusters of small aphides	Aphides
Young leaves spotted, becoming brown and torn ; shoots may be stunted	Common Green Capsid Bug
Fruit	
Fruit fails to swell and ripen properly, remaining small, brown, hard and deformed, maggoty	Raspberry Beetle

Note.—Once the trouble has been diagnosed, the reader is advised to consult the paragraph dealing with the particular Disease or Pest, and also the Guide to Spraying, page 109.

DISEASES

DWARF

A virus disease recognized in spring by the bushy, stunted appearance of the new growths when a few inches high. There are many such growths instead of the usual few strong ones, and the normal purplish colour at the tips is often absent, giving place to light green. The virus, probably carried about by insects, gets into the sap, and the only satisfactory means of checking the disease lies in the prompt removal and destruction of affected plants.

CANE SPOT (*Elsinoë veneta*)

This disease attacks blackberries and can be controlled as recommended for Loganberries on page 202.

DISEASES : DIAGNOSIS TABLE

THE BLACKBERRY

DAMAGE	PROBABLE CAUSE
Shoots and Foliage	
New growths light green, bushy and stunted when a few inches high	Dwarf Virus

DESCRIPTIVE NOTES ON VARIETIES

BLACKBERRY

The best varieties are :

Parsley-leaved Blackberry (*R. laciniatus*). A self-fertile variety, which bears a heavy crop of large black fruit of excellent flavour and, on account of its beautifully-shaped leaves, is extremely valuable for decorative purposes in the garden.

Himalaya Berry. A strong-growing, heavy cropper, bearing large round black berries, excellent for making tarts and jams. This is usually considered the best variety to grow for market. Thought by some to be synonymous with Black Diamond.

John Innes. (Cross between *R. rusticanus inermis* and *R. thysiger*.) Raised by Mr. M. B. Crane at the John Innes Horticultural Institution, Merton—one of the latest to ripen, having a long picking season. Considered to be very promising.

Merton Thornless. Raised by Mr. M. B. Crane at the John Innes Horticultural Institution. Entirely without prickles. Fruit large with wild blackberry flavour. In season from mid-August to the end of September.

HYBRID BERRIES

Boysenberry. Raised about 1930 in California. A good cropper yielding very large fruits. Susceptible to " dwarf " disease.

Japanese Wineberry (*R. phœnicolasius*). A useful species for decorative purposes, bearing small, round, sweet to sub-acid flavoured, bright orange berries, enclosed in a hairy calyx. Hardy and prolific. Useful for jam or culinary purposes.

King's Acre Berry. An early-fruiting variety, bearing large, black, longish fruits of distinct blackberry flavour.

Ready from the end of June to early in July. Useful as dessert or for culinary purposes.

Laxtonberry. A cross between a raspberry and a loganberry. It is a strong grower and bears large bright red, raspberry-like fruit. Inclined to be self-sterile and should be grown only in conjunction with various other berries.

Loganberry. (See page 198.)

Lowberry. This bears long, black loganberry-like fruits with a distinct blackberry flavour.

Phenomenal Berry. The fruit resembles the loganberry and is, perhaps, a little larger. (See page 198.)

Youngberry. Not such a strong grower as the loganberry or blackberry. Exceptionally large fruits, which are of excellent flavour. Susceptible to " dwarf " disease.

BUSH FRUIT

See separate articles in this chapter under the heading : Currant, Gooseberry, Raspberry, etc.

THE CHERRY *(Prunus avium)*

SOIL AND SITUATION

Sweet Cherries.—Cherries always appear to grow and crop best under conditions of moderately light rainfall in soils which are really deep and freely drained, overlying a chalk subsoil. They are always unhappy in very wet soils and seldom do well in sandy loams which dry out early in the season, or in soils with a coarse, sandy or gravelly subsoil. They need shelter from the east winds at times of blossoming and protection from spring frosts. Trees on walls should preferably face south or west.

Sour Cherries.—One variety of sour or " red " cherry known as the *Wye Morello*, much esteemed for the manufacture of Cherry Brandy, grows and crops well on its own roots in Kent on the light, sandy loams of the Folkestone sands. The other varieties of sour cherries, including the ordinary Morello, appear to thrive under the same conditions as the sweet cherries, except that they have the additional advantage of doing well on a north wall.

ROOTSTOCKS FOR CHERRIES

The cherry is usually propagated by means of budding in July or August on cherry rootstocks. The " mazzard " or wild cherry, is the rootstock in general use for both sweet and sour cherry varieties. The mazzards are sometimes dug up in the woods, but in recent years they have been propagated vegetatively from layers (see page 28). Up to the present no really dwarfing stock for cherries in this country has been discovered. It is always difficult to grow sweet cherries satisfactorily as wall trees because both the varieties themselves and the rootstock on which they are worked are much too strong growing to conform with the limitations of a wall.

The sweet cherry is happiest when grown in its natural shape as a forest tree, and any attempt to grow it in artificial form will inevitably produce its own problems.

If means can be found to keep them in check, cherry trees trained as fans on walls have the obvious advantages of shelter from wind and frost. They are, moreover, easy to net against birds, which form one of the chief pests of the cherry.

The Morello, the most popular form of sour cherry in this country, is grown widely for market as a bush tree under conditions of clean cultivation, and for plantations or for large gardens without walls this is probably the best form. On the other hand, the Morello and most of the sour varieties, with the possible exception of the *Dukes*, are so much less vigorous in growth than the sweet cherries that where wall space is available, they are much more suitable for this purpose than the sweet varieties, especially as they will do quite well on the north side of the wall.

PLANTING

Planting may take place any time when the weather and conditions are favourable, between leaf fall and bud burst, October and early November for preference, if favourable. So far as possible, varieties should be planted in order of picking in order to facilitate the moving of ladders. This, however, is a secondary consideration when compared with planning for cross-pollination.

MANURING

The cherry may be classed among the fruits which normally require fairly high nitrogen feeding to produce regular crops of good quality fruit. At the same time, potash is undoubtedly necessary as a basic dressing, and in Kent, at any rate, the best cherry growers have always been keen on giving their cherry orchards periodical applications of phosphatic manures. In Kent it used always to be the custom to graze sheep in large numbers in the cherry orchards, feeding them on cake, and managing the grass in such a way that the sheep grazed it closely and evenly all over the orchard. The result was a smooth, fine turf like a tennis lawn, and it used to be the proud boast of the best orchardists, that anyone could throw a threepenny piece as far as he could in the orchard without losing sight of it.

Phosphatic manures such as basic slag or superphosphates at 5 or 6 cwt. per acre were applied every few years, to keep the clovers going, and potash was given at similar intervals as kainit 4 cwt. or as muriate 1 cwt. per acre. The nitrogen, it was reckoned, was provided in the sheep droppings, distributed evenly all over the orchard by the sheep. Doubtless such a method of manuring is almost ideal for grass orchards in districts of relatively low rainfall, and at times when there is money to be made out of sheep. Of recent years there has been a tendency to look for other ways of manuring cherry orchards. Poultry are, perhaps, the best substitute for sheep to supply the nitrogen, but they must not be run too thickly under the trees.   Others, again, apply nitro-chalk, nitrate of soda or sulphate of ammonia at rates of from 5 to 10 cwt. per acre, and keep cutting the grass throughout the season with a tractor-drawn " gang-mower " such as is used on golf-courses. In such cases phosphatic and potash manures are given as well; slag, steamed bonemeal, or supers at 5 to 6 cwt., and kainit at 4 cwt. or muriate or sulphate of potash at 1 to 2 cwt. per acre.

Cherry trees grown on walls, especially wall trees, must not be given much nitrogen until they are carrying a really heavy crop of fruit, otherwise they are likely to make too much shoot growth.

It is very widely held by some of the best fruit-growers that cherries, like plums, should not be allowed to be short of lime, and for this reason where cherries are being grown on soils which are known to be deficient in lime, it is probably wise to apply lime at intervals of four or five years.

The exact part played by soil moisture in the setting and the development of the cherry is not known, but it is certainly important.   Cherries on walls should be given a good mulching of farmyard manure as soon as the fruit is set to conserve the moisture, and the trees should be watered at intervals throughout the hot weather in June and July.

PRUNING SWEET CHERRIES

Once the framework has been formed the less a cherry tree is pruned the better.   The silver leaf fungus is liable to infect pruning cuts made in autumn and winter, so that any pruning should be carried out either in August and September, or in April.   In standard trees dead and crossing branches should be cut out once a year, preferably in August.

Wall trees or bush trees grown in confined spaces need very careful pruning.   Once the tree has been shaped, pruning should be confined to summer pinching of growing shoots to five or six leaves with the finger and thumb, and to the shortening back of these laterals to three or four buds in September.   The leading shoots should not be pruned once the tree is shaped.   On walls there is always the temptation, when the tree gets to the top of the wall, to cut the leading shoots hard back every winter.   If instead of doing this, the leaders are bent over and tied down for a year the new growth will be weakened, and in the following autumn it is often possible to shorten the leaders back to a weak lateral.

PRUNING THE SOUR CHERRIES

The sour cherries, particularly the Morello, should be pruned differently from the sweet cherry, the object being to promote fresh shoot growth every year.   This makes the Morello a peculiarly difficult subject for wall training. The only way is to be ruthless and cut out one or more whole branches from each tree in the early autumn or late spring and to train new shoots in their place. The Morello being very subject to the Brown Rot fungus, there will nearly always be a certain number of twigs killed by the fungus, and these must be cut out before the tree blossoms the following spring.

GATHERING

Cherries should be picked when dry: early varieties such as *Early Rivers*, about the middle of June and late varieties such as *Noble*, about the middle of August. The fruit should be gathered with the stalks intact as it reaches the ripening stage, without actually handling the fruit itself. Morello cherries may be clipped off with special thin-pointed scissors. Each tree is usually gone over once or twice, removing those fruits which are ready first, before finally clearing the tree. The fruit should be placed into paper-lined baskets and forwarded to market the same day.

It is profitable to grade the choicest fruit for market purposes. See also Gathering, page 87.

MARKETING

Cherries are sent to market in half-sieve (24 lb.) wicker baskets; in boxes (6 or 12 lb.); chip baskets or cartons (2, 3, 4, 6, and 12 lb.). Punnets (1 and 2 lb.) may be used in the case of selected choice fruit. See also Marketing, page 91.

INSECT PESTS

CATERPILLARS

See Winter Moth under Apple, page 121.

SLUGWORM *(Caliroa limacina)*

See Pear and Cherry Slugworm, page 222.

CHERRY BLACK FLY *(Myzus cerasi)*

Masses of these black aphides may be found in the summer feeding on young shoots and on the leaves, which become curled and often turn a reddish colour, finally blackening and falling off. Its chief damage is done to rootstocks, young trees and Morello cherries.

The winter is spent as a shiny black egg on the twigs and branches. From this egg a stem-mother, the ancestor of the summer colonies, hatches out in the spring.

Control.—Summer outbreaks of this pest should be treated with nicotine before the leaves become too tightly curled.

RED CURRANT BUSH BEFORE WINTER PRUNING

Copyright Photos]   [East Malling Research Station.
RED CURRANT BUSH AFTER WINTER PRUNING

 [*East Malling Research Station.*
SHOOT OF A BLACK CURRANT, SHOWING TYPICALLY DISTORTED LEAVES—THE CHIEF
SYMPTOM OF "REVERSION"

The winter eggs can easily be killed by spraying with tar-oil washes in December. Rootstocks and young trees should always receive such a spray, which will obviate the use of much summer work, but watch should also be kept in the summer for the appearance of colonies of the aphis (established by winged aphides flying in from elsewhere) and immediate steps taken to eradicate them with nicotine and soft soap.

CHERRY FRUIT MOTH (*Argyresthia nitidella*)

This insect is not widespread, but is important in some orchards. As soon as the flower buds burst, the small green caterpillars enter them, making pinholes in their sides. Then, when the petals fall, they bore into the developing cherries and destroy them.

In the middle of May the caterpillars drop to the ground and turn to chrysalides in the soil, in small silken cocoons from which the adult moths emerge after about a month. These are small, delicate, white and brown creatures, which fly in a curious dancing manner. They lay eggs on leaf scars, under scales and in crevices.

The eggs are laid in July and hatch out in September. The minute caterpillars, after feeding for a short while on the leaves, spin cocoons and hibernate in them in crevices and other convenient spots on the trees.

Control.—A few eggs remain unhatched throughout the winter and these are easily killed by tar-oil washes. Such sprays will not, however, have much effect on the hibernating caterpillars, which are well protected by their silken cocoons. For these the best treatment is an application of lead arsenate or D.D.T. just before the blossoms open.

CHERRY FRUIT FLY (*Rhagoletis cerasi*)

This is a very serious pest on the Continent, but has not yet been found in this country except in imported cherries. Legislation has been introduced with a view to preventing its introduction.

PESTS : DIAGNOSIS TABLE

THE CHERRY

DAMAGE	PROBABLE CAUSE
Branches and Twigs	
Small, round holes in trunk	Shot-hole Borers
Shoots and Foliage (Including Blossom)	
Leaves and blossom attacked by small, " looping," green caterpillars	Winter Moth
Upper surface of leaves attacked in August by black, slug-like larvæ, leaving pale-brown blotches	Slug-worm
Young shoots and leaves curled in summer, infested with masses of black aphides ; may be reddish, turning black and falling off	Cherry Black **Fly**

PESTS : DIAGNOSIS TABLE

THE CHERRY (*continued*)

DAMAGE	PROBABLE CAUSE
Fruit	
Small fruits eaten by green, " looping " caterpillars	Winter Moth
Fruit eaten from within and destroyed by tiny, pale-green caterpillars with brown heads	Cherry Fruit Moth

DISEASES

LEAF-SCORCH (*Gnomonia erythrostoma*)

The main characteristic of this disease is that the leaves fail to drop in autumn but persist, dead, on the tree throughout the winter. The new leaves produced in spring are infected by spores shot from fruit-bodies of the fungus in the dead leaves on the tree. The first sign of attack is the appearance of yellowish patches on the leaves. These later turn brown. The fungus passes down the leaf-stalk and prevents the leaf from falling. The disease can be severe in some seasons.

Control.—In young trees it can be controlled by stripping the dead leaves from the trees in winter and burning them, but this is hardly practicable with large trees.

Spraying just before the blossoms open with Bordeaux Mixture 6–9–100 and at petal-fall with the same at 4–6–100 will prevent infection of the new leaves.

BACTERIAL CANKER AND LEAF SPOT (*Pseudomonus mors-prunorum* and *P. prunicola*)

This is a very serious disease, especially in the nursery and in young plantations. The sweet cherry varieties *Napoleon, Bigarreau de Schrecken, Florence, Bradbourne Black, Ohio*, and *Early Rivers*, and the acid cherry varieties, are particularly susceptible, while *Frogmore, Turkey Heart*, and *Governor Wood* are much more resistant. The leaves of badly attacked branches turn yellow, often become rolled, and wilt, usually any time from May to August, and the branches eventually die. Inspection will reveal the presence of a cankered area on the branch. Frequently whole trees are killed when infection occurs in the trunk and spreads far enough to girdle it. Infection is often accompanied by copious gumming of a cloudy yellow colour in the region of the canker. Natural recovery is known to occur, for if the branch or tree is not girdled before the bacteria die out, the canker heals. In such cases, although the affected branch or tree may be enfeebled during the ensuing year, it continues to live and eventually recovers. Experiments have shown that infection occurs most readily through wounds in October, November, and December, while the bacteria have usually died out by the following summer when the canker ceases to grow. There is also a leaf-spot phase. Small circular spots, at first pale yellow, and later turning brown, when often surrounded by a yellow translucent halo, are produced on the leaves in spring. These brown areas eventually fall out, thus giving to the leaves a "shot-hole" effect. The organism that causes these leaf-spots is able to produce cankers in the branches.

Control.—Trunks and branches should be thoroughly sprayed during the second or third week in October with Bordeaux Mixture (10–15–100) and again, just before the flower-buds open in spring, with Bordeaux Mixture (6–9–100). This treatment should be continued every year to give the best results, and particularly during the first ten or fifteen years of a susceptible tree's life, when it is most likely to be attacked. It is important to spray susceptible trees in the nursery. The spring spray will help also to control Cherry Leaf Scorch (see page 162).

High-worked trees of susceptible varieties are preferable to low-worked trees because the stock is usually more resistant than the scion.

BROWN ROT BLOSSOM WILT

Acid cherries and certain varieties of sweet cherry, *Governor Wood* in particular, are susceptible to this disease, caused by the fungus *Sclerotinia laxa* (see Plum, page 240). Spores infect the flowers and the fungus grows down the flower stalk and into the young shoot of acid cherry, or spur of sweet cherry, and these, on being killed, become conspicuous in summer when the withered, brown leaves and flower-trusses hanging stiffly show up clearly against the normal green. On bush trees of acid cherries such as the Morello, on which the disease can be very serious, it is possible to cut out and burn the dead shoots in summer when they are best seen, but on standard sweet cherries the cutting-out of affected spurs would be impracticable, and growers must rely on spraying with tar-oil when the trees are dormant, and with Bordeaux Mixture if necessary just before the blossoms open (see Plum, page 241).

Control.—Spraying as well as cutting-out is highly desirable on acid cherries also, the object being to burn up completely (with tar-oil) or sterilize (with Bordeaux) the surface of the greyish fungus cushions or pustules that arise in late winter on the parts killed by the fungus in the previous year. Even where the cutting-out has been thoroughly done on acid cherries, it is very easy to overlook small infections, especially where the attack has been severe, and spraying is a necessary second line of attack.

BROWN ROT
See Plum, page 240.

CHERRY LEAF CURL

This is a similar disease to Peach Leaf Curl (see page 213), and is caused by a similar fungus. Affected leaves are swollen, perhaps curled, and tinged brownish-red. It is rarely serious and can be controlled by the spring spray of Bordeaux (6–9–100) already mentioned for Bacterial Canker and Cherry Leaf Scorch. A disease caused by another closely allied fungus is known as *Witches' Brooms* or *Bull Wood*. It can be recognized by the characteristic cluster of non-fruiting branches reminiscent of a besom. The same Bordeaux spray will help to control this, too.

SILVER LEAF

See Plum, page 242.

DISEASES : DIAGNOSIS TABLE

THE CHERRY

DAMAGE	PROBABLE CAUSE
Branches and Twigs	
Cankered area on branch or trunk—may be " gumming " (see also Shoots and Foliage)	Bacterial Canker
Shoots and Foliage (Including Blossom)	
Yellowish patches on leaves, which turn brown and fail to drop in autumn, remaining on tree throughout winter	Leaf Scorch
Flower-trusses withered and persistent with surrounding leaves brown and dead. Shoots dead on acid cherries	Brown Rot Blossom Wilt
Leaves swollen, often curled, tinged brownish-red	Cherry Leaf Curl
Leaves turn yellow, may be rolled and withered ; small, circular, brown spots appear, fall out, and leave " shot-hole " effect	Bacterial Canker and Leaf Spot
Leaves silvery on branch affected	" Silver Leaf "
Fruit	
More or less concentric rings of " pustules," buff or greyish, appear on fruit, which is rotting	Brown Rots

Note.—Once the trouble has been diagnosed, the reader should refer to the paragraph dealing with the particular disease or pest.

DESCRIPTIVE NOTES ON VARIETIES

DESSERT CHERRIES

Amber Heart (Kentish Bigarreau). Medium-sized, heart-shaped fruit ; pale yellow with red cheek. Ready mid-July. Good flavour. Hardy and prolific cropper. Grown as standard, bush, or fan. Pollinated by Waterloo, Napoleon and Florence. An old favourite with Kentish growers and still widely grown. Used for canning.

Bedford Prolific. Large, heart-shaped fruit; glossy purplish-black in colour. Closely resembles Roundel. Ready early July. Good flavour. Grown as standard, bush, or fan on a wall. Free in habit and a prolific bearer. Pollinated by Elton, Frogmore and Waterloo.

Bigarreau de Mezel. A very large, white, sweet cherry, ready in the second half of July. In recent years it has gained favour in Kent as a promising commercial variety.

Bigarreau Gaucher. A large, black, sweet cherry in season in the second half of July. Planted as a commercial variety in some Kentish orchards. Makes a good tree.

*Bigarreau Napoleon. Very large, heart-shaped fruit; bright red. Ready late July. Rich flavour. Grown as standard, bush, or fan. A prolific cropper. One of the most popular cherries in the market, especially among the extra-selected grade. Transports well. Pollinated by Waterloo, Roundel and Florence. Highly susceptible to bacterial canker and silver leaf.

*Bigarreau de Schrecken. Large, roundish, shiny black fruit. Ready late in June. Delicious flavour. Grown as standard or fan on wall. A prolific bearer. Highly susceptible to bacterial canker. Pollinated by Bigarreau de Mezel.

Black Eagle. Large, roundish fruit; purplish-black in colour. Ready early to mid-July. Rich, sweet and juicy. Grown as standard, bush, or fan on wall. Hardy, a good bearer and travels well to market, where it is a popular cherry. Pollinated by Bigarreau de Schrecken.

Bradbourne Black (Géant de Hedelfingen). A large, black cherry, ready in the second half of July. Has a very good flavour, and makes a strong tree; very susceptible to bacterial canker.

*Early Rivers. Large, heart-shaped fruit; glossy black. Ready from the middle of June to early in July. Rich in flavour, tender and juicy. Grown as standard. One of the best cherries for all purposes. Forces well and keeps well. A popular market cherry and travels nicely. Pollinated by Governor Wood, Noir de Guben, Turkey Heart, Emperor Francis. Hardy and a good cropper. Makes an enormous tree. Probably the most widely planted cherry in Kent.

*Elton. Large, heart-shaped fruit; pale yellow, mottled bright red. Ready in July. Superb flavour, sweet and tender. Grown as standard, bush, or as fan on wall. A poor cropper in most localities. Not so popular at market as it used to be. Self-sterile. Pollinated by Black Heart and Early Rivers. Highly susceptible to brown rot.

Emperor Francis. Large, heart-shaped fruit; dark red. Ready in August. Fine flavour, juicy and sweet. Grown as standard or bush. Hardy and a good bearer. One of the best late cherries for market, particularly in northern areas. Pollinated by Turkey Heart.

Florence. Large, heart-shaped fruit; bright red. Ready early to mid-August. Good flavour, juicy and sweet. Grown as standard, bush, or fan on wall. Pollinated by Bigarreau Napoleon. A good late variety for market. A heavy cropper, but very susceptible to bacterial canker.

* Denotes varieties specially recommended by the Royal Horticultural Society for private gardens.

*Frogmore Early Bigarreau. Medium, heart-shaped fruit; pale yellow, tinged with red. Ready early in July. Fine flavour, juicy and sweet. Grown as standard, bush, fan on wall, or pot plant. Hardy and a good bearer. A popular cherry at market, but soft. Self-sterile. Pollinated by Roundel.

Géant de Hedelfingen. See Bradbourne Black.

*Governor Wood. Large, heart-shaped fruit; bright red over pale yellow, and thin skinned. Ready late June to early July. Moderate flavour, sweet and juicy. Grown as standard, bush, as fan on east wall, or pot plant. Hardy and prolific. A popular market cherry but needs careful handling. Pollinated by Early Rivers, Turkey Heart and Emperor Francis. Highly susceptible to brown rot and cherry leaf scorch.

Kentish Bigarreau. See Amber Heart.

Knight's Early Black. Large, heart-shaped fruit; dark purplish-black to dead black in colour. Ready late June to early July. Rich and sweet in flavour. Grown as standard, bush, or fan on wall. Hardy and a medium cropper. One of the best black cherries and a market favourite. Transports well. Pollinated by Noir de Schmidt.

May Duke. Large, roundish fruit; deep red-purple in colour. Rich flavour, juicy and sweet. Ready about the end of June. Grown as standard, bush, fan on wall, or pot plant. Hardy and good cropper. Said to be partially self-fertile. Cross-pollinated by Morello. Excellent for bottling.

Napoleon. See Bigarreau Napoleon.

Noble. See Tradescant's Heart.

Noir de Guben. Large, handsome, roundish fruit; dark reddish-brown. Early flowering. Ready late June. Good flavour and heavy cropper. Suitable for garden or orchard culture.

Noir de Schmidt. A large, black sweet cherry, ready in the first half of July; a strong grower, not yet widely planted in this country, but said to be promising.

Peggy Rivers. A new variety, somewhat similar to Governor Wood, that shows considerable promise. Ready in July.

*Roundel. Very large, heart-shaped fruit; purplish-black in colour. Ready early in July. Dark red and very juicy flesh. Grown as standard, bush, or as fan on a wall. Hardy and prolific cropper. One of the best flavoured cherries. Transports well. Pollinated by Waterloo.

Tradescant's Heart (Noble). Large, heart-shaped fruit; dark red to purple in colour. Ready early in August. Rich flavour, sub-acid. Grown as standard or bush. Unreliable. Pollinated by Napoleon.

Ursula Rivers. A new black variety of good flavour that promises well. Ready in July.

*Waterloo. Medium, heart-shaped fruit; glossy reddish-black in colour. Ready end of June to early in July. Rich flavour, juicy and sweet. Grown as standard, bush, or as fan on wall. Hardy and a fairly regular cropper. An old market favourite. Hangs well on tree after ripening

---

* Denotes varieties specially recommended by the Royal Horticultural Society for private gardens.

and transports well. Pollinated by Amber Heart, Roundel, Florence, and Bigarreau Napoleon. One of the best flavoured black cherries.

COOKING CHERRIES

Carnation. A good representative of the cooking, red, or sour cherry class. Ready in early August. Makes a strong bush tree.

Flemish Red. Rather small fruit, roundish and bright red in colour. Ready about the end of July. Sharp and acid in flavour. Grown as standard or bush. Hardy and grows almost anywhere, producing good crops. Said to be self-fertile.

*Kentish Red. Medium-sized, roundish fruit; deep red in colour. Ready about the middle of July. Sharp, juicy and acid flavoured. Grown as standard or bush. Bears well, particularly when associated with Flemish Red.

A good cherry for preserves and cooking. Self-sterile.

*Morello. Large, flattish, roundish fruit; deep red to black in colour. Ready from August to September. Sharp, juicy and acid in flavour. Grown as half-standard or bush on north, east or west walls. Hardy, a prolific cropper and said to be self-fertile. Undoubtedly the best of the cooking cherries.

A small distinct type known as the Wye Morello is used in the manufacture of cherry brandy.

POLLINATOR VARIETIES

All the best varieties of sweet cherry are largely self-sterile so that if any one variety is planted by itself, and there are no wild cherries or sour varieties near by, the trees will blossom freely but will never set a good crop. Hence the absolute necessity for planting pollinator varieties for sweet cherries. Fortunately, most sorts which flower together will cross-pollinate each other, but there are small groups of varieties which have been shown to be inter-sterile, and varieties within these groups cannot be relied on to pollinate each other.

In choosing varieties to plant together, the following tables should be consulted.

Early Flowering Varieties of Cherry

Variety	Season of Picking
Elton	Early July
Emperor Francis	End of July
Noir de Guben	End of June

* Denotes varieties specially recommended by the Royal Horticultural Society for private gardens.

Mid-Season Flowering Varieties of Cherry

Variety	Season of Picking
Early Rivers	Middle to the end of June
Bigarreau de Mezel	Early July
Bigarreau de Schrecken	Middle to the end of June
Black Eagle	Early July
Knight's Early Black	End of June
Noir de Schmidt	Early July
Waterloo	Early July

Late-flowering Varieties of Cherry

Variety	Season of Picking
Bigarreau Napoleon	End of July
Bradbourne Black (Géant de Hedelfingen)	Late July
Florence	End of July
Frogmore Bigarreau	Early July
Governor Wood	Early July
Kentish Bigarreau (Amber Heart)	Mid-July
Noble (Tradescant's Heart)	End of July
Roundel	Early July

Note.—1. *Flemish Red, Kentish Red, Morello* and the *Dukes* are all late-flowering.
Note.—2. From the above lists it will be seen that a variety may flower early and yet be a late season fruit and *vice versa.* This is equally true of some other fruits.

SELECTION IN ORDER OF RIPENING

Early (end of June to early July)

Variety	Colour	Pollinators of same Flowering Period
Early Rivers	Black	Waterloo, Noir de Schmidt
May Duke	Dark Red	Napoleon, Kentish Bigarreau
Frogmore Bigarreau	White	Roundel
Noir de Guben	Black	Emperor Francis
Noir de Schmidt	Black	Bigarreau de Mezel
Bigarreau de Mezel	White	Black Eagle
Elton Heart	White	Noir de Guben
Governor Wood	White	Frogmore

Mid-Season (Mid-July)

Variety	Colour	Pollinators of same Flowering Period
Black Eagle	Black	Bigarreau de Schrecken
Kentish Bigarreau (Amber Heart)	White	Waterloo, Napoleon, Florence
Roundel	Black	Waterloo
Waterloo	Black	Roundel, Napoleon, Kentish Bigarreau, Florence

Late (end of July to early August)

Variety	Colour	Pollinators of same Flowering Period
Bradbourne Black	Black	Napoleon, Florence, Noble
Emperor Francis	Dark Red	Turkey Heart
Florence	White	Napoleon
Napoleon	White	Roundel, Florence, Kentish Bigarreau
Noble	Black	Napoleon

VARIETIES FOR GROWING IN POTS

Variety	Season	Colour
Bigarreau Napoleon	Late	White
Bigarreau de Schrecken	Early	Black
Elton	Early	White
Florence	Late	White
May Duke	Early	Red
Noble	Late	Black
Roundel	Medium	Black
Waterloo	Medium	Black

SELECTION OF TWELVE LEADING SORTS

Amber Heart (Kentish Bigarreau)	Mid-Season (Mid-July)	White
Bedford Prolific	Mid-Season (Mid-July)	Black
Bigarreau Napoleon	Late (Late July)	White
Bigarreau de Schrecken	Early (End June)	Black
Elton Heart	Early (Early July)	White
Early Rivers	Early (End June)	Black
Frogmore Bigarreau	Mid-Season (Mid-July)	White
Governor Wood	Early (Early July)	White
Kentish Red	Mid-Season (Mid-July)	Red
Morello	Late (End July)	Red
Roundel	Mid-Season (Mid-July)	Black
Waterloo	Mid-Season (Mid-July)	Black

COBNUT AND FILBERT (vars. *Corylus Avellana*)

ASPECT

When planting a cobnut or filbert plantation, a site should be chosen which is sheltered from east and north-east winds. The bushes thrive in sunny, open situations in gravelly and rough, stony ground with a clay subsoil, but good drainage is essential.

PROPAGATION

This is usually done by layering two-year-old wood in autumn.

Young layered plants, when rooted, are separated from their parents and are planted in the nursery 10 inches apart in rows 3 feet apart, only one straight stem being allowed to grow. In three years' time this stem should be strong and firm with a framework of 5 or 6 strong branches and a stem of about 15 inches. The young trees may then be planted in their permanent positions.

PLANTING

The trees should be planted 15 feet apart in the late autumn or early spring. After planting the main shoots are cut back to two or three buds, always cutting back to a bud pointing outwards. This procedure is repeated each year until the trees have attained a height of 6 feet, at which height the main shoots are maintained. Nuts are very slow to come into cropping and cannot be expected to give large crops for several years after planting.

PRUNING

Cobnuts and filberts are early flowerers, and depend largely on wind for the dispersal of pollen and the consequent fertilization of fruit. They flower in February, and should this month be wet and cold few nuts will be produced. The catkins are long and of a downy yellow appearance. These are the male flowers, the female flowers being small, reddish pink in colour and brush-like in appearance. The male flowers are borne on the last season's wood, the female mostly on the older wood and the lower few inches of the young. It is consequently well not to cut the tree at all until the male flowers have shed their pollen, or there is a great likelihood that the female flowers will not be fertilized. As soon as the pollen is shed, usually early in March, pruning may be begun. Vigorous side shoots should be cut back to a catkin a few inches above the base, some of the oldest wood being cut out each year. The small, twig-like wood of the previous year's growth must be left in, for this bears the fruit. Wood that has borne fruit the previous year should be cut hard back to two or three buds.

All sucker growth must be twisted off from the roots in winter and the centre of the trees kept well open. In August all vigorous side-shoots should be " brutted " or broken off by hand about 5 or 6 inches from their base, the ends being left hanging. This will check secondary growth and let light and air in to the centre of the bush.

CULTIVATION

If large nuts are required the ground should be kept cultivated through the season ; the bushes will grow and crop under grass or weeds but the nuts tend to get very small under such growth conditions.

MANURING

A good dressing of organic nitrogenous manure, preferably dung, shoddy or feathers, should be spread round the trees annually, and the soil should be well dug over each year, preferably in December. Sulphate of potash, 2 to 4 cwt. per acre, and steamed boneflour or superphosphate, 5 to 6 cwt. per acre, if applied at the same time, will ensure a complete manurial dressing. A dressing of lime may be given occasionally.

GATHERING AND STORING

The nuts should not be gathered until they are perfectly ripe, late in September ; they should be left on the bushes until the husks are quite brown, and if they are to be stored, they had better hang until they fall naturally. After gathering they should be laid out in a dry place for a time before being stored. If the husks contain moisture when the nuts are packed away, they will soon turn mouldy. When quite dry, pack the nuts away in earthenware jars, barrels or tubs, covering each layer with salt before adding another layer. For marketing, however, the nuts are usually picked a little earlier as the nuts then do not so easily leave the husk in which they are marketed.

MARKETING

Cobnuts and filberts are usually marketed in sieves (40 lb.) or half-sieves (20 lb.), wicker baskets. When large quantities are being sent, they may go in 100-lb. sacks. The first pickings are often sent to market in " flats," flat wicker baskets with lids, holding about 20 lb.

VARIETIES

Good varieties include the *Kentish Cob** (Lambert's Filbert), the largest of the cobs, a prolific bearer, largely grown for market purposes ; the *Cosford Cob**, a roundish and thin-shelled nut, a heavy bearer and of good flavour ; *Webb's Prize Cob*, claimed to be of better flavour than the Kentish Cob ; *Pearson's Prolific*, a medium-sized, thick-shelled nut, and a reliable cropper of good flavour ; *Prolific*, a large nut and a good cropper ; *Cannon Ball, Duchess of Edinburgh, Marquess of Lorne* and *Duke of Edinburgh*.

Filberts.—The *White Filbert** and the *Red Filbert** are among the best flavoured filberts, the former so-called on account of its white skin, and the latter on account of its red skin. Other good varieties include *Princess Royal, Prolific**, a very free early cropper, with peculiar long-fringed husks to the nuts, *The Shap, Garibaldi, Daviana, Webb's Prize*, and *Bergeri.** The last-named opens its catkins very early and is therefore a useful variety to plant with other filberts.

* Specially recommended.

INSECT PESTS

NUT WEEVIL *(Balaninus nucum)*

There are frequently to be seen nuts that have a small round hole in the side from which the maggot of the nut weevil has escaped. The maggot hatches from an egg laid in the nut by the adult beetle, a brown or greyish creature, about one-third of an inch in length, with long legs and a long, curved snout, the tip of which is furnished with small, powerful jaws. The maggot feeds on the kernel and destroys it. It then leaves the nut and enters the soil, from which it emerges as a beetle the following May or June.

Control.—Since many nuts are also lost from a Brown Rot disease which gets in through the small punctures made by the weevil in the course of feeding, control of the pest is doubly important. Fortunately it is very susceptible to the effect of D.D.T., which should be applied as a 5 per cent. dust at the beginning of June.

GALL MITE *(Eriophyes avellanæ)*

This animal is closely related to the Big Bud Mite of black currants, which it resembles in appearance, in habits and in the damage it does. The nut mite does not, and cannot, attack black currants, although it is often popularly supposed to do so. When sufficiently numerous this pest can do a lot of harm, as the swollen, infested buds are nearly always abortive.

Control.—Lime-sulphur should, if necessary, be applied in May.

CATERPILLARS

These may be of the Winter Moth or the Tortrix families. They eat the foliage, often doing serious damage. The remedy is arsenate of lead or D.D.T., applied earlier than is necessary for the weevil, but this earlier spraying may suffice for both pests.

PESTS : DIAGNOSIS TABLE

THE COBNUT AND FILBERT

Damage	Probable Cause
Shoots and Foliage (including Blossom)	
Leaves, opening buds and flowers attacked by " looping," green caterpillars	Winter Moth
Leaves spun together by small brown, green or yellowish caterpillars which quickly wriggle backwards when disturbed	Tortrix Moths
Swollen buds, infested with mite similar to " big bud " in currants, usually abortive	Gall Mite
Nuts	
Holes in side	Nut Weevil

Note.—Once the trouble has been diagnosed, the reader should refer to the paragraph dealing with the particular disease or pest.

RED AND WHITE CURRANTS *(Ribes)*

SOIL AND SITUATION

There are few garden soils in which red and white currants cannot be grown successfully, although they prefer a deep loam of medium texture and plenty of sunlight. Shelter from wind is essential to prevent breaking of the shoots, especially in early years. They come into bearing two to three years after planting and should last for fifteen years or longer if kept free from disease.

SUITABLE FORMS

The most usual form is that of the open bush, with eight to ten leaders, shaped like a vase, on a short leg or stem, at least 5 or 6 inches above ground level. For late picking these fruits may be trained on a north wall or on wires as single, double or triple cordons at 1, 3 or 4 feet apart respectively, in rows 5 to 6 feet apart, or as espaliers at 6 to 8 feet apart in the row. In gardens the half-standard form is popular and for exhibition purposes, or where space is limited, the cordon forms are most to be recommended.

PROPAGATION

Red and white currants are easily propagated from hardwood cuttings. These consist of healthy shoots made during the summer, cut off soon after leaf-fall in autumn. They are cut into lengths of 12 to 15 inches and all but the top three or four buds are removed, see diagram, page 175. There are various ways of inserting the cuttings. One of the best methods is to dig a narrow trench or " grip " about 6 or 7 inches deep and then to push the cutting vertically down to about 1 inch below the

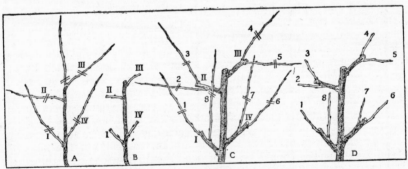

SHAPING RED AND WHITE CURRANTS.

A. A two-year-old plant to be trained as a bush. B. The same cut back to the points indicated in A. C. The same after another season's growth, showing the new shoots and points to cut back to. D. The same, pruned.

bottom of the trench. After that, the trench is half filled and the soil is trodden firmly down round the base of the cuttings. The trench is then filled up and stamped well down with the heel. Consolidation of the soil immediately around the cuttings is one of the main secrets of success in getting cuttings to strike roots. They are usually spaced about 6 inches apart in the row, leaving about 2 feet to 2 feet 6 inches between the rows. At the end of the first season the yearlings are lifted, and the upper roots are cut clean away in order to prevent suckering. They are then replanted at about 12 inches apart and left for one more season, by which time they will be ready to plant out in their permanent quarters. For cordon and standard forms, the terminal shoot is encouraged to grow on by cutting out the side shoots. For espaliers, the central shoot is cut back by about half its length and the side shoots are cut out.

SHAPING THE BUSH FORM (*see diagram, page 173*)

When a two-year-old plant is planted out to be trained as a bush, there are usually three or four strong lateral shoots as well as the terminal shoot (Fig. A). The latter is cut clean out at the base, and the laterals are cut hard back to within 2 or 3 inches of the base, each to a bud pointing outwards (Fig. B). After one season's growth the young bush will be beginning to take shape as in Fig. C. Eight or nine strong shoots should be selected and cut back hard to outside buds, thus giving a framework of about eight or nine leading branches to the bush (Fig. D). Suckers from below these main leaders must be kept cut out, or they will spoil the shape of the bush.

PRUNING (Illustration facing p. 160)

In red and white currants the fruit buds are formed in clusters at the base of the new lateral shoots. These shoots should be pinched back in summer, just as the fruit is beginning to colour, to five or six leaves, and then cut hard back to within half an inch of the base during the dormant season. The leading shoots should be shortened by at least one-half in the dormant season, care being taken to cut back close to a good healthy outside bud. Old wood must periodically, though not too frequently, be cut away to permit young shoots to be trained in to take its place. Summer-pruning must not be too rigorous at one time ; a little should be done each day. The " leaders " must not be summer-pruned. Since birds are apt to peck out the buds in winter the bushes should be " cottoned " with black cotton threaded by means of a bobbin, and pruning should be delayed until just before bud-break in spring.

In exposed places, and particularly with brittle varieties of the *Versailles* group, including *Fay's Prolific* and *Laxton's Perfection*, it is as well to give some form of artificial support to young bushes in the way of stick supports for the branches, to prevent the leaders being broken off by the wind in the summer.

MANURING RED AND WHITE CURRANTS

Potash is generally considered to be much more important for red and white currants than for black currants. Hence sulphate of potash at rates varying from 2 to 4 cwt. per acre (1 to 2 oz. per square yard) should be given according to requirements, poor sandy soils always receiving the larger quantities.

At the same time, red and white currants respond to generous dressings of nitrogenous manures and growers usually like also to apply phosphates in one form or another. Farmyard manure, stable manure, pig dung, shoddy, steamed boneflour, fish-meal, all these make useful fertilizers provided the potash basic dressings have been given.

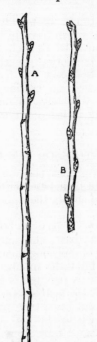

CURRANT CUTTINGS.
A. Red and White.
B. Black.

GATHERING AND MARKETING
As for Black Currants, page 177.

BLACK CURRANTS

SOIL AND SITUATION

Black currants prefer a rich soil containing plenty of humus and a high nitrogen content. They have the reputation of doing well on heavier soils than would be suitable for red or white currants, but this does not mean that they can be grown on badly-drained, clay soils. Shelter from east winds at the time of blossoming is important, because with most varieties pollen has to be carried by insects from the anthers to the stigma, and these insects will fly freely only in a sheltered situation. The bushes start to bear from two to three years after planting; their length of life depends on keeping them free from diseases and pests; if well looked after, they should last eight years and may even last longer than this under exceptionally favourable conditions.

SUITABLE FORM

As already stated, red and white currants form fruit buds in clusters at the very base of the young shoots. In black currants fruit buds are formed singly along the whole length of the young shoots. Hence with black currants the main object is to provide for a yearly succession of strong new shoots. Such shoots grow best from the base of the bush and even from buds below the surface of the ground. Thus the best form for the black currant is the stool or bush, rising straight out of the ground without any leg or with as short a leg as possible. Artificial forms are quite unsuitable.

Black currant bushes may be planted at distances of from 6 to 8 feet between the rows, and from 4 to 6 feet between bushes in the row, according to circumstances.

PROPAGATION

Cuttings are taken from bushes carefully selected in summer for freedom from reversion and big bud (see page 178), and for their good cropping. Such bushes should be labelled late in June as " stock bushes."

The cuttings should be taken early in the autumn, preferably in October, and are cut from the lower part of shoots which have just completed one season's growth. They are cut about 8 to 10 inches long and all the buds are left on with the idea of promoting sucker shoots. They are inserted in the ground as described on page 173 for red and white currants, except that with the black currant cuttings only two buds are left above ground level, and as they usually remain two seasons in the nursery they can be spaced to 12 inches apart in the rows.

SHAPING AND PRUNING THE BLACK CURRANT STOOL OR BUSH

As soon as the young plant is put out in its permanent position, all the shoots should be cut off to within two inches of their base, with a view to stimulating the growth of more strong new shoots the same season.

After that the pruning practice varies only in degree. Every winter a certain number of shoots are cut clean out at the base, choosing always the oldest branches for removal, with the idea of replacing them with strong young shoots. There is no attempt to limit the number of main shoots, nor to keep the centre open. All that is required is a constant succession of strong new shoots to carry fruit the next season. Very often when three or four laterals have grown out on a two- or three-year-old shoot, that shoot can be shortened back to the lowest lateral, thus leaving some fruiting wood, and at the same time stimulating fresh growth lower down.

No summer pruning is necessary for black currants, since each new shoot is needed in its entirety for next year's cropping.

MANURING BLACK CURRANTS

Nitrogen is the chief manurial requirement of black currants, and potash, though necessary in moderation, appears to be a secondary consideration.

All forms of animal dung are suitable, good farmyard manure being the best of all. Pig dung is widely used, dry poultry manure, fish manure, guano, hoof and horn, blood, rabbit flick and meat meal, are all used at relatively high rates of application with the object of stimulating strong new shoots. Phosphates are not usually considered essential, but are often applied periodically in the organic forms such as bonemeal or steamed boneflour at rates of from 5 to 6 cwt. per acre. Sulphate of potash at 1 cwt. per acre per annum should provide the necessary basis of potassium. Inorganic chemical forms of nitrogenous fertilizers, such as nitro-chalk, sulphate of ammonia, or nitrate of soda, are often used to supplement light dressings of dung or of organic nitrogenous fertilizers when these are obtainable only in small quantities. The usual practice is to apply these in March or April, but some experts recommend applying them after the fruit is picked. The chemical fertilizers are usually applied at from 1 to 5 cwt. per acre, according to circumstances.

GATHERING

Gathering the fruit for market may commence as soon as a fair proportion of the fruit has begun to colour. The bushes should be gone over again a few days later, and then finally stripped. When the whole crop is intended for a jam factory, the grower may prefer to wait and then strip the bushes completely in one picking. The fruit should be gathered in the early part of the day but on no account should it be picked in a wet condition.

The berries should not be handled, but picked by the strig. Leaves and damaged berries must not on any account be included in the packages.

MARKETING

The old returnable market baskets, the strike, rimpeck, and half-sieve basket at one time in general use for currants have fallen into disfavour and the non-returnable chip baskets (4 lb., 6 lb. and 12 lb.) are the popular market packages for currants to-day.

Selected berries may be sent up in No. 2, 3, 4, 6 and 12 chip baskets, while punnets (No. 1 in case) are sometimes used for extra selected. No. 3 and 4 veneer boxes (12 lb. and 6 lb.) are also used, and so are No. 2 bonnet ($\frac{1}{4}$ bushel), as well as the old returnable baskets referred to above.

F.G.H.   M

INSECT PESTS OF CURRANTS

LACK CURRANT GALL MITE OR " BIG BUD " *(Eriophyes ribis)*

" Big Bud " is, perhaps, the worst pest of black currants, since not only is it so destructive itself, but it is frequently followed by the disastrous " Reversion " disease. Infested buds swell till they are several times the normal size and globular in shape. When cut open and examined under a powerful lens, they are seen to contain hundreds of minute white creatures, each of which is no more than a hundredth of an inch in length.

Since attacked buds usually fail to open, it can readily be seen that an attack of " Big Bud " soon leads to a falling off in the yield. Moreover, the spread of the pest, once it is established, is rapid and certain.

At blossom time the mites leave the diseased buds and live for a while on the flowers and leaves. Many migrate to other bushes by clinging to insects or by jumping and being carried by the wind. But as soon as new buds are formed, the mites enter them and breed prolifically.

Control.—Badly-attacked bushes should be destroyed, since for them there is no satisfactory cure. Neither should diseased shoots be used for cuttings, as they will never make satisfactory bushes.

When the flower racemes have appeared, but before the flowers actually open, the bushes should be sprayed with lime-sulphur. This deals with the mite effectively but is apt to scorch, particularly when used on varieties of the Goliath group, which will seldom tolerate a concentration greater than 1 in 25.

When the pest is well under control and spraying is carried out as a routine preventive measure, 1 in 50 suffices to keep the bushes reasonably clean. Only on cutting beds and on bushes exposed to serious risk of infection need a stronger dose be used.

CURRANT APHIS

Several species of " greenfly " commonly attack currants and gooseberries. The insects feed on the leaves and stems in early summer, causing, according to the severity of the attack, leaf-curl, shoot distortion and early leaf fall. An accompaniment of severe aphis attack is the sooty mould which grows on drops of honey dew deposited by the aphides on the leaves and fruits.

Currant Aphis (Capitophorus ribis).—This pest attacks both red and black currants and, sometimes, gooseberries. Often reddish-coloured blisters are seen in the summer on the leaves. The pale green aphides are to be found on the undersides of the leaves, feeding in the blisters. In July or August the insects forsake the bushes and breed on other plants such as dead nettle till the autumn, when they return to lay their eggs.

Leaf Curling Currant Aphis (*Amphorophora cosmopolitana*).—This feeds on red and black currants, but is a darker green than the *Capitophorus* and curls the terminal leaves of the young shoots. The insects hatch early in April from shiny black eggs laid the previous autumn in crevices on the shoots. They then feed on the young leaves till June, when they fly off to other plants (such as sow thistles) and do not return till October.

Currant Root Aphis (*Eriosoma ulmi*).—This infests the roots of gooseberries and currants and much resembles Woolly Aphis. Winged forms of the insect emerge in the autumn and fly to elm trees to lay eggs. Return migrants fly from the elms to the gooseberry and currant bushes in the summer.

It is a comparatively minor pest and does far less damage than either of the other two species.

Control.—Since the leaf-feeding aphides spend the winter on the bushes in the egg stage, infestation can usually be prevented by spraying with a tar-oil wash in the winter. This effectively destroys the eggs but cannot, of course, protect the bushes from infestation by aphides flying in from neighbouring bushes in the summer. If summer spraying has to be resorted to, nicotine and soap or derris and soap should be used.

CATERPILLAR

See Winter Moths, under Apple.

COMMON GREEN CAPSID BUG *(Lygus pabulinus)*

This is a very common and widespread pest with a very large range of host plants. It feeds on the leaves and shoots of blackberries, black and red currants, gooseberries, apples and pears. On currants and gooseberries it makes small brown spots on the young leaves. Affected leaves become " torn " and distorted, and often the shoots are stunted or even killed, excessive side branching then resulting.

The young bugs and the adult insect itself much resemble the Apple Capsid in appearance and habits (page 124). Like that pest, too, the Common Green Capsid lays its eggs beneath the rind of the shoots. These hatch in April and May into the young bugs which cause so much damage to the bushes. When only half-grown the bugs are apt to leave the bushes and complete their development on various weeds. In any case, when mature, they migrate to herbaceous plants, such as potatoes and various weeds, in July, and there produce a second generation. When mature, this second generation returns to the currant bushes or some other suitable woody nest in order to lay winter eggs.

Control.—The use of a winter petroleum-oil spray is a good way of dealing with this pest, or a dual-purpose winter wash (D.N.C. or tar-petroleum) can be used to destroy both Capsid and Aphis. Failing this, D.D.T. can be applied just after blossoming, to control Capsid and Caterpillar at the same time. Even if it is used before blossoming, in the Big Bud spray, D.D.T. is likely to give a good control of Capsid and Caterpillar, on account of its lasting effect.

APPLE CAPSID BUG *(Plesiocoris rugicollis)*

Currants, especially reds, are sometimes attacked by this bug (see under Apple, page 124).

Its damage is similar to that of the Common Green Capsid Bug and it is amenable to the same remedies.

BLACK CURRANT SHOOT MOTH *(Incurvaria capitella)*

This is a pest sometimes met with. Its eggs are laid in the young fruits, but no appreciable damage is done to the fruit by the caterpillars when they are small. It is after spending the winter in the soil in little silken cocoons, that the half-grown caterpillars emerge and attack the shoots, boring into the stem and causing buds to wilt when they have grown out an inch or so.

Control.—The only effective measure is to cut the currant bushes down to the ground in the spring, preferably after the larvæ have entered the shoots. This drastic course entails the sacrifice of a year's crop, but the bushes will, in many cases, benefit by being cut down, especially if they are young. Old, badly-infested bushes are best removed altogether ; this should be done during April or May if it is proposed to replant with other black currant bushes the following autumn.

No reliable spraying method has yet been devised.

MAGPIE MOTH

See under Gooseberry.

CURRANT CLEARWING MOTH *(Conopia tipuliformis)*

This can be a severe pest where it occurs. Mainly red currants but also black currants and gooseberries are attacked. The moth lays her eggs on the branches in early summer, and the damage is done by the fat white caterpillars which bore into the branches and tunnel in the pith. Affected shoots frequently break off.

Control.—No satisfactory means can be recommended. Where only a few bushes are grown, cut out the infested shoots, although this may involve ruining the shape of the bush with the consequent need to grow fresh shoots.

BLACK CURRANT LEAF MIDGE (Dasyneura tetensi)

In a few districts this has become a troublesome pest. In the summer, the leaves at the tips of the shoots become rolled and twisted and tiny white maggots can be found in them. There are several generations, the first midges laying their eggs just before the flowers open.

Control.—The only material that has so far given promising results is D.D.T., which can be added to the " grape stage " lime-sulphur spray.

EELWORM (Aphelenchoides ribes)

This pest is not widespread but in some parts of the country has caused a good deal of trouble. The worms, which are microscopic, live and feed in the buds, which if severely affected fail to open. At times the worms migrate and it is then possible to see them congregated together in white cottony masses, protruding from the buds.

Control.—No satisfactory remedy is known. Warm water treatment (20 minutes at 100° F.) should kill the worms in cuttings from suspected bushes but it is, of course, inadvisable to take cuttings from any bush that is not known to be in robust good health.

PESTS : DIAGNOSIS TABLE

BLACK CURRANTS

DAMAGE	PROBABLE CAUSE
Shoots and Foliage	
In spring buds grow out about one inch and then wilt. Small caterpillars may be found inside shoot	Black Currant Shoot Moth
Shoots break off. Fat white caterpillars in stems	Currant Clear Wing Moth
Abnormally large buds, which fail to develop	Big Bud Mite
Leaves, opening buds, and blossom attacked by small " looping " caterpillar	Winter Moth
Reddish-coloured blisters on leaves in summer, pale green aphides on undersides	Currant Aphis
Leaf-curl and shoot distortion, foliage infested by dark green aphides. Sooty Mould on leaves and fruit	Leaf-curl Currant Aphis
Leaves torn and distorted, shoots stunted and may be killed	Common Green Capsid Bug
Leaves attacked by black-and-white marked caterpillars	Magpie Moth

RED AND WHITE CURRANTS

Shoots and Foliage	
Shoots break off. Fat white caterpillars in stems	Currant Clear Wing Moth
Reddish-coloured blisters on leaves in summer, pale green aphides on undersides	Currant Aphis
Leaf-curl and shoot distortion, foliage infested by dark green aphides. Sooty Mould on leaves and fruit	Leaf-curl Currant Aphis
Leaves torn and distorted, shoots stunted and may be killed	Common Green Capsid Bug

DISEASES OF CURRANTS

LEAF-SPOT *(Pseudopeziza ribis)*

This disease sometimes assumes serious economic importance by causing premature defoliation of red, white, and black currant bushes on an extensive scale. It is usually pronounced in wet seasons. It can readily be recognized by the numerous small, brownish, angular spots produced on the leaves, mainly on the upper surfaces. In a severe attack, these spots merge together and the leaves wither and fall off in August, sometimes earlier. The fungus has also been found on leaf-stalks, fruit-stalks, young shoots, and fruits. Infection comes from the old leaves of the previous year, and possibly from the shoots, and is usually first noticed in July.

Control.—It can be controlled by spraying the bushes, immediately after the crop has been gathered, with Bordeaux Mixture made to the formula : 4 lb. copper sulphate, 6 lb. hydrated lime, 100 gal. water.

Where the fruit is intended for canning, a copper-containing spray should not be applied *before* the fruit is picked because a copper residue, even in very small amounts, is inimical to the fruit vitamins.

RUST *(Cronartium ribicola)*

This disease, sometimes known as " orange rust of currants," is readily recognized in its early stages by the bright orange spots produced by the fungus on the undersides of red, black, and white currant leaves.

In severe cases nearly the whole of the underside of the leaf is affected, and premature leaf-fall may result. After a time the orange colour changes to dark brown when the resting-spore stage is reached. The spores protrude in short columns, which gives a rough, hairy appearance to the underside of the leaf. Another stage in the life-cycle of the fungus occurs on the Weymouth Pine (*Pinus Strobus*) and other five-needled pines. Infection of currants comes from the pines and thus completes the life-cycle of the fungus on its alternate host.

Control.—Spraying as described for Leaf-Spot (see above).

CORAL SPOT *(Nectria cinnabarina)*

This is found on a wide range of hosts, and usually attacks red and white currants through wounds at the base of the bush, probably made during cultivation.

An affected branch wilts and dies, and in time becomes covered with bright pink cushions of fungous tissue. These later become studded with small, red, globe-shaped fruit-bodies of the fungus as it passes to its perfect stage.

Control.—Affected branches should be removed and destroyed when the wilting is seen. All dead wood should be cut out and burnt.

REVERSION *(Virus)*

This is a serious disease of black currants and is most easily recognized by its leaf-characters in May and June. Reverted leaves, found usually in the middle region of the new growth, are deficient in sub-main veins and marginal serrations as compared with normal leaves (which have five or more sub-main veins) and they are often rather longer and narrower. The blossoms on reverted shoots rarely set fruit, and are of abnormal appearance, the trusses being longer and more highly coloured than healthy ones. The virus is now believed to be transmitted by the " Big Bud " mite (and, perhaps, by other insects), which can be controlled by spraying with 2 to 5 per cent. lime-sulphur, according to severity of attack, at a time when the majority of the flower-trusses look like tiny bunches of grapes. The disease does not always affect a whole bush at first ; reverted branches may be found among healthy ones. Reverted shoots should not be used for propagation, and where whole bushes are affected, they should be destroyed.

Care should be taken to distinguish this disease from " false reversion " found in the lower leaves. Distortion of these is usually caused by injury to the terminal bud during the early stages of seasonal growth.

DISEASES : DIAGNOSIS TABLE

BLACK CURRANTS

DAMAGE	PROBABLE CAUSE
Foliage	
In May and June reverted leaves appear in the midst of the new growth. These are deficient in main veins and serrations—long and narrow. Blossom abnormal and sets no fruit	Reversion
Small, brownish spots on leaves, mainly on upper surfaces, may merge together, and leaves wither and fall	Leaf Spot
Bright orange spots on undersides of leaves. Premature leaf-fall may follow	Rust

RED AND WHITE CURRANTS

Branches and Twigs	
Branch wilts and dies—becoming covered with raised cushions of fungous tissue of a bright pink colour	Coral Spot
Foliage	
Small, brownish spots on leaves, mainly on upper sides, may merge together and leaves wither and fall	Leaf Spot
Bright orange spots on undersides of leaves. Premature leaf-fall may follow	Rust

Note.—Once the trouble has been diagnosed, the reader should refer to the paragraph dealing with the treatment of the particular disease or pest and should also consult the Guide to Spraying, see page 110.

RED CURRANT VARIETIES

Variety	Group	Colour	Size	Season	Remarks
Fay's Prolific	Versailles (R. vulgare)	Deep Red	Very Large	Early to Mid-season	Long truss—exhibition, even ripening, needs protection from wind. One of the most popular commercial varieties
Versailles (La Versaillaise)	Versailles (R. vulgare)	Bright Red	Very Large	Early to Mid-season	One of the best red currants for all purposes. Needs protection from wind
La Constante (Southwell Red)	Scotch (R. rubrum)	Bright Dark Red	Medium	Very Late	Attractive appearance
Earliest of Fourland	Prince Albert (R. petræum)	Pale Bright Red	Medium	Early	Vigorous, upright grower
Prince Albert (River's Late Red) (Murie Red)	Prince Albert (R. petræum)	Pale Bright Red	Medium	Very Late	Long truss—useful to prolong the season
Laxton's Perfection	Ungrouped	Very Dark Red	Very Large	Mid-season	Long truss—exhibition, needs protection from wind
Laxton's No. 1	Ungrouped	Shining Scarlet	Large	Mid-season	One of the most promising new varieties
Victoria (Wilson's Long Bunch)	Ungrouped	Pale Red	Medium	Very Late	Long truss. Suits all districts

WHITE CURRANT VARIETIES

Variety	Group	Colour	Size	Season	Remarks
Transparent	Ungrouped	Yellowish	Large	Late	Long truss. Exhibition
Wentworth Leviathan	Ungrouped	Deep Yellow	Large	Very Late	Strong growth
White Versailles (White Versaillaise)	Ungrouped	Pale Yellow	Large	Early	Sweet

BLACK CURRANTS—GROUPS AND VARIETIES

Group	Variety	Growth	Season	Fruit	Remarks
French	French	Vigorous, compact, branched	Mid-season	Truss medium; fruit small to medium, acid; skin tough	
French	Seabrook's Black	ditto	ditto	ditto; fruit large	One of the most widely-planted varieties. Gives large fruit
Boskoop Giant	Boskoop Giant	Very vigorous, drooping	Early	Truss long; fruit large, sweet; skin tender	Needs shelter. Fruit apt to "run off"
Goliath	Edina	Compact	Mid-season	Truss short; fruit very large and sweet; ripens unevenly; skin tender	Rather susceptible to aphis, and leaf definitely sulphur-shy. (See page 108)
Baldwin	Baldwin	Weak, compact	Late	Truss medium; fruit medium, acid; skin very tough	Probably the most widely-grown group. Needs best growth conditions

Group	Variety	Growth	Season	Fruit	Remarks
Baldwin	*Daniel's September*	Rather more vigorous than Baldwin	Very Late	Truss medium; fruit medium, acid; skin very tough	
Intermediate Group	*Wellington Triple X*	Vigorous, drooping	Early to Mid-season	Truss long; fruit large, sweet; skin moderately tough	A cross between *Baldwin* and *Boskoop*. A promising variety, but apt to spread too much
	Westwick Choice	Moderately vigorous	Late	Truss medium, sweet	Strongly recommended
	Davison's Eight	Moderately vigorous	Early to Mid-season	Truss medium, large; skin moderately tough	Leaf highly susceptible to sulphur damage
	Mendip Cross	Vigorous, drooping	Early	Truss long	A promising variety from Long Ashton Research Station

THE DAMSON *(Prunus domestica damascena)*

Because of its peculiar virtues as a jam fruit the damson has acquired a special reputation in this country. Grown as a special crop in certain areas, especially Buckinghamshire, Shropshire, Westmorland and Cumberland, the damson is also generally to be found on any large fruit farm and in most private gardens.

The conditions of soil and management are the same as for other plums and for these the reader is referred to pages 233–6.

VARIETIES OF DAMSONS

Name	Size	Season	Quality
Aylesbury Prune	Large	October–November	Late bearer. Dependable
*Bradley's King of the Damsons	Large	Mid-September	Almost too large for a damson and without the true damson flavour. Susceptible to bacterial canker.
*Farleigh (Crittenden's) or Cluster Damson	Small	Mid-September	Hardy and very prolific. A market favourite, but not the best for canning or preserving.
*Merryweather	Very Large	September–October	Very prolific. For cooking or dessert
Prune (or Shropshire)	Large	September	Good cropper. Described by E. A. Bunyard as the " Greengage of Damsons "
Westmorland	Medium	November	Hangs late. Excellent for canning

Note.—These are all usually grown as standards or half standards, and are more or less self-fertile.

Note.—Aylesbury Prune is considered by some fruit growers to be more resistant than other sorts to the attacks of the Silver Leaf Fungus.

* Recommended by the Royal Horticultural Society for garden culture.

THE FIG *(Ficus Carica)*

SOIL AND SITUATION

The fig should have a situation fully exposed to sun throughout the day, and it must have a free supply of air to enable the branches to ripen. Success depends ultimately upon ripe wood, and this can be attained in the English climate only by root restrictions and the exposure of the wood to the maximum of sunlight. At the same time, the plant should be effectively sheltered so as to preserve as much warmth as possible. Its rooting space should be strictly limited, and it is well to prepare the actual site rather carefully. Indeed, the actual hole, which should be about 3 feet deep and 4 feet square, is often walled in by bricks and cement, so that the roots cannot possibly escape beyond the space allotted to them. At the bottom of this hole should be placed about a foot in depth of broken bricks or gravel. On this should be laid about a foot depth of turves, grass side downwards, and the top foot should consist of a mixture of fibrous loam and broken rubble. Some successful growers, however, prefer to grow in a 12-inch pot and plunge the pot. The roots will climb over the top of the pot and can, if necessary, be pruned at any time.

PROPAGATION

Figs are propagated by means of cuttings made of semi-ripe one-year-old wood, 4 to 6 inches long, and inserted in pots or under a hand-light in September. Or cuttings 10 to 12 inches long, made of firm, woody shoots, may be inserted against a sheltered wall outdoors in autumn. For two years the cuttings are kept in a warm, sunny spot, and are then planted in permanent situation. Suckers are also a possible mode of propagation.

PLANTING

The trees should be planted in late autumn. No manure must be added at planting time, nor at any other—save in exceptional circumstances ; excessive root growth must be guarded against. The borders should be liberally watered every ten days in a dry summer. Fifteen to twenty feet should be allowed between trees. The trees will bear for thirty to forty years.

FORMS OF TREE

Fan.—Details for producing a fan tree are given in full on page 61. In training figs to this form each fruit-bearing shoot must be allowed as much sun and air as possible.

Bush.—In the mild climate of the south and west of England figs ripen on bushes in the open, provided they get enough sunlight, but in most localities the fan form is to be preferred.

PRUNING, DISBUDDING AND PINCHING

Winter pruning consists of cutting out last year's fruit-bearing shoots and tying in the replacement shoots in their place. Where space allows the retention of last year's fruit-bearing shoot and its extension shoot, the replacement shoot may be tied in beside the old fruit-bearing shoot. In early summer disbudding should be carried out to limit the number of new shoots arising from each fruit-bearing shoot. Where space allows one is allowed to grow out at the apical end, as an " extension " shoot, and one from the base for replacement. Towards the end of August or beginning of September, these young shoots should be " stopped " by pinching above the fifth or sixth leaf. This stopping, the object of which is to induce the formation of fruit for the ensuing season, is a matter of much nicety. The fruit for next year must not be much larger than a pea when winter sets in. Larger fruits intermediate on the tree between these, and those of full size should be removed.

ROOT PRUNING

If fig trees are to be induced to crop their roots must be prevented from growing too strongly. In the south of France they are often to be seen with their roots growing on what appears to be almost pure rock. In this country it often happens that in spite of root space being restricted at time of planting, the roots succeed in growing over or round the obstruction. When this happens the tree grows much too strongly, with the result that there is little or no fruit. For this condition root-pruning is the remedy. (See Root Pruning, page 47.)

PROTECTION FROM FROST

Severe winter and spring frosts will often kill the shoots of the fig. For this reason the French growers near Paris used to grow the plants as low bushes or stools, burying the entire plant in the autumn in shallow trenches, and uncovering them the following spring when frosts were over. In this country, with the possible exception of the south-west, the fig tree needs protection in severe winter. Wall-trained trees may be covered over with nets, mats, straw or bracken. Trees grown in pots may be brought indoors for the winter.

GATHERING AND PACKING

The ultimate success in marketing figs depends upon gathering them at a moment when they will arrive on the market in a perfect condition of ripeness. The fruit must be as nearly dead ripe as handling will permit, and should be packed in shallow boxes in the softest of wool, or cotton, a single layer in a box, carefully supported on all sides, or better still, in punnets protected in the same manner.

VARIETIES OF FIGS

Name	Colour	Size	Qualities
*Black Ischia	Purplish-black	Medium	Sweet and juicy. Hardy
Bourjasotte Grise	Reddish-brown	Medium–Large	Excellent flavour. Sweet and rich
*Brown Turkey	Brownish-purple	Medium–Large	Prolific. Good under glass, and best for outdoor culture. Excellent flavour
*Brunswick	Brownish Red-purple	Very Large	Excellent flavour. Forces well, and good outdoor sort
Castle Kennedy	Light Brown	Large	Hardy. Good and early bearer
Negro Largo	Brown-red	Large	Not hardy enough for outdoor. Good flavour
Osborne's Prolific	Brown-red	Medium	Free bearer. Best for pot culture under glass
St. John's	White-fleshed	Large	Excellent. Early bearer under glass
White Ischia	Pale Yellow	Small	Prolific and well adapted for forcing. Not hardy. Sweet and delicious
*White Marseilles	Pale Yellowish-green	Large	Hardy and prolific. Good pot sort. Forces well. Excellent flavour

* Recommended for outdoor garden culture.

DISEASES AND PESTS

The fig suffers little from pests. Scale insects and Red Spider, should they appear, can be checked with petroleum-oil emulsions.

DISEASES

CANKER (Phomopsis cinerescens)

This fungus disease sometimes attacks the branches, gaining entry through wounds. It may cause death of an affected branch, the bark of which is roughened at the seat of the canker, often reminiscent of the markings of an oyster shell. In damp weather the spores of the fungus are released in whitish tendrils from tiny points scattered over the surface of the canker, from whence they can be splashed about by rain.

Control.—Removal and burning of cankered branches, and painting of all wounds with white-lead paint. Branches should be cut out flush so that no snags are left.

DIE-BACK AND FRUIT ROT (Botrytis cinerea)

This common fungus, the cause of Grey Mould disease in many plants, sometimes attacks the young shoots and fruits. The young shoots wilt and the developing fruits rot and usually drop off, though they may become mummified and remain on the tree through the winter, producing spores in the following spring for further infections. The fungus can be recognized by its greyish, fluffy felt produced on affected parts in wet weather.

Control.—Affected shoots and fruits should be removed and burnt.

DISEASES AND PESTS: DIAGNOSIS TABLE

THE FIG

DAMAGE	PROBABLE CAUSE
Branches and Twigs	
Encrusted with scale-like formation	Scale
Twigs die off, patches and cracks in bark, red dot-like fungus	Canker (*Fungus*)
Foliage	
Leaves turn yellow, then silvery, falling early	Red Spider
Fruit	
Damaged	Ants
Eaten	Wasps
Stolen	Mice

THE GOOSEBERRY (*Ribes Grossularia*)

SOIL AND SITUATION

To produce the best bushes and fruit it should be planted in a deep, rich, well-drained loam exposed to full sun and air. It must have potash, and cannot stand waterlogged conditions; very sandy soils and heavy undrained clay soils should equally be avoided. The gooseberry starts to bear two years after planting, and if it is well cared for, should remain productive for ten to fifteen years. If neglected, growth soon becomes stunted.

SUITABLE FORMS

The gooseberry is usually grown as a bush on a short leg in the same way as a red currant, but with rather more leading branches, planted at 5 or 6 feet apart in rows, and at the same distance between the rows.

Where space is limited, the gooseberry may be trained as standards, as pyramids, as single, double, or triple-cordons, as grid-irons, or in fan or espalier form. These are planted at the same distances as for red and white currants (page 173).

PROPAGATION

The gooseberry is raised from hardwood cuttings which are inserted before the middle of October, in the manner described for red currants (page 173). The yearlings are lifted, the upper roots are cut off, and they are replanted for one more season in the nursery. The following autumn they are ready for planting out in their permanent positions as two-year-olds.

SHAPING THE ARTIFICIAL FORMS

Gooseberries and red and white currants can usually be obtained from the nurseries already trained as standards, or in other artificial forms, so that it is not essential to do all the shaping at home. The technique for shaping the tree into these forms is given on page 174.

PRUNING

Pruning for Quantity of Berries.—The gooseberry bears fruit on both one and two-year-old shoots. Hence it can be pruned by either of two methods, according to whether quantity or quality of fruit is required. Where the fruit is to be picked green for jam or bottling, *number of fruits* rather than size of berry is to be considered. In such cases, pruning follows more on the lines of that advised for the black currant, and consists of cutting out whole branches of old wood, in order to keep the bush sufficiently open to allow easy picking; at the same time, such cutting back stimulates strong new shoots to replace the old ones. As a rule little or no " spurring back " of new shoots is practised when gooseberries are being grown for jam or bottling, but the extension or " leader " shoot is cut back from one-half to two-thirds according to the general vigour of the bush.

Pruning for Quality of Berries.—When the main object is to get *a really large fruit*, a different method of pruning is employed, more on the lines laid down for the red currant. The number of main branches is strictly limited, and all the new lateral growths on these are shortened or " spurred back " in winter or early spring to within about 2 inches of their base. In commercial plantations summer pruning of gooseberries is seldom practised, but in gardens when time allows, it pays to carry out this operation when growing the berries for size on cordon and other artificial forms. Summer pruning in this case consists of spurring back the new laterals to within about 5 inches of their base in June or July. This is followed automatically by the winter spurring previously referred to.

In subsequent years the shoots growing from the ends of these " spurs " are shortened right back to their base.

The treatment of the leader or extension shoot depends very largely on the form of tree used. In bush trees it is usual to cut the leaders back annually about one-half from the time the framework is formed, until the bush is in full bearing. When the bush is large and carrying heavy crops, the leaders may need shortening by two-thirds, but this can be determined only by experience.

Some varieties of gooseberry are of a very drooping habit of growth.

The leaders of these varieties should always be cut to an inward and upward-pointing bud. Other varieties have a bad habit of sending up strong " gourmand " suckers from the base. These should be ruthlessly suppressed in the growing season.

Birds are very fond of eating out the buds of gooseberries and red currants, so that it is best to leave the winter pruning of these fruits to the last. Many people cover the bushes all over with black cotton at the beginning of winter by means of a special bobbin which can be bought for the purpose. The birds catch their feet in the cotton, and this acts as a deterrent.

MANURING

Gooseberries are potash and nitrogen lovers. Potash is the more important element and, if it is not available in sufficient quantity, the leaf of the plant becomes scorched and brown round the edges and cannot perform its normal functions. This condition is known as " leaf-scorch " (see under Apple, page 135). Potash should be given every winter, preferably in the form of sulphate of potash, broadcast and pricked in at rates of from 1 to 4 cwt. per acre (½ to 2 oz. per square yard), according to requirements. *The lighter the soil, the more potash will be required.* Provided they have plenty of potash, gooseberries respond to generous applications of bulky nitrogenous manures such as farmyard manure, stable dung, pig dung, shoddy, or meat and bonemeal.

These organic manures help to keep the moisture in the soil through the dry season. It is risky to give very heavy dressings of concentrated nitrogenous fertilizers, because these promote too rapid growth of young shoots, which are apt to break off in the wind, and which readily become attacked by American Gooseberry Mildew where there is a source of infection.

CULTIVATIONS

Clean cultivations without going deep enough to injure the roots are necessary to keep the bushes in a vigorous state of growth throughout their lifetime.

GATHERING THE FRUIT

In some districts the green berries are gathered as soon as they reach marketable size, three-eighths of an inch in diameter, so as to catch the early market. In the later districts this is inadvisable, it being best to wait until the berries are at least half an inch in diameter. The main crop is usually graded at about eleven-sixteenths of an inch in diameter and under eleven-sixteenths of an inch. No damaged berries or leaves should be gathered. The main crop is usually picked into 6-lb. or 12-lb. chip baskets, and is graded afterwards. A start can usually be made with the dessert kinds in July. First all the fruit from the centre of the bush should be gathered, then the large fruit on the lower branches ; after this the fruit is picked in successive gatherings as it swells and ripens. Thinning is recommended in the case of special dessert kinds, such as *Leveller*, when large fruit is required for market or exhibition, the berries being carefully thinned in the early stages, when about half to three-quarters of an inch long.

MARKETING

The first early green berries are usually sent to market in 6-lb. chip baskets ; the main crop usually in 12-lb. chip baskets. The old half-sieve, rim peck and strike, returnable measures have fallen into disfavour. Select dessert berries go up graded in No. 1 and 2 punnets and in No. 2 chip baskets.

INSECT PESTS OF THE GOOSEBERRY

CATERPILLAR

Caterpillars, chiefly of the Winter Moth group (see page 121), can do a great deal of damage to gooseberries by eating the leaves, blossom and young berries.

Control.—Tar-oil and petroleum-oil sprays, particularly the latter, help to control these pests by killing many of the eggs, but the best plan is to apply lead arsenate, derris or D.D.T. immediately after blossoming.

SAWFLY (*Nematus ribesii*)

About blossom time the eggs of this pest can be found laid in rows along the veins on the underside of the leaf—as many as thirty or more often occurring on a single leaf. They soon hatch into tiny green caterpillars with black heads and small black spots on the body. At first the caterpillars feed on one side of the leaf only and keep very much together, but later they consume whole leaves and spread over the entire bush in search of food. Branches or even entire bushes can rapidly be defoliated by a severe attack of sawfly.

When fully fed and about to leave the bushes, the caterpillars are about two-thirds of an inch long, bluish green in colour with an orange-coloured patch behind the head and another on the tail. By now they have lost the rows of black spots, which are, until the final moult, a very conspicuous feature. Like many other sawflies, they spend their pupal period in the soil, in brown parchment-like cocoons.

Control.—It is advisable to spray for this pest soon after blossoming, as the larvæ are then small and easily killed and have not moved far from the spots where the eggs were laid. Lead arsenate, derris

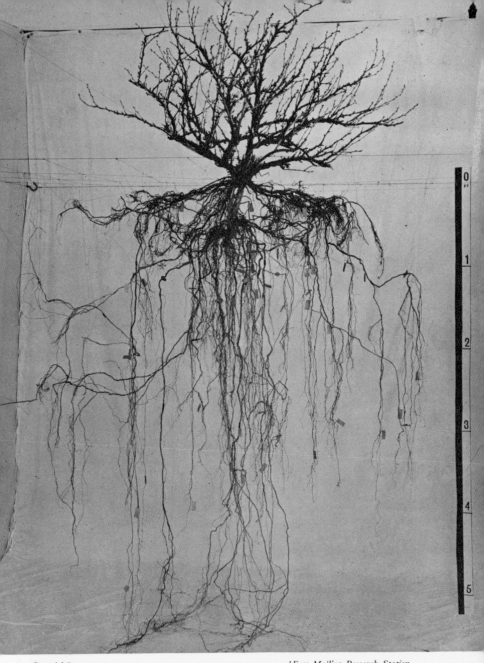

[*East Malling Research Station.*

The rootsystem of an eight-year-old gooseberry bush, excavated from sandy soil, and reconstructed to show the positions occupied by the roots when in the soil.

WINTER PRUNING

or D.D.T. can be used, and an effort should be made to apply the spray to both sides of the leaves. If spraying later in the season becomes necessary (either on account of a second generation of the pest or because the post-blossom spray was omitted), lead arsenate must not be used. A 5 per cent. D.D.T. dust provides a quick and easy means of dealing with this and other species of leaf eating caterpillars.

GOOSEBERRY APHIS (Aphis grossulariæ)

The Gooseberry Aphis is the chief greenfly pest. Others, such as the Lettuce Aphis (Myzus lactucæ), occur now and then.

The Gooseberry Aphis is deep green or greyish green in colour, and occurs in colonies on the shoots in May and June. It sucks the sap and causes young shoots to become stunted and malformed. Migration to other host plants takes place in the summer, but aphides return in the autumn to lay eggs which hatch in the following spring.

Control.—The pest is not particularly easy to kill with nicotine in the summer, as the leaves serve to protect it from the spray. Fortunately, the eggs are easily killed by means of a tar-oil wash, which can be used at any time in the winter up to the end of February.

COMMON GREEN CAPSID (Lygus pabulinus)

Gooseberries are seldom attacked by the Apple Capsid, but do suffer occasionally from attacks of *Lygus*. (See Black Currants, page 179.)

RED SPIDER (Bryobia ribis)

This pest must not be confused with the Fruit Tree Red Spider (*Metatetranychus ulmi*), from which it differs in appearance and in habits. Attacked foliage turns grey or silvery through loss of sap, and when the attack is severe, the young leaves are stunted. Later many of the leaves fall off, and the fruits either drop or fail to grow out properly.

Both spiders and eggs may be found on the bushes in the winter. The spiders, which are red, green or grey in colour, reach a length of about one-thirtieth of an inch. After June, very little damage occurs. Eggs are then laid on the branches and may or may not hatch before the winter.

Control.—Good results can be obtained by winter washing with a tar-oil preparation ; this kills the hibernating mites. After blossoming, lime-sulphur may be applied at a concentration of 1 in 100.

MAGPIE MOTH (Abraxas grossulariata)

This is one of the minor pests of gooseberries and currants. The caterpillars are marked with black and white, and feed on the leaves. If spraying has to be resorted to, non-poisonous material such as derris or D.D.T. should be used.

CURRANT CLEARWING MOTH
See Red Currants, page 180.

PESTS : DIAGNOSIS TABLE

THE GOOSEBERRY

DAMAGE	PROBABLE CAUSE
Shoots and Foliage (Including Blossom)	
Leaves, opening buds and blossom attacked by small green " looping " caterpillars	Winter Moth
Leaves attacked by green larvæ with black heads ; as these grow, they may cause defoliation	Sawfly
Young shoots stunted and malformed and infested with deep or greyish-green aphides	Gooseberry Aphis
Leaves torn and distorted, shoots stunted and may be killed	Common Green Capsid Bug
Foliage turns grey or silvery, young leaves may be stunted and fall early	Gooseberry Red Spider
Leaves attacked by black-and-white marked caterpillars	Magpie Moth
Fruit	
Drops or fails to grow	Gooseberry Red Spider

DISEASES OF THE GOOSEBERRY

AMERICAN GOOSEBERRY MILDEW *(Sphærotheca mors-uvæ)*

This is most commonly found on the tips of the young shoots and on the berries as a thick felt of " mycelium," white in its summer stage but turning brown by autumn. It can be peeled or rubbed off. Occasionally the disease reaches epidemic intensity, when the results are disastrous, the berries being ruined and the young growths distorted. Affected leaves are white and mealy. The brown felt may remain on the bushes in winter, or it may break up and fall to the ground, thus serving as a source of infection the following spring.

Control.—There are various ways in which the risk of infection may be minimized.

Correct pruning to remove any affected growths and to allow of free air circulation amongst the bushes is helpful. Heavy nitrogenous manuring should not be practised, for this encourages succulent growth, which is very susceptible to infection. Bad soil drainage also fosters the disease. Affected portions of shoots removed in pruning should be destroyed and not left lying about.

Lime-sulphur ($2\frac{1}{2}$ per cent.) should be sprayed on to the bushes just before flowering and again (1 per cent.) just after flowering, to protect the new growth from infection. A further application (1 per cent.) may be given if necessary, but the use of this fungicide should be discontinued sufficiently early so that an unsightly spray-deposit does not mar the appearance of the berries at picking-time. The varieties *Leveller, Cousen's Seedling, Yellow Rough (Early Sulphur)*, and *Golden Drop* should not be sprayed post-blossom with lime-sulphur as they are very sulphur-shy, and will drop their leaves and fruits, especially during hot weather. *Leveller*, indeed, is best not sprayed with lime-sulphur at any period. Alternative sprays are colloidal sulphur or dispersed sulphur at a strength recommended by the makers, or soda-soap solution (20 lb. washing soda and 5 lb. soft soap made up to 100 gallons with water) on lime-sulphur-shy varieties. The last-named is a contact spray and is best applied after the appearance of the disease, in its earliest stages. Its effect does not persist, however; it is readily washed off by rain; and frequent sprayings may be necessary to keep the disease in check.

This disease occasionally affects red, white, and black currants as well as gooseberries.

DIE-BACK *(Botrytis cinerea)*

This disease attacks the main stem and branches of the bush, and is occasionally found on the young shoots, leaves, and berries. An affected bush or branch suddenly wilts and ultimately dies. After death, the bark begins to peel off in flakes and the ashy-grey tufts of the fungus appear profusely all over the dead parts, especially in damp weather. The fungus grows within the host tissues and can spread from one affected branch to another. It is important, therefore, to remove affected branches as soon as they are seen, and to cut out and burn any dead wood. Dying bushes should be dug out and destroyed. In cultivating among gooseberry bushes, care should be taken not to injure the plants, for cracked or wounded branches are frequently attacked by the fungus. The fungus can endure for long periods in a resting stage in the form of small, black bodies embedded in the bark of attacked branches. These are highly resistant to weather conditions, and they can give rise to spores, which spread the disease. The fungus is a very common saprophyte on decaying vegetation, and sources of infection for gooseberries are, therefore, extremely numerous.

CLUSTER CUP RUST *(Puccinia Pringsheimiana)*

This disease is not very common but it sometimes turns up in the plantation or garden, and can be recognized by characteristic orange-coloured patches mostly occurring on leaves and berries. The patches are usually found as thickened cushions covered in tiny, saucer-like depressions (" cluster cups ") with frilled edges, but if found before that stage is reached the cushions may appear to be covered in warts or pimples. The depressions arise when these warts burst open to liberate spores, which, however, infect sedges and not gooseberry. On sedge a rust is produced that is an essential part of the life cycle of the fungus. Certain spores are produced in spring on the sedges, and it is these spores that are capable of causing infection on gooseberries when the Cluster Cup stage arises again, and so on.

Control.—Good cultivation and drainage to eradicate sedges in the gooseberry plantation is a necessary preliminary. Where the disease persists and is really troublesome the bushes should be sprayed when the leaves first appear with Bordeaux Mixture (4–6–100) or with a colloidal copper preparation.

LEAF SPOT *(Pseudopeziza ribis)*

This disease, already described for currants (see page 182), is frequently found on gooseberry and can be severe.

Treatment as recommended for currants.

DISEASES : DIAGNOSIS TABLE

THE GOOSEBERRY

DAMAGE	PROBABLE CAUSE
Branches and Stems	
Main stem and branches wilt and die	Die-back
Shoots and Foliage (Including Blossom)	
Leaves, berries and young shoots coated with felt of fungus tissue—white, later turning brown	American Gooseberry Mildew
Orange-coloured patches on leaves, covered in warts or saucer-like depressions	Cluster Cup Rust
Small brownish spots on leaves, mainly on upper surfaces, may merge together, and leaves wither and fall	Leaf Spot
Fruit	
Orange-coloured patches on berries, covered in warts or saucer-like depressions	Cluster Cup Rust

Note.—Once the trouble has been diagnosed, the reader should refer to the paragraph dealing with the particular disease or pest, and should also consult the Guide to Spraying, see page 110.

GOOD VARIETIES

Seasons—Early ; End of June to early July.
Mid-season ; Middle to end of July.
Late ; End of July to August.

GREEN

Berry's Early Kent (see Keepsake).

Green Ocean. Very large, smooth-skinned and of good flavour. Mid-season and of spreading habit.

Howard's Lancer. Medium to large-sized oval, downy-skinned, greenish-white fruit of excellent flavour. Regular cropper. For dessert, cooking or exhibition. Recommended for garden culture and a market favourite. Susceptible to American Gooseberry Mildew. Makes a large, spreading bush. Suckers freely. Should be grown on a leg. Mid-season.

Keepsake. Large, oval, hairy-skinned fruit of excellent flavour. One of the best for picking early for market. A heavy cropper. Recommended for garden culture and is a market favourite. Dessert or cooking. Very susceptible to Mildew. Early.

Langley Gage. Small to medium, rounded, smooth, pale green and very sweet. Strong, upright growth. Suitable for gardens. Mid-season.

RED

Lancashire Lad. Large, oblong to oval, hairy-skinned fruit of fair flavour. Ripens to a dark claret red in mid-season, but is useful also for picking green. Dessert, cooking and exhibition ; a heavy cropper and a very old market favourite in Kent. Probably the best all-round red gooseberry for garden or market.

Lord Derby. Very large, smooth-skinned fruit of moderate flavour, ripening to a deep red. Late season.

May Duke. Medium to large, roundish, smooth-skinned fruit of excellent flavour when cooked. Ripens a deep red, early, and useful for picking green as early as May. Dessert or cooking. Upright growth.

Whinham's Industry. Medium to large, oval-shaped, hairy-skinned fruit of fine, sweet flavour. Mid-season. Hardy and a good cropper. Good for picking green. Recommended for garden cultivation and is a market favourite. Dessert or cooking and makes excellent jam. Rather susceptible to American Gooseberry Mildew.

YELLOW

Brighton Dessert and **Brighton Mammoth** (see Leveller).

Broom Girl. Very large, roundish-oval, hairy-skinned fruit of fine flavour. Early.

Gunner. Large, round-oval, slightly hairy, dull, greenish yellow berry. Good flavour and bears well. Mid-season to late.

Leader. Large, roundish-oval, greenish-yellow fruit of excellent flavour. Late. A market dessert favourite.

Leveller. Very large, oval, smooth-skinned, yellowish-green fruit of excellent flavour. Mid-season. Heavy cropper. One of the best dessert fruits. Recommended for garden culture, and much the most sought-after market variety at present. Is also known under other names. Needs rich soil, good drainage, and heavy dressings of potash and of organic nitrogenous manures. *Very susceptible to lime-sulphur damage.*

WHITE

Careless. Very large, oval, smooth-skinned, creamy or whitish-green fruit of excellent flavour. Second early or mid-season. A very heavy cropper and a market favourite, especially in the Eastern counties. Makes a large bush.

Freedom. Very large, oblong, smooth-skinned, white to yellowish and vigorous.

White Lion. Very large, oval, slightly-flattened, downy-skinned, white fruits of excellent flavour. Mid-season. Popular at market. Makes a very large bush.

Whitesmith. Medium-sized oval, smooth and downy-skinned, whitish-green fruits of fine flavour. Mid-season, hardy and crops well. A popular market berry, and one of the best all-round varieties. Recommended for garden culture.

VARIETIES WITH VERY LARGE FRUITS

Green

Green Ocean		Keepsake

Red

Lancashire Lad		Lord Derby

Yellow

Broom Girl	Leader	Leveller

White

Careless	Freedom	White Lion

All the above are suitable sorts to grow for exhibition.

LOGANBERRY AND *PHENOMENAL BERRY

SOIL, SITUATION AND ASPECT

The Loganberry likes a well-drained deep, rich loam, and any aspect which gives a fair degree of protection from wind. Owing to their late flowering season loganberries may be planted in comparatively low situations.

PROPAGATION

If any quantity of Loganberry canes are to be raised, the parent plants may be bought as " yearlings " in autumn and should be planted out at once in a cane nursery at 6 foot square, and cut back to within 6 to 9 inches of the ground. The following spring several young canes will spring up from each " stool " and these will be used for " tip-rooting." The method consists of bending over the young growing cane until it is nearly perpendicular, and burying the tip in the soil, by digging a hole and heeling it in firmly. The cane continues to grow for a short time underground, growth becoming more and more abnormal as the cane pushes down against the hard soil. The new growth underground becomes short-jointed, swollen and fleshy, and before long adventitious rooting takes place from this region. Then

* Similar to the Loganberry. The fruits ripen somewhat later, and are a little larger.

a bud breaks from near the base and forms a shoot which grows upwards and soon emerges above the ground to become the new " tip-rooted " cane. This process is best done in June or July, though in a normal season Loganberry tips can be rooted as late as mid-August and blackberries until the beginning of September. The " tip " is left in place all through the winter. About February it is severed from the parent cane about a foot above ground level, and is then dug up and planted out in its permanent position. At this time the cane is usually 12 or 18 inches long. When digging up the young " tip," care should be taken to preserve intact as much of its new root system as possible, because the new roots are very brittle and are liable to get knocked off with rough treatment.

When all the " tips " have been cut off and dug up in this way, the remaining part of each parent cane is cut back to within 9–12 inches of the base and the cane nursery is ready to produce a new crop of canes for next season's " tip-rooting."

PLANTING AND TRAINING

Loganberries may be planted as " tips " or as two year plants in the spring or autumn in rows 6 to 7 feet apart, the tips being spaced at from 8 to 12 feet apart in the row, according to the method of training to be adopted. After planting the young cane is cut back to within about 9 inches of ground level. No fruit can be expected in the season of planting, but each plant should make from three to six strong new canes in their first year, and up to twelve new canes in subsequent years.

TRAINING

The canes which are to carry next year's crop are usually tied to horizontal wires at 3 feet and 5 feet above the ground level. Of the various training methods employed, the Fan is the most popular for gardens (see diagram). Immediately after pruning (page 200) the new

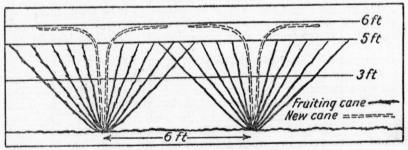

FAN METHOD OF TRAINING LOGANBERRIES.

canes are spread out like the ribs of a fan, each cane being tied with soft fillis string to the wires at 3 feet and 5 feet.

The tips of any canes which extend beyond the 5 foot wires are cut back to it. As the new canes shoot up during the following summer, they are taken up through the middle of the fan and tied up along the top wire (6 feet) to right and left. In commercial plantations of Loganberries, the Rope method of training is often used. This is described under blackberries on page 154.

PRUNING

The pruning of Loganberries takes place as soon as possible after the fruit is picked, and consists of cutting to the ground the whole of the cane which has been fruiting during the summer. This should be done with a stout knife or pair of secateurs.

MANURING

The Loganberry has to form fruiting laterals to carry this year's crop as well as new cane for next year. Hence nitrogen is the main manurial requirement, with potash next in importance.

Farmyard manure, which contains nitrogen, potash and phosphates, is the ideal manure for Loganberries as for all soft fruits and may be dug in at rates up to 30 tons per acre. Failing this, pig-dung, poultry manure or shoddy may be spread evenly over the ground round the plants in the winter and forked in, or such artificials as guano, hoof and horn or meat meal, may be applied in the same way at about 5 cwt. per acre (2 oz. per square yard) supplemented in February or March with sulphate of ammonia, nitrate of soda, or nitro-chalk, at from 1 to 2 cwt. per acre ($\frac{1}{2}$ to 1 oz. per square yard). Sulphate of potash at 2 to 3 cwt. per acre (1 to $1\frac{1}{2}$ oz. per square yard) may be applied at any time during the winter and pricked in or dug in. Steamed bone-flour at 5 cwt. per acre (2 oz. per square yard) may be applied in the spring as a phosphatic manure for Loganberries.

The ground round the roots of the plants must be hoed throughout the spring and summer, or a good mulch of rotted dung, grass mowings, old hay or rotted bracken may be applied after the spring hoeings.

GATHERING AND MARKETING

Loganberries commence to ripen towards the middle of July and thence on, according to locality, through July and into August. Where intended for immediate use or for canning, the fruit should be picked as it ripens, but when required for the fresh fruit market, the berries should be gathered when a bright red, without the " strig." They must be perfectly dry when gathered and are usually sent to market in 4-lb., 6-lb., or 12-lb. paper-lined chip baskets.

INSECT PESTS OF THE LOGANBERRY

Loganberries, fortunately, have very few important pests.

RASPBERRY AND LOGANBERRY BEETLE *(Byturus tomentosus)*

This is a pest of long standing and can, if sufficiently numerous, destroy the whole crop. The fat, curved grubs, dirty white in colour and with pale brown patches on the back are a familiar sight in Loganberry fruits. They hatch from eggs laid in the blossoms by the adult beetle, a small, active, brown or grey creature about one-sixth of an inch in length.

The grubs burrow in the plug and feed on the surrounding drupelets. Badly-attacked fruits of Loganberries and blackberries fail to swell out or to ripen properly, but become, instead, small, brown, hard and deformed. The damage done to the flesh of raspberries, although considerable, is relatively less, since these fruits are much nearer ripening when the larvæ attack them.

Control.—Fortunately, the pest can easily be controlled by the use of derris and soap. This should be applied towards the end of June to both raspberries and Loganberries; one application is normally sufficient, but an additional and earlier (mid-June) spraying is often worth while on Loganberries. Blackberries should be sprayed in the middle of July. Thorough spraying is important as it is essential to wet the fruits thoroughly. An alternative method is to apply a derris dust during the blossom period. This is effective, but not good for the bees. D.D.T. preparations can be used in place of derris and are equally effective.

BRAMBLE SHOOT WEBBER *(Notocelia uddmanniana)*

The fat, dark brown grubs of this moth are to be found feeding in the young tips of the new canes, the leaves of which they spin together in tight bunches. As a rule, the shoots eventually grow out of the attack, but they are then usually distorted and the check to growth is apt to cause excessive side branching.

Control.—On a small scale, the pest can be combatted by hand picking. When laterals are attacked, the tip containing the grub may be pinched out, but in the case of main shoots wanted later for training, the bunched tips should be unrolled and the grubs killed. On a larger scale, hand picking is impracticable. Then the young growing canes should be protected by sprayings of lead arsenate or D.D.T. applied often enough to maintain a good deposit on the tips until about the middle of May.

GREENFLY *(Aphides)*

Various species of aphides occur in Loganberries, but are not particularly troublesome. They can easily be killed with nicotine or by the derris spray used for the Raspberry Beetle.

RASPBERRY MOTH *(Incurvaria rubiella)*
See Raspberry, page 256.

PESTS : DIAGNOSIS TABLE
THE LOGANBERRY

DAMAGE	PROBABLE CAUSE
Shoots and Foliage	
Tips of young shoots attacked and leaves spun together by fat, dark brown larvæ	Shoot Moth
Young shoots, about one inch long, wither and die, eaten by small red caterpillars	Raspberry Moth
Undersides of leaves infested with long-legged, pale greenfly	Raspberry Aphis
Tips of shoots infested with greenfly	Blackberry Aphis or *Aphis idaei*
Fruit	
Fails to swell or ripen properly ; is small, hard, brown and deformed ; fat, dirty-white grubs in fruit	Raspberry Beetle

Note.—Once the trouble has been diagnosed, the reader should refer to the paragraph dealing with the particular disease or pest and consult the Guide to Spraying, page 111.

DISEASES OF THE LOGANBERRY

CANE SPOT *(Elsinoë veneta)*

This is the fungus that causes Cane Spot on the raspberry (see page 255). The symptoms of the disease are similar on the two hosts but severe infection of the leaves is a more dominant feature in Loganberry than in raspberry. Severely infected Loganberry leaves may be almost covered in rounded, purple-coloured spots, which, as they become older, develop grey centres, so that the spots are very conspicuous. The canes, too, can become so badly attacked that cankers are formed and the ends of the canes are killed. Infection has occasionally been found on the berries. Spores are produced on the spots and splashed about by rain, so that the disease is worst in wet weather.

Control.—The promotion of good conditions for adequate aeration amongst the foliage, and thus quicker drying after wet weather, can be achieved by allowing ample space between plants and rows at planting time, and also by suitable distribution of the canes on the wirework. As the new canes grow, their chances of becoming infected by spores splashed downwards from the current season's fruiting canes are greatly reduced if they are trained above and not below the fruiting canes. First-class control of this disease can be secured if, to the measures already suggested, be added spray-treatment with a copper fungicide. Bordeaux Mixture (4–6–100) should be put on just before the flowers open, and this should be followed by a colloidal copper preparation put into the derris and soap spray recommended for the control of Raspberry Beetle on Loganberry (see page 201). Bordeaux must not be used on the berries, because it would leave a persistent visible deposit on them.

DWARF (Virus) (see Blackberry, page 155)

WATERLOGGING

Functional disease.—See Apple, page 133.

DISEASES : DIAGNOSIS TABLE

THE LOGANBERRY

DAMAGE	PROBABLE CAUSE
Canes, Foliage and Shoots	
Purplish spots on young canes and leaves in early summer ; getting larger and having grey centres	Cane Spot
Apparently healthy canes wilt after bud-burst and fail to grow	Waterlogging

MEDLAR (*Mespilus germanica*)

SOIL, SITUATION AND ASPECT

The medlar is grown in any good, well-drained but retentive soil. It requires an open, sunny situation where it is protected from cold winds, and in northern districts a protecting wall is necessary.

FORMS AND PLANTING

The medlar may be grown in standard form, allowing 15 to 20 feet between trees.

PRUNING

The cultivation of the medlar is almost identical with that advised for the apple. Pruning consists in merely thinning out weak and old wood in winter, and in keeping the tree open. The fruit is borne on old spurs, and on the ends of the branches.

PROPAGATION

Propagation is carried out by means of budding named varieties in July in the open, using the thorn as stock. Pear and quince stocks are also used, and by some grafting may be preferred to budding.

GATHERING AND STORING

The fruits should be gathered about the middle of November, and should be stored in a single layer, " eye " downwards, on some dry silver sand, placed on a shelf in the store room. The stems should point upwards. It is usually necessary to store the medlars for at least a fortnight before they are sufficiently ripe for eating ; that is, when they lose their green tint and become soft.

VARIETIES

The best varieties to grow are *Nottingham* or *Narrow-leaved Dutch*, with small to medium pear-shaped, russeted, yellowish-brown fruits, and *Royal* with medium-sized, roundish, reddish-brown fruits, both of which are of excellent flavour and prolific. *Dutch Giant*, or *Monstrous*, makes a large, spreading tree and produces very big fruits, but the fruit is not so prolific or good flavoured.

DISEASES AND PESTS

The medlar is particularly free from diseases and pests. Should any put in an appearance, the reader is referred to the diseases and pests of the apple.

MULBERRY (*Morus nigra*)

SOIL, SITUATION AND ASPECT

The mulberry likes a sunny position and deep, well-drained, rich, moist loam. In the south and most of the British Isles the mulberry can be grown in the open as a bush or standard, but in northern districts it should be grown on a warm south wall.

PROPAGATION

The mulberry is easily propagated by cuttings which readily root if taken in September and October ; shoots a foot or more in length, root with little trouble in sandy soil in a cold frame. Layers also root readily if put down in October. Suckers for propagating should not be taken from round the base of a tree because this may have been grafted on *Morus alba*, the wild mulberry, used for feeding silkworms.

PLANTING

The best time for planting is in October or November, although the trees may be put in late in February or early in March. They should be planted at least 25 to 30 feet apart. When planting, do not cut back the long, thick roots of this tree, as is usual when planting fruit trees, or they will " bleed " and the tree may die.

PRUNING

As the fruit is borne on spurs and on short-jointed young wood, it is well to cut back young shoots to about four or five buds, only removing in winter such as are necessary to keep the tree shapely and from becoming overcrowded. Wall-trees should have their main branches trained some 15 inches apart and should be allowed to grow until they have covered the wall. Side-shoots should be cut back in July to five or six leaves.

GATHERING THE FRUIT

The fruit should be allowed to remain on the tree until it falls from ripeness. Cloths spread under the tree will catch the ripe fruit if the tree is shaken, or hand picking may be preferred. When the tree is heavily laden with fruit, some of the branches may need support, otherwise they are apt to break off.

VARIETIES

The *Large Black* is one of the best varieties.

DISEASES AND PESTS

The mulberry is practically immune from diseases and pests, birds being the most troublesome enemy.

CANKER *(Gibberella moricola)*

This fungus disease causes cankers and death of the young shoots, and pale-brown, waxy spore-pustules or cushions appear on the cankers in damp weather.

Control.—All affected parts should be promptly cut out and burnt.

THE PEACH AND THE NECTARINE

(Prunus Amygdalus Persica)

The nectarine is a smooth-skinned variety of the peach.

SOIL AND SITUATION

The peach and nectarine, like the apricot, need great summer heat to ripen their wood. For this reason they do best in this country either under glass or on a south wall, as fan trained trees. In recent years two or three varieties have been grown in the bush form in the open air with some degree of success.

PROPAGATION

Peaches and nectarines are usually propagated by budding on to plum stocks in the summer. For large trees the Brompton has proved to be one of the best rootstocks, while for trees of medium size the Common Mussel stock is to be recommended. Other Plum stocks making good trees of medium size are Pershore (Yellow Egg) and St. Julian C. One grower also recommends Broad Leaved Shiny Mussel.

PLANTING

Planting should take place in the autumn. Wall-trained trees should be planted about 4 inches from the wall and not less than 15 feet apart. The bottom of the hole should be made firm previous to planting and all injured roots should be cut away. The roots should then be covered to a depth of at least 6 inches with fine soil, well pressed down, care being taken to see that the union between stock and scion is left uncovered. If a drought should occur during the summer following planting, the ground should be well watered and mulched with old stable manure.

FORMS OF TREE

Peaches and nectarines can be grown in a number of artificial forms and, in sheltered situations, certain varieties can be grown as bush trees. In this country the fan shape is generally considered the most satisfactory form for trees when grown against walls or fences. (See diagrams, pages 60 and 61.)

For those who wish to buy maiden trees and do their own training the notes on page 62 will form a guide. But it should be emphasized that the training of a fan tree is essentially a slow process, needing patience and experience to obtain uniformly successful trees, and one which for that reason is best left to the skilled nurseryman.

PRUNING AND DISBUDDING OF TRAINED TREES OF PEACH AND NECTARINE

On peaches and nectarines the best fruits are borne on good shoots of the previous season's growth. Good fruits are sometimes produced

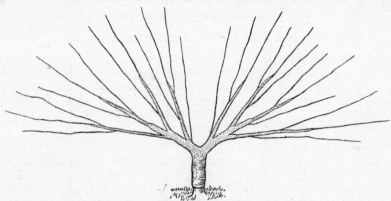

FAN-TRAINED TREE AT END OF FOUR YEARS' GROWTH.
For early training, see pages 61 and 62.

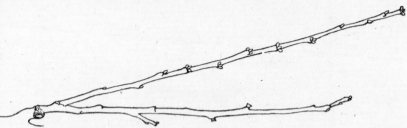

Fig. 1.—Fruit-bearing shoot after fruit is picked, showing replacement shoot ready to replace it. See also page 208.

on comparatively short and weak growths, but attention should be devoted mainly to shoots from 15 to 18 inches long, bearing in winter mixed fruit and wood buds. These shoots, usually $\frac{1}{4}$ to $\frac{1}{2}$ inch thick, are referred to in the following section as fruit-bearing shoots.

Fruit-bearing Shoots.—The fruit-buds on these shoots will blossom and carry fruits which in due course must be drastically thinned out. The wood-buds on the same shoots, if allowed to grow unchecked, will starve the fruit and smother in the tree, so it is important to know how to deal with them by means of disbudding. The expression " disbudding " in this connection does not mean the actual rubbing out of the bud between finger and thumb, but it means pinching out the tip of the embryo shoot when it is not more than an inch long. This process is vital to the successful control of all wall-trained trees, especially apricots, peaches and nectarines. Disbudding should begin at the top of the tree as soon as the wood buds begin to push out into shoots in the late spring. All " fore-right " shoots, namely, those growing straight outwards from or inwards to the wall are disbudded first. After that the principle is to restrict the number of shoots so that when these are ultimately tied in to the supporting wires, there will be a clear 5-inch lateral space between each. Most trees on walls are allowed to carry far too many shoots, especially at the top, for want of regular pinching.

The only way to avoid this is to lay down a " rule of thumb " regulation for the pruner something as follows :

Wood-bud for Replacement Shoot.—At the base of every fruit-bearing shoot, whether fruit has set or not, at least one good shoot must be left to grow. This must be situated at the base of the fruit-bearing shoot, and is known as the " replacement shoot." By the end of the season the fruit-bearing shoot, having done its work and being of no further use, will be cut off just above the replacement shoot which

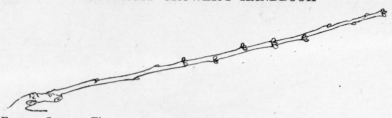

FIG. 2.—Same as Fig. 1 on page 207 after fruit-bearing shoot has been cut off at base, and replacement tied in to take its place.

will then be tied in its place to carry out the same function, namely, carrying fruit the next season.*

Extension Shoot.—In early years, when there is plenty of room on the wall, one wood-bud at the end of the fruit-bearing shoot is also retained to form an extension shoot growing in the same direction as the fruit-bearing shoot, its subsequent treatment being the same as described for the replacement shoot.

Shoots next Fruits.—Shoots growing next to fruits left from the final thinning should not be disbudded. These, however, must be pinched out later as described under Summer Pruning.

All other Shoots growing from Fruit-bearing Shoots.—All other shoots except those mentioned above should be disbudded over a period of two to three weeks in May and June. When the process is complete each fruit-bearing shoot should be seen to have either one, or occasionally two, shoots growing strongly away from its base, and one at or near the tip, *where space allows.* No other wood shoots should be tolerated with the exception of those actually next a fruit.

FIG. 3.—Peach Pruning—Pinching and Disbudding.
1. Replacement shoot growing away unchecked.
2 and 3. Fruits, each with one shoot " pinched " to two good leaves.
4. Unwanted shoots disbudded.
5. Extension shoot growing away unchecked.

* Some pruners like to leave two wood-buds at the base of each fruit-bearing shoot in order to make certain of having something to replace the old shoot.

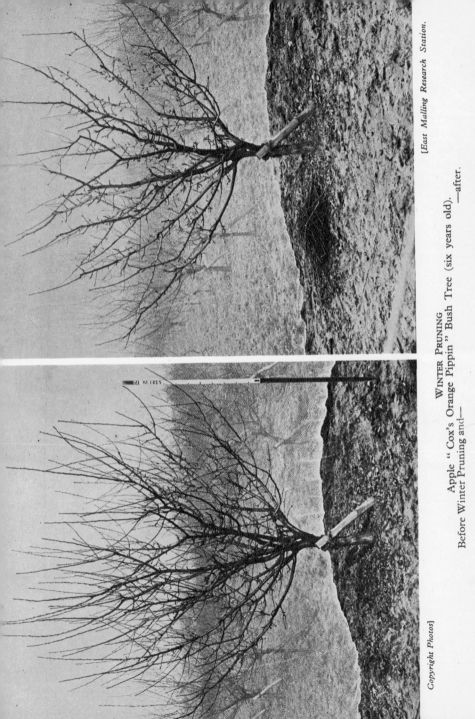

WINTER PRUNING

Apple "Cox's Orange Pippin" Bush Tree (six years old).

Before Winter Pruning and——

——after.

INFLUENCE OF STOCK ON GROWTH OF TREE

"Victoria" Plum (thirteen years old) on Common Plum Stock. "Victoria" Plum (thirteen years old) on Myrobolan Plum Stock.

SUMMER PINCHING AND STOPPING

Replacement of Extension Shoots.—Should the extension shoots grow too strongly, showing signs of much exceeding 18 inches in length, they should have their tips pinched out at this length. Where wall-space is limited extension shoots on established trees should be pinched out above the fifth good leaf when they have attained that length. As a result of summer pinching, especially if rainy weather follows, the buds below the pinch are likely to send out one or more " secondary " shoots after a week or two. These should be pinched or " stopped " above the first good leaf.

Shoots next Fruits.—Shoots that have been allowed to grow next fruits should be pinched above the second good leaf, and secondaries above the first leaf.

PRUNING AND TYING-IN AFTER FRUITING

The next pruning operation takes place after the fruit has been picked. Where there is plenty of wall-space available, the extension shoot is tied in, carrying on the direction of the fruit-bearing shoot, and the replacement shoot is tied in beside last year's fruit-bearing shoot. In an established tree, or where wall-space is limited, the old fruit-bearing shoot with its terminal extension shoot is cut off at the base immediately in front of the new replacement shoot. The replacement shoot is then tied in to the space formerly occupied by the fruit-bearing shoot. Thus the replacement shoot of this season becomes the fruit-bearing shoot for next season, and in this way the whole tree is refurnished annually. The pinching programme described above may be expressed in tabular form as follows :—

SUMMER PINCHING PROGRAMME—PEACHES AND NECTARINES

Replacement Shoot. (At base of fruit-bearing shoot.)
    (1) Terminal bud pinched out at about 18 inches.
    (2) Secondaries stopped at first leaf.
Extension Shoot. (At end of fruit-bearing shoot.)
  (a) *On Young Trees where Wall-space is Plentiful.*
    (1) Terminal bud pinched out at about 18 inches.
    (2) Secondaries stopped at first leaf.
  (b) *On Established Trees where Wall-space is Limited.*
    (1) Terminal shoot pinched out above fifth leaf.
    (2) Secondaries stopped at first leaf.

SUBSEQUENT TREATMENT OF SHOOTS

  (a) *On Young Trees where Wall-space is Plentiful.*
    (1) Extension shoot tied in in the same direction as the fruit-bearing shoot.

F.G.H.   O

(2) Replacement shoot tied in alongside last-season's fruit-bearing shoot.

(b) *On Established Trees where Wall-space is Limited.*

(1) Fruit-bearing shoot cut back to base.

(2) Replacement shoot tied in in its place.

The method of disbudding and pinching here described is only one of various systems employed by gardeners, and does not attempt to deal exhaustively with the treatment of all the shoots which may grow in the course of the season. For the sake of simplicity, it has been thought best to concentrate on the treatment of the fruit-bearing shoots, since these are the most important. Shoots arising in other parts of the tree which are not disbudded, and which are clearly not going to be required, are best dealt with by cutting them clean out after the fruit has been picked.

In peaches and nectarines when tying in, a space of not less than 4–5 inches should be left between all fruit-bearing shoots. In plums and cherries this space may be reduced to about 2 inches.

PRUNING OF BUSH TREES

Mr. Justin Brooke, in *Peach Orchards in England*, recommends pruning young bush trees in May by cutting back all but the most vigorous shoots to strong side shoots near the base with the idea of annually renewing fruit-bearing shoots. Should the tree become too thick in the centre, crossing or awkwardly placed branches are cut off in May.

ROOT PRUNING WALL TREES

One of the difficulties inherent in the maintenance of peaches and other stone fruits in artificial forms and in confined spaces lies in the fact that they are naturally strong-growing trees for which there is no really dwarfing stock. Hence the everlasting problem of what to do with a wall tree when it gets to the top of the wall. Gardeners on the whole are agreed that the only thing to do is to meet trouble half-way by root-pruning a few years after the trees are planted. A trench 15 to 18 inches deep is dug in winter underneath the tree, and all strong roots are severed at a distance of about 4 feet from the stem.

PROTECTION FROM FROST

Owing to their early flowering, apricots, peaches and nectarines are always liable to be injured by severe spring frosts. Any form of over-head shelter will give a measure of protection and where this is impracticable, a double thickness of fish-netting may be hung 9 inches in front of the trees every evening from the time of bud-burst throughout the blossoming period. On fine days this shelter should be removed to allow pollinating insects free access to the flowers.

PROTECTION FROM HAIL

Wall trees may be protected to a certain extent from damage by hailstones in March and April by fastening a single thickness of fish-netting, about mid-February, above the top of the wall, and carrying it down and out at an angle of about 45 degrees to the wall. The netting is then fastened to a wire stretched on posts, about 3 feet high, and about 6 feet out from the foot of the wall (see diagram, page 85).

MANURING

Like all other stone fruits peaches like plenty of farmyard manure or equivalent organics, supplemented by a complete artificial fertilizer.

FRUIT THINNING

Thinning should start when the fruits are the size of a hazel nut, leaving twice as many fruits as will ultimately be required. A natural process known as " stoning " begins when the fruit is about an inch in diameter, in the course of which many drop off. After stoning, the fruits again begin to swell and thinning should then be continued, leaving the fruits approximately 9 inches apart for peaches, and rather less for nectarines. In the final thinning, only the largest and best-placed fruits should be left on the tree, spaced at about one to every square foot of tree, but leaving more at the top of the tree.

WATERING

In very hot weather when the fruit is swelling, the trees will benefit from a good watering, but when the fruit is actually ripening, watering must cease.

GATHERING AND MARKETING

The test for time of picking is to feel the fruit at the base, but never to press the sides. When picking the whole hand is placed over the fruits with fingers extended under it. If ready for picking, a slight pull with the fingers will detach the fruit without causing a bruise.

The usual practice is to send peaches and nectarines to market in specially-constructed " peach boxes." These are supplied as returnable packages by the salesman and are lined with cotton wool to hold 12, 15, or 18 fruits according to size. Failing this single layer trays well padded with some soft lining material may be used.

NECTARINE

The nectarine requires exactly the same treatment as the peach (see page 205). The fruit is smaller, smooth-skinned and more delicate in flavour. For best varieties see list on page 212.

NECTARINES—GOOD VARIETIES

Name	Colour	Size	Season	Qualities	Soil, Aspect, etc.
*Dryden	Red and purple	Very large	August	Sweet and juicy	
*†Early Rivers	Bright red	Large	July–August	Good flavour. Excellent cropper	
*Elruge	Pale green and red	Small	August–September	Good flavour. Very popular. Very sound	
*Hardwicke	Pale green, flushed dark purple	Large	End of August	Good flavour and prolific	Open, deep calcareous soil; not too moist.
*†Humboldt	Orange and crimson	Good size	August–September	Good flavour and sound variety	Aspect East to South-west Winter pruning, autumn; Summer pruning, April–May
*†Lord Napier	Pale green, red cheek	Good size	July–August	Excellent for forcing. Best of the earlies	
*†Pineapple	Orange and red	Large	August–September	One of the best flavour	
*Pitmaston Orange	Orange, flushed reddish-brown	Large	Early September	Good flavour and prolific	
†River's Orange	Orange	Large	September	Excellent for forcing	
Spenser	Dark crimson	Large	Mid-September	Fine flavour. Good exhibition fruit	
*†Victoria	Yellow, with brownish-red flush	Large	September–October	Prolific. Good flavour	

PEACHES—GOOD VARIETIES

Name	Colour	Size	Season
EARLY			
†‡Alexander	Yellow, red flush	Medium	July–August
*Amsden June	Greenish-white, dark red flush	Medium	Early July
Dagmar	Yellow, red flush	Medium	Early August
Dr. Hogg	Yellow, flushed red	Medium to large	August
*‡Duke of York	Bright crimson	Large	Mid-July
Duchess of Cornwall	Pale yellow	Medium	Mid-July
Earliest of All	Yellowish, flushed red	Medium	Early July
*†‡Hale's Early	Crimson	Medium	July–August
*†‡Peregrine	Bright crimson	Large	Early August
*†Waterloo	Yellow with red flush	Medium	July–August
MID-SEASON			
*Crimson Galande	Crimson	Medium	Late August to September
Dymond	Greenish-yellow, red cheek	Large	Early September
Prince of Wales	Greenish-yellow, mottled red	Large	Mid-September
†Royal George	Pale, speckled red	Large	August and September
Violette Hative	Pale Yellow, flushed red	Large	Mid-September

Note.—*Denotes those kinds which will grow on south walls in the open.
†Denotes a good market variety.

‡ Varieties suitable for growing out of doors.

Name	Colour	Size	Season
LATE			
*Barrington	Yellowish-green, marbled red	Large	Mid-September
*Bellegarde	Dark crimson	Large	Mid-September
Golden Eagle	Lemon	Very large	October
†Gladstone	Greenish-yellow, slight flush	Large	End of September
Late Devonian	Greenish-yellow, crimson cheek	Large	Mid-September
†Late Admirable	Yellowish-green, and pale red	Very large	September
Princess of Wales	Cream and red	Large	September to October
*Sea Eagle	Pale yellow, crimson flush	Very large	September to October
Téton de Vénus	Pale yellow, crimson flush	Large	End of September

Note.—* Denotes those kinds which will grow on south walls in the open.
    † Denotes a good market variety.

Various plum stocks are used for grafting. See notes on Stocks, page 27.

NECTARINES FOR GROWING ON A SOUTH WALL

Early Rivers (End of July) ; *Lord Napier* (Early August) ; *Humboldt* (Mid-August) ; *Elruge* and *Hardwicke* (End of August) ; *Darwin* and *John Rivers* (September) ; *Pitmaston Orange* and *Pineapple* (Early September) ; *Victoria* (End of September).
For details of these varieties, see list, page 212.

DISEASES OF THE PEACH AND NECTARINE

LEAF-CURL *(Taphrina deformans)*

This disease is commonly found on peaches grown in the open, and, to a less extent, on those grown under glass. It also attacks nectarines and almonds. Chiefly the leaves are affected. These become crinkled and swollen and, when young, are yellowish in colour with tinges of red. The older the leaf, the more pronounced are the symptoms and the more striking is the red coloration. When the fungus is producing spores, affected leaves develop a whitish bloom mostly on the upper surface. Diseased leaves ultimately wither and die prematurely, and this saps the vitality of the tree, and, in bad cases, causes the immature fruits to drop. The shoots are sometimes attacked ; they become swollen and twisted.

Infection of the leaves in early spring is believed to arise from spores that have passed the winter dormant on the tree, possibly entangled in the bud-scales ; the disease is favoured by a wet spring. Affected leaves produce large numbers of spores throughout the spring and early summer, and these serve to spread the disease to healthy leaves.

Control.—Good control can be obtained by spraying with lime-sulphur at 3 per cent., or with Bordeaux Mixture at 8–12–100, just as the buds are bursting. The collection and burning of diseased leaves also is helpful.

BROWN ROTS (see Plum, page 240)

SILVER LEAF (see Plum, page 242)

DISEASES : DIAGNOSIS TABLE

PEACHES AND NECTARINES

DAMAGE	PROBABLE CAUSE
Foliage	
Leaves crinkled and swollen ; when young, yellowish with tinges of red	Leaf Curl
Leaves turn silvery on affected branches	Silver Leaf
Fruit	
More or less concentric rings of " pustules " of fungous tissue appear and produce spores	Brown Rot

Note.—Once the trouble has been diagnosed, the reader should refer to the paragraph dealing with the particular disease or pest and should also consult the Guide to Spraying, page 111.

INSECT PESTS OF THE PEACH AND NECTARINE

Peaches and Nectarines sometimes suffer from attacks of greenfly, the Green Peach Aphis (*Myzus persicæ*) and the Leaf-curling Peach Aphis (*Anuraphis amygdali*), feeding on the young leaves and blossoms. They can be kept in check with a tar-oil wash in December or with nicotine or derris and soap in spring and summer. Peach Scale (*Lecanium*) may also occur, but can be killed with strong lime-sulphur or with tar-oil washes. Red Spider (*Tetranychus telarius*) is the chief pest. The same species attacks hops and is troublesome on almost all glasshouse plants ; it hibernates as an adult and emerges in the spring and soon causes silvering or browning of the foliage. The lime-sulphur applied at bud-break for Peach Leaf-curl will also destroy this Red Spider.

CATERPILLARS

See Winter Moth, under Apple, page 121.

PESTS : DIAGNOSIS TABLE

PEACHES AND NECTARINES AND APRICOTS

DAMAGE	PROBABLE CAUSE
Branches and Twigs	
Reddish-brown scaly formations on branches and twigs	Peach Scale

DAMAGE	PROBABLE CAUSE
Foliage and Shoots	
Shoots and young leaves infested with greenfly	Green Peach Aphis
Leaves infested with aphis and curled up	Leaf-curling Peach Aphis
Leaves turn silvery or brownish	Red Spider

THE PEAR *(Pyrus communis)*

SOIL AND SITUATION

The best soil for all varieties of pear is a deep, well-drained medium loam of a " brick earth " type. Most varieties of pear can be grown in any good garden soil, in the milder districts of the south and west of England.

To produce some of the best quality late-keeping pears at their right season, and in perfect condition, is one of the most severe tests of skill in hardy fruit-growing in this country. For such varieties perfect shelter, a sunny position and a warm, dry ripening season, are just as important as ideal soil. Unless *all* these conditions are obtainable, it is wise to avoid planting any but the more hardy varieties of mid-season pears.

ASPECT

It is useless to plant dessert pears in a north aspect, even against a wall, since abundance of sunshine and warmth is essential. One or two stewing varieties such as *Catillac* might succeed on a north wall. In the case of trees grown against walls, protection from frost may easily be afforded by hanging netting about 9 inches from the face of the wall as in the case of peaches and nectarines. Pears planted in the open need good shelter from East winds.

FORMS OF TREES

Pears are naturally more slow to come into bearing than apples, and require full exposure to the sun if their flavour is to be of the best. Hence they favour the more artificial forms of tree. In France, the land of pear-growing, the pyramid, the espalier, the fuseau, various forms of cordon, the single and double U, and many forms of candelabra and of palmette Verrier or " grid-irons," are all extensively used for the pear, the open bush or vase forms being seldom used. In this country the bush, cordon, espalier and grid-iron forms are the most popular. For garden trees of small and medium size, the single oblique cordon form is the cheapest to produce, and one of the most convenient to handle, but where space allows, the three- or four-tiered espalier is to be recommended. The standard and half-standard forms cannot be recommended for any but the most vigorous varieties such as *Pitmaston Duchess* or *Catillac.*

PROPAGATION

The pear is usually propagated by means of budding in the open in July and August, and by grafting in March and April, on quince or pear stocks. New varieties may be raised by means of seed, as described in Chapter IV, page 26.

ROOTSTOCKS FOR PEARS

Where space is limited and small trees of any form are required, *Quince C* rootstock is to be recommended. Maiden trees on this stock are often inclined to be weak, but if planted in good soil and well-cared for, they will make sturdy, healthy little trees which come into cropping earlier than on any other known rootstock. For the next size of tree, as bush, dwarf pyramid, fuseau, espalier or grid-iron, or for cordons on poor soil, *Quince A*, known in this country as *Angers Quince*, and *Quince B*, or *Common Quince*, appear to be equally suitable rootstocks.

In the case of very weak-growing varieties such as *Olivier de Serres* to be trained as espaliers, and for any form requiring strong extension growth, the quince stocks cannot be recommended. In such cases a selected seedling pear stock should be used.

Incompatibility between Quince Stock and Pear Scion.—When certain varieties of quince are used as rootstocks, most varieties of pear, when grafted or budded on them, fail to make good trees.

In some cases the trees remain small and stunted, in others growth is normal for a few years and then suddenly in a gale the whole tree breaks off at the graft union. This trouble also occurs with plums on certain stocks. The best safeguard is to ensure that trees are worked on one of the more compatible quince stocks such as A, B, or C. There are, however, some varieties of pear, such as *Dr. Jules Guyot* and *Williams Bon Chrétien*, which often show a certain degree of incompatibility when grafted or budded direct on to any quince stocks. For such varieties the method known as " double-working " is advocated for making a good tree. In double-working, a scion of a variety such as *Pitmaston Duchess, Beurré d'Amanlis, Fertility* or *Hessle*, which take well on quince, is first budded or grafted on to the quince stock. A scion of the incompatible variety is then budded or grafted on to this " intermediate " or " first scion." Varieties which are said to do best when double worked, apart from those already mentioned, are *Souvenir de Congrès, Calebasse Bosc, Beurré Clairgeau, Beurré Rance, Comte de Lamy, Doyenné d'Eté, Jargonelle, Marie Louise, Monarch, Nec Plus Meuris,* and *Thompson's.*

Scion Rooting in Pears on Quince.—When trees are planted with the graft or bud union below ground, or when soil has been drawn up to cover the union, the part of the pear stem so covered sometimes forms strong pear roots which compete with the quince roots to such an extent that these often die. When this happens, the tree grows very strongly, with an upright habit of growth, and shows a disinclination to fruit. When such symptoms suggest scion rooting, it is wise to dig the soil away from round the stem, and if young scion roots are seen to be growing out above the union, they can be cut off flush with the stem. If there is only one scion root and it is of any size, it is risky to cut it off completely, in case the quince roots have already perished. In this case, the single scion root can be cut off about a foot away from the stem, or alternatively the tree can be bark-ringed (see page 45).

When a pear tree on quince is showing the signs of incompatibility between stock and scion mentioned above, and no amount of pruning or manuring will increase its vigour, the balance may be restored either by inarching it with a vigorous seedling pear stock (see page 216) or by inducing the tree to send out scion roots. To do this, the soil should be drawn up to the stem until the union is well covered, and conditions for root growth should be encouraged by mulching the soil round the stem.

PLANTING

Standards, or half-standards on pear stock, unless planted for a shelter belt, should be planted from 18 to 25 feet apart all ways, according to soil and variety. Bush trees on quince should be from 12 to 15 feet apart all ways. The fuseau and dwarf pyramid can be planted as closely as 6 feet by 3 feet, but a square plant of 6–9 feet is probably better, and even this is rather close under really good soil conditions.

Espaliers, and most of the various other forms of wall- or wire-trained trees on pear stock should be planted at from 15 to 20 feet apart, according to variety and stock, in rows not less than 6 feet apart. Single cordons require 2 feet, double cordons 5 feet, treble cordons (grid-irons) 8 feet in the row.

In the more natural forms, the younger the trees are when planted the better. Bush, pyramid, fuseau and cordon trees should be planted as maidens ; standards or half-standards as two-year-olds. The espaliers and other artificial forms, if bought already trained, are likely to be four or five years old. Those who wish to shape the trees into these forms, should plant maidens and follow the directions in Chapter VI.

PEARS FOR GROWING AS ESPALIERS

Belle Julie	Durondeau	Le Brun
Beurré Six	Emile d'Heyst	Louise Bonne d'Avranches
Conference	Glou Morceau	Marie Louise
Doyenné du Comice	Laxton's Superb	Williams (Bon Chrétien)

PEARS RECOMMENDED FOR CORDON CULTURE

Belle Julie	Conference	Olivier de Serres
Beurré Alexandre Lucas	Doyenné du Comice	Seckle
Beurré Easter	Durondeau	Thompson's
Beurré Six	Emile d'Heyst	Triomphe de Vienne
Beurré Superfin	Marie Louise	Williams (Bon Chrétien)

PEARS RECOMMENDED FOR BUSH AND PYRAMID FORMS

Belle Julie	Conference	Le Brun
Beurré Alexandre Lucas	Doyenné d'Eté	Louise Bonne d'Avranches
Beurré Giffard	Durondeau	Marguerite Marillat
Beurré Hardy	Emile d'Heyst	Souvenir de Congrès
Beurré Naghin	Fondante d'Automne	Thompson's
Beurré Six	Laxton's Superb	Williams (Bon Chrétien)
Comte de Lamy		

PEARS FOR WALL CULTURE (see page 221)

PRUNING OF PEARS

Winter Pruning.—In commercial plantations, pears are generally pruned in the winter in the same way as apple trees, the leaders or extension shoots being left uncut, tipped or cut hard back according to the age and vigour of the tree. The less winter pruning a young tree receives, the sooner it will come into bearing ; when the tree has carried one or two good crops, pruning again becomes necessary to keep up the vigour of the tree by stimulating fresh shoot growth. Trees which become covered with fruit buds and which set enormous crops will require severe winter pruning.

Trees which grow many strong shoots and produce little or no blossom should be winter pruned as little as possible until they again come into cropping.

It is generally considered that in winter pruning pear trees, the new lateral side shoots may be cut back or " spurred " fairly drastically.

Summer Pruning.—Although opinions differ as to the best time for summer pruning pears, it will generally be found that the new green shoots begin to lignify in July, and this is probably the best period at which to cut or brutt them at about the fifth leaf. Leaders, or extension shoots, should never be summer pruned in this way. Lorette pruning in France was concerned mainly with pears, and although the system has been severely criticized in this country, there seems no reason in theory why it should not prove successful in normal seasons, with certain varieties such as *Pitmaston, Beurré Hardy* and *Laxton's Superb,* which make a lot of strong wood-growth. The system depends on stimulating dormant buds at the base of strong new shoots of the current season's growth by cutting those shoots right back to the base when they are beginning to get woody. Lorette fixed more or less arbitrary dates for this, beginning in May and repeating the process three or four times at intervals of about a month.

Unfortunately in this country short summer pruning does not always have the desired effect of stimulating basal fruit-buds, and a forest of weak secondary growth springs up. When this happens, the only thing to do is to cut or brutt these growths back and try again next season.

Lorette advocated pruning each extension shoot or " leader " in the normal way, but he did it late in the spring when the new terminal shoot was already about an inch long. This is an important part of the Lorette pruning process, and is likely to prevent or weaken the growth of very coarse laterals immediately below the terminal.* (See also page 44.)

PRUNING IN RELATION TO VARIETAL HABIT

Like all fruit trees, pears have marked varietal habits which should be taken into account when pruning or shaping the trees. Upright-growing varieties like *Comice* should have their leaders cut to outside buds, but drooping varieties like *Beurré d'Amanlis* should be pruned to upward buds. Tip-bearing varieties like *Marguerite Marillat* are very difficult to grow as cordons because the fruit is borne at the end of long, slender, twiggy shoots, and if these are " spurred " back, little or no fruit-buds remain on the tree.

PEARS NEEDING HARD PRUNING AT CERTAIN STAGES

Variety	Season	Cooking or Dessert
Beurré Diel	October to November	Dessert
Doyenné d'Eté	July to August	Dessert
Olivier de Serres	February to March	Dessert
Seckle	October to November	Dessert

PEARS NEEDING LIGHT PRUNING AT CERTAIN STAGES

Variety	Season	Cooking or Dessert
Bellissime d'Hiver	November to March	Cooking
Beurré Clairgeau	October to November	Cooking
Beurré Hardy	October	Dessert
Clapp's Favourite	August to September	Dessert
Conference	October to November	Dessert
Doyenné du Comice	November	Dessert
Durondeau	October to November	Dessert
Hessle or Hazel	September to October	Dessert
Joséphine de Malines	December to February	Dessert
Marguerite Marillat	September to October	Dessert
Pitmaston Duchess	October to November	Cooking or Dessert

* The Lorette pruning method was given a thorough trial with apples by the late Mr. A. H. Lees when on the staff at Long Ashton Research Station, and a detailed report of his findings was published in the Annual Report of that station for the year 1920. See also *Lorette Pruning*, by Lorette, translated by W. H. Dykes.

CROSS-POLLINATION

However " self-fertile " a variety of pear may be said to be, it is always wise to plant one or more pollinating varieties within easy flying distance for insects, and to ensure that the flowers of these varieties overlap to a certain extent in their blossoming period.

To plant a single pear tree in a garden or plantation without any other variety of pear from which pollen may be carried to it by insects, is a practice which cannot under any circumstances be recommended. Where space will not permit of the planting of another tree, the difficulty can usually be got over by top-grafting or frame-working one or more limbs of the solitary tree with scions of another variety with a similar blossoming period. From what has been said above it will be realized that a hive of bees in the vicinity of the garden or plantation is an invaluable aid to cross-pollination and fruit productivity. (See tables, page 231.)

MANURING

The most successful pear growers are unanimous in recommending generous dressings of nitrogen and potash, and most of them apply phosphates, also, to be on the safe side. Nothing can beat really good farmyard manure dug in round the trees in winter, or failing that, shoddy, pig-dung or poultry manure, meat and bonemeal, dug in during the winter and supplemented in February or March by 2 cwt. per acre (1 oz. per square yard) of sulphate of potash.

In the spring if the trees set a really heavy crop, some growers like to apply, in addition, a complete application of artificial fertilizers such as would be given for potatoes; i.e. sulphate of ammonia 1 cwt. per acre ($\frac{1}{2}$ oz. per square yard); superphosphates 5 cwt. per acre ($2\frac{1}{2}$ oz. per square yard); sulphate of potash 1 cwt. per acre ($\frac{1}{2}$ oz. per square yard).

MULCHING AND WATERING

Trees grown against walls or in very dry situations may find it difficult to hold their crop in a hot summer. Under these conditions a good mulching with some decaying organic matter, such as old compost or lawn mowings, will help to keep moisture in the soil. Before applying the mulch, the ground must be hoed to break any pan that may have formed on the surface.

There are occasions when pear trees on quince carrying a heavy crop of pears, will respond to a good drenching of water, but this should be regarded rather as an emergency measure for wall trees in drought conditions where it is obvious that the tree is wilting for want of moisture. A mulch put on after watering is a great help in preventing rapid evaporation.

THINNING

Fruits should never touch one another on the tree. Each fruit should have ample room to develop.

Varieties bearing small fruit naturally need thinning more drastically than the larger fruited kinds, which may be allowed to carry two or even three pears on each spur.

PROTECTION FROM BIRDS AND WASPS

Choice individual fruits should be protected whilst still hanging on the tree from the attacks of birds and wasps by means of nets or muslin bags, and if these are tied to the branch or spur, they will prevent the fruit falling and incurring damage.

PEARS FOR WALL CULTURE

Amiral Gervais (South)
Bergamotte d'Esperen (South)
Beurré Diel (South)
Beurré Easter (South)
Beurré Hardy (West)
Beurré Rance (South)
Beurré Superfin (West)
Comte de Lamy (South)
Doyenné du Comice (South or West)
Doyenné d'Eté (East)
Emile d'Heyst (West)
Glou Morceau (South or West)

Joséphine de Malines (South or West)
Le Lectier (South)
Marie Benoist (South)
Marie Louise d'Uccle (South)
Nec Plus Meuris (South or West)
Nouvelle Fulvie (South)
Olivier de Serres (West)
Passe Crassane (South)
Williams (Bon Chrétien) (North East or East)
Almost any good Dessert variety will do well on a South Wall.

GATHERING AND STORING

The fruit of the early and mid-season kinds should be gathered before it easily separates from the tree, when gently raised on a level with the stalk. *Williams* must not be yellow when picked or it will quickly go soft. Early fruit intended for market requires very careful selection, handling and packing. It is best sent away as soon as gathered. Early fruits for private consumption should be laid out singly and allowed to ripen for a few days, being eaten at once, as few of the early varieties keep. The mid-season and late kinds must be stored for a time, as they are not in condition for use when picked. Pears need to be stored at an even temperature of between 40° F. and 45° F. The fruit is best stored in trays in single layers, and not allowed to touch one another. Every care should be taken not to bruise it. The fruit should be inspected from time to time so that any decayed pear may be removed before it contaminates other pears near it. It is not always easy to tell when pears are beginning to ripen. With several varieties, however, the skin becomes a golden yellow, or the tinge of red, if present, will become brighter. Late dessert pears, especially, need care, and should be allowed to hang on the trees as long as possible. Most of the fruit, however, should be gathered before the beginning of November.

Recent investigations suggest the desirability of keeping pears separately from apples in store. It may even be wise to store pears of different seasons separately, varieties of the season of *Beurré Hardy*, *Conference* and *Doyenné du Comice* being kept away from early varieties like *Williams* and *Laxton's Superb* and from really late-keeping varieties like *Joséphine de Malines*, *Glou Morceau* and *Winter Nelis*.

Before attempting to place pears in gas storage, the advice of the county horticultural officer should be sought as to the varieties which can safely be stored in this way, and as to the temperature and gas concentration required for such varieties. (See Gas Storage, page 90.)

MARKETING

Pears are sent to market in much the same manner as apples ; cookers in sieves or bushels, and dessert pears in boxes, half-boxes or trays. (See Apple.)

INSECT PESTS OF THE PEAR

PEAR APHIS *(Yezabura Pyra)*

This is the only one of the several species of greenfly occurring on Pears that does much damage. In appearance and habits it very much resembles the Rosy Apple Aphis (see Apple, page 122), and it is amenable to the same remedies.

COMMON GREEN CAPSID *(Lygus pabulinus)*

The corky, dimpled patches sometimes found on pear fruits are caused by the feeding of this Capsid Bug, which is best known, however, as a pest of bush fruits. (See Currants, page 179.)

APPLE BLOSSOM WEEVIL (see Apple, page 123)

CATERPILLARS

See Winter Moths, under Apple, page 121.

CODLING MOTH *(Cydia pomonella)*

The habits of this pest are much the same on pears as they are on apples, but there is a greater tendency for the larvæ to enter the eye rather than at the side, making control somewhat easier. Arsenical sprays should be applied late in June or early in July. (See also Apple, page 125.)

PEAR AND CHERRY SLUGWORM *(Caliroa limacina)*

The black slug-like larvæ of this pest occur on pears and cherries in August, and feed on the upper surface of the leaves, eating away the tissue to leave pale brown blotches. Severely attacked leaves turn brown and fall, and small trees have been known to be almost defoliated. The "slug" is really the young stage of a sawfly and hatches from an egg laid in the leaf tissues. Although green in colour, it exudes a very dark slime which makes it resemble a black slug. When fully fed it spins a cocoon in the soil wherein it pupates and whence the adult sawfly ultimately emerges the following July.

Control.—This pest, which can be very serious is, fortunately, easy to destroy. Almost any kind of dry powder such as derris, nicotine or D.D.T. dust will get rid of it. If preferred, sprays of any of these materials may be used.

PEAR MIDGE (Contarinia pyrivora)

In some districts this insect is a serious pest and considerably reduces the yield, since attacked fruitlets invariably fall off. An attack of this pest is readily diagnosed. Infested fruitlets swell abnormally, often becoming deformed ; within a few weeks they begin to crack and decay and drop off the trees. Their centres will be found to consist of wet, black debris together with a number of small, white, legless maggots, up to about one-sixth of an inch in length.

These maggots escape when the damaged fruits fall to the ground and burrow into the soil, their curious jumping powers enabling them to travel short distances. They pupate in the soil and emerge as small, inconspicuous midges the following April, ready to lay eggs in the pear blossom.

Control.—On small trees in gardens the infected fruit can be collected and destroyed. It is little use doing this, however, if the pest is allowed to go unchecked in neighbouring gardens.

In commercial orchards little can be done beyond frequent cultivation in June and July and stocking with poultry in April, May and June, but D.D.T. applied at the white-bud stage has shown some promise.

Some pears suffer to a greater extent than others, e.g., *Williams* are often attacked, whilst late-flowering varieties usually escape altogether.

PEAR LEAF BLISTER MITE (Eriophyes pyri)

This pest causes reddish pimples or blisters on the young leaves, first noticeable in the spring. Severely attacked leaves may eventually turn brown and fall. The fruitlets too are often attacked and become deformed or die altogether.

The creature responsible for the damage is a mite of microscopic dimensions (less than one-hundredth of an inch in length) which spends the winter under the bud scales and comes out in spring to feed on the leaves and fruits. Eggs are laid in the blisters which the mites produce and in which they feed and multiply during the whole summer. In the autumn they return to the shelter of the bud scales.

Control.—Either lime-sulphur or a petroleum-oil spray should be applied to the trees as soon as the leaves have fallen or when the buds open in the spring.

MINOR PESTS

Pears are not quite so prone to attack by the host of minor pests which infect apples. Occasionally the black and yellow caterpillars of the Social Pear Sawfly (*Pamphilus flaviventris*) may be encountered. These live in a " tent " much after the fashion of those of the Lackey Moth. Sometimes also an attack of Leaf-curling Midge (*Dasyneura pyri*) may be seen.

PESTS : DIAGNOSIS TABLE

THE PEAR

DAMAGE	PROBABLE CAUSE
Shoots and Foliage (*Including Blossom*)	
Leaves, opening buds and blossom attacked by small " looping," green caterpillars	Winter Moths
Leaves spun together by small, brown, green or yellowish caterpillars, which wriggle quickly backwards when disturbed	Tortrix Moths
Leaves curled and infested by masses of small, bluish-purple aphides. Young shoots twisted, stunted and deformed	Pear Aphis
Flower buds eaten from within in April by black-headed white grub. Blossom remains " capped," turns brown, drops	Apple Blossom Weevil
Leaves torn and distorted, shoots stunted and may be killed	Common Green Capsid Bug
Intervenal tissue of leaves eaten by black, slug-like larvæ in August ; leaving pale brown blotches ; foliage may turn brown and fall	Pear and Cherry Slug-worm
Pimples or blisters on young leaves in spring, often reddish ; may turn brown and leaves fall	Pear Leaf Blister Mite
Fruit	
Small fruits eaten by green, " looping " caterpillars	Winter Moth
Maggoty. May drop just before picking-time	Codling Moth
Fruitlets swell abnormally, are deformed, crack, decay and drop—centres, wet black débris and white maggots	Pear Midge

DISEASES OF THE PEAR

PEAR SCAB (*Venturia pirina*)

Much of what is written under Apple Scab applies also to Pear Scab, but the two diseases are quite distinct biologically ; that is, the Pear Scab fungus cannot infect apples, and vice versa. The symptoms of the two diseases are similar, but, with Pear Scab, the fruits are usually infected before the leaves, which, until blossom time, are tightly rolled and present very little surface on which spores can alight and cause infections.

Infection of young pear shoots, especially of the variety *Fertility*, is often much more severe than with apples, and the individual " pustules " are much larger and more open. They present a ready means of entry for the canker fungus, and indeed, areas are known where it is impossible to grow *Fertility* pears unless very efficient spraying for Scab-control is carried out ; they succumb to Canker.

Control.—Unlike most apple varieties, pears can safely be sprayed with Bordeaux Mixture in most seasons. Many pear varieties, however, are injured by lime-sulphur, especially when this is applied post-blossom. To control the disease, a spray should be applied at the same periods of tree development as recommended for Apple Scab, that is, twice before, and at least twice after blossom. Lime-sulphur at $2\frac{1}{2}$ per cent. pre-blossom, followed by Bordeaux Mixture at 4–6–100 post-blossom, or a colloidal copper preparation, is an effective combination, or the copper spray can be used pre- and post-blossom quite satisfactorily. Copper spray is likely to russet the fruits, but this is not a serious blemish in pears, provided the injury is not severe enough to cause cracking of the young fruits. The russeting is more extensive in a wet summer than in a dry one, but it is preferable to the risk of severe leaf-burn and fruit-drop consequent upon the use of lime-sulphur strong enough to be fungicidally effective.

Fertility, Comice, and *Clapp's Favourite* are among the most susceptible varieties.

BROWN ROTS *(Sclerotinia fructigena and S. laxa)*

See Plum, page 240.

CANKER and EYE ROT *(Nectria galligena)*

See Apple, page 129.

ARMILLARIA *(Armillaria mellea)*

See Apple, page 132.

BITTER PIT *(Functional)*

This disease appears to be of similar origin to that on apple (see page 136), though some workers now suspect that it may be a virus disease. It differs in appearance from that on apple in that the pits are usually deep so that an affected fruit is dimpled and misshapen. The pits consist of very hard areas that resist the knife when an attempt is made to cut them open, and a badly affected fruit is ruined as a dessert pear.

WATERLOGGING *(Functional)*

See Apple, page 133.

DISEASES : DIAGNOSIS TABLE
THE PEAR

DAMAGE	PROBABLE CAUSE
Branches and Twigs	
Cankerous formations—patches of small, whitish pustules or crimson spherical bodies grouped together	Canker
Sheets of fungous tissue under bark at base of trunk. Long, black strands like " boot-laces " on roots and in adjacent soil in autumn. Tree dies	Armillaria Root Rot
Shoots and Foliage (Including Blossom)	
Blister-like " pustules " on shoots and possibly on bud scales in spring. Circular, olive-green spots, turning corky and scab-like later	Pear Scab
Blossom trusses and surrounding foliage of apparently healthy tree wilts about blossom-time	Waterlogging
Brownish, roughly circular, indefinite smudges on skin (usually near picking time)	Sooty Blotch
Deep pits giving fruits a dimpled appearance ; fruits often misshapen ; brownish pockets in flesh after picking	Bitter Pit
Brown, soft rot of fruit either on the tree or in store ; buff spore pustules or cushions mostly in concentric form	Brown Rot

Note.—Once the trouble has been diagnosed, the reader should refer to the paragraph dealing with the particular disease or pest, and should also consult the Guide to Spraying, see page 111.

VARIETIES OF PEARS

Before deciding which varieties to grow, it is advisable to make a careful study of local conditions, and if possible to find out which varieties are most satisfactory. This is best done by consulting the county advisory officer and local fruit growers.

DESSERT PEARS

Amiral Gervais. A medium-sized, round oval pear, dark russet green ripening to yellowish green. Excellent flavour and good cropper. Ready November to December.

Belle Julie. A small to medium-sized, oval pear, a russeted golden-brown, flushed red. Of excellent flavour and recommended for garden culture as a cordon, bush, or espalier. Hardy and prolific. Ready for use in October and November. Self-sterile.

Beurré Alexandre Lucas. A large, roundish, conical fruit, a patchy russeted yellow when ripe. Of juicy and aromatic flavour. Ready November and if gathered before it is ripe, will store for use up to January. Recommended for culture as cordon or bush. Self-sterile. Triploid.

DESSERT PEARS (*continued*)

Beurré d'Amanlis. A medium to large, round, pyriform, yellowish-green fruit with reddish-brown cheek. Of excellent flavour and a good cropper. Growth very spreading.

Hardy and recommended for the Midlands and northern districts. Ready September. Self-sterile. Triploid.

Beurré Diel. A very large, roundish, oval, pale green pear turning yellow with russet spots and reddish-brown flush. Of excellent sweet aromatic flavour when grown as bush or pyramid on the quince stock. Ready October to November. Prefers a warm sheltered site and needs a wall in colder districts. Prune hard. Triploid.

Beurré Hardy. A medium, round to conical, brownish, russet-spotted fruit, that does well as an espalier on a west wall on quince stock. Very vigorous grower. Of excellent flavour and should be gathered just before it is ripe. Ready October. Prune lightly. Mid-season flowering. Usually considered a shy cropper. Self-sterile.

Beurré Six. A large, pyriform, light green pear, changing to russety-yellow. Of good flavour. Ready for use in November and December. Hardy and prolific. Self-sterile.

Beurré Superfin. A medium-sized, pyriform, golden-yellow fruit, patched with russet, that thrives on west walls in espalier form. Does well on quince stock and is a fine garden fruit. Prune regularly. Of excellent flavour. Ready October.

Requires to be picked early and eaten while still firm. Early flowering and rarely self-fertile.

Bon Chrétien (Williams). A medium-sized to large, pyriform, uneven, pale green fruit turning yellow, with faint red lines and russet spots, when ripe. Of delicious musky flavour. Recommended for garden culture by the Royal Horticultural Society. Does well as a cordon, on a north or east wall, as a half-standard, standard, trained tree, or bush. Ready September. *Should be picked green.* Mid-season flowering and said to be self-fertile. Prune lightly. Should be double worked on quince. (See page 216.)

Conference. A medium-sized to large, pyriform, long-necked, handsome, deep green fruit russeted reddish-brown. Of delicious and aromatic flavour. Ready for picking in late September and a very valuable market pear from October to November. Hardy and a reliable cropper in all forms and on most soils, particularly when grown against a south or west wall. Recommended for garden culture by the Royal Horticultural Society. Said to be self-fertile and a useful pollinator to mix with second-early flowering, self-sterile varieties. Incompatible with *Beurré d'Amanlis.*

Dr. Jules Guyot. Large, oval, pyriform, yellow fruit with small black dots and slight flush, very similar to Williams (Bon Chrétien) in appearance. Delicious flavour and a hardy and reliable cropper. A popular market pear, but it must be picked before it ripens as it does not keep long. Ready early in September. Self-fertile. Should be double-worked when on quince. (See page 216.)

DESSERT PEARS (continued)

Doyenné d'Eté. A small, roundish, yellow fruit, but flushed with reddish-brown, of excellent flavour and ready July to August, but does not store. The earliest pear, but somewhat delicate. Recommended for cultivation as bush, cordon or espalier against an east wall. Self-sterile. A weak grower. Prune hard. Best on pear stock.

Doyenné du Comice. A medium-sized, oval, pyriform, golden-russet fruit of delicious flavour. Does best as cordon, or espalier against a warm and sheltered south or west wall in a deep brick-earth soil. The best-flavoured market dessert pear. Ready for picking early in October and does not keep long after November in ordinary storage. Recommended for garden culture by the Royal Horticultural Society. Late flowering and self-sterile. Highly susceptible to scab. Pollinators recommended are Glou Morceau, Nouveau Poiteau, Laxton's Superb, Winter Nelis, Beurré Bedford, Clapp's Favourite, André Desportes. One of the most difficult of all pears to induce to crop. Subject to scab.

Durondeau. A large, pyramidal, brown russet fruit flushed red, of good flavour, that is popular at market. Hardy and prolific in all forms and recommended for garden culture. Ready in September, and stores until October and November. Early flowering; sometimes self-fertile. Prune lightly. Highly susceptible to scab.

Emile d'Heyst. A medium-sized, long, oval, yellow, russeted pear, of excellent flavour that is ready for picking in September, and is popular at market in October and November. Recommended for garden culture by the Royal Horticultural Society and does well in all forms and in all soils on a pear or quince stock, particularly against a west wall. Hardy and prolific in northern counties. Mid-season flowering. Rarely self-fertile.

Fondante de Thirriot. A large, conical, clear yellow fruit, with russet spots and rosy-flushed cheek. Of fine flavour. Ready for use in November and December. Hardy and prolific in all forms except standard. Has very long stalk. Self-sterile.

Glou Morceau. A large, roundish light green to greenish-yellow fruit of rich flavour. Hardy and prolific as espalier on warm south or west wall and in light soil. Late blossomer and a good pollinator for Doyenné du Comice. Ready for picking late October and stores until December or January. Very difficult pear to finish. Self-sterile. A strong grower. Prune regularly.

Joséphine de Malines. A small, conical, greenish-yellow pear russeted round the stem. Of delicious flavour and probably the best of the late pears, particularly for market, where it is popular. Hardy and prolific, especially when grown as an espalier against a wall. Recommended for garden culture by the Royal Horticultural Society. Ready early in October and keeps well for use from December to February. Self-sterile. Prune lightly.

Lammas. A small, conical fruit, of second-rate flavour, somewhat similar to Hessle. Ready in August for immediate use. Strong, upright grower. Often grown as a half-standard for shelter. Not a garden fruit.

Laxton's Superb. A fair-sized fruit of good flavour obtained by means of a cross between Beurré Superfin and Williams (Bon Chrétien). Ready early September. Hardy and prolific. Precocious cropper. Partially self-fertile.

Louise Bonne d'Avranches (Louise Bonne of Jersey). A medium-sized to large, handsome, conical, yellowish-green pear, with a dark red cheek. Rich flavour. A heavy and regular cropper, especially in the milder districts and in any form. Recommended for garden culture by the Royal Horticultural Society and useful for pot culture. Ready October, but must be picked before it is ripe. Mid-season flowering. Partially self-fertile.

Marguerite Marillat. A very large, long, uneven-shaped, golden-yellow pear, tinged red and russeted. Of fair flavour. It should be gathered before it is ripe and stored for use in September and October. Recommended for culture as a bush. Hardy and prolific in warm and sheltered positions. Early flowering. Said to be self-fertile. Prune lightly, leaving tip-bearing laterals full length in early years.

Marie Louise. Long, oval fruit, pale greenish-yellow. Good flavour. Straggling growth and makes many spurs. Season, October to November. Self-fertile. Makes a small tree ; very suitable for garden culture, but subject to scab.

Marie Louise d'Uccle. A large, pyriform, pale green to yellow fruit with russet patches. Ready October to November. Of delicious flavour. Hardy and prolific in all forms. In colder districts requires wall protection. Should be picked before it is ripe if for market as it does not keep long. A tip-bearer. Subject to scab. Mid-season flowering. Self-fertile.

Nec Plus Meuris. A small to medium-sized, greenish-yellow fruit, slightly russeted and of delicious flavour. Stores well, and is ready for use from February to March. Hardy and prolific as bush, cordon, pyramid or espalier. Difficult to ripen in the open, except on wall. Self-fertile.

Passe Crassane. A large, flattish, round, russeted green fruit of fine flavour. Stores well for use from January to March. Hardy and prolific in favourable conditions in a mild climate and good pear soil. Self-sterile.

Pitmaston Duchess. A very large, long, pyriform, golden-yellow, russeted pear of good flavour for dessert or cooking. Ready for use in October and November, but should be gathered towards the end of September. Hardy and very vigorous in all forms. Too vigorous for small gardens. A popular market and exhibition pear. Late flowering. Partially self-fertile. Prune lightly. A shy cropper in many districts. A triploid and therefore not to be recommended as a pollinator for other varieties.

Seckle. A small, spotted, brownish-red fruit of honey-like sweetness. Ready for use from October to November. Hardy and prolific in all forms. Rarely self-fertile. Very weak growing. Incompatible with *Louise Bonne*.

Souvenir de Congrès. Very large, handsome, pyriform, yellow fruit, russeted and rosy cheeked. Fine flavour. Best when double grafted on quince stock. Ready for use from August to September. Hardy and a good bearer in all forms. Rarely self-fertile.

Thompson's. A medium-sized, uneven-shaped, yellow fruit slightly russeted. Of delicious flavour and crops well as a standard. Ready from October to November. Self-sterile. A good pear, now seldom grown.

DESSERT PEARS (*continued*)

Triomphe de Vienne. A medium-sized, conical, russeted, yellow fruit, flushed red. Of good flavour. Ready in September, but best picked before it is ripe. Hardy and prolific in all forms in good pear soil. Rarely self-fertile.

Williams. See Bon Chrétien.

Winter Nelis. A small, dull-green pear, changing to yellow and spotted with black specks. Of delicious flavour and a market favourite. Ready for picking early in October, and stores for use from December to January if gathered before it is ripe. It is hardy and a good cropper if grown in warm and sheltered situations and makes a good wall fruit or espalier. A weak grower. Difficult to ripen. Rarely self-fertile.

COOKING PEARS

Bellissime d'Hiver. A large, yellow fruit with red flush, and of good flavour when cooked. Ready November to March and stores well. Hardy and prolific as a pyramid or standard, and may also be grown as a cordon or bush. Prune lightly. Said to be self-fertile.

Beurré Clairgeau. A large, handsome and remarkably fertile, oval, lemon-yellow to golden-brown fruit, flushed orange and red. Ready from November to December. Hardy and prolific even in the northern counties. Stores well for a short time and is a profitable market pear. Makes a large upright bush or standard on pear stock and needs only light pruning. Said to be self-sterile.

Beurré Naghin. A medium-sized, round, bright green pear with a long stalk. Medium growth; good cropper and excellent quality. Ready December.

Catillac. A large, roundish, dull green pear, tinged reddish-brown and ripening to a deep reddish-brown. Ready to pick in October and stores well. A profitable market fruit from December to April. Recommended for garden culture by the Royal Horticultural Society. Does well as standard, espalier, pyramid, or trained tree on north or east walls. Hardy and prolific, but an uncertain cropper on some soils. Mid-season flowering. Self-sterile. Triploid. Prune lightly. Too vigorous grower for small gardens.

Vicar of Winkfield. A large, longish, bright green fruit, turning yellow. Of excellent flavour and may be used for dessert. Ready early in October and storing for use from November to January. Hardy and prolific in all forms. Prune lightly. Triploid.

Many dessert pears, if gathered when they are hard and green, cook splendidly, and when the trees are cropping heavily, it is wise to thin out and cook a quantity, and thus give the remaining fruit more chance to develop into choice specimens. For the small grower the following three varieties make a highly satisfactory combination: **Conference, Laxton's Superb** and **Dr. Jules Guyot.** If only one tree is to be selected, it had better be the first of these.

THE CROSS-POLLINATION OF PEAR VARIETIES

When only one pear tree is planted, it is essential to select one of the self-fertile varieties, unless, of course, other pear trees, flowering at the same period, are growing in other gardens close by.

SELF-FERTILE VARIETIES

Early Flowering	Mid-season Flowering	Late Bloomers
Conference Durondeau Marguerite Marillat	Bellissime d'Hiver Beurré Bedford Bon Chrétien (Williams) Marie Louise	Dr. Jules Guyot

PARTIALLY OR SOMETIMES SELF-FERTILE

Early Flowering	Mid-season Flowering	Late Bloomers
Beurré Superfin	Laxton's Superb Louise Bonne of Jersey	Pitmaston Duchess

The John Innes Horticultural Institution have proved that Beurré d'Amanlis cannot be cross-pollinated by Conference, nor Louise Bonne by Seckle. Apart from these any of the fertile or partially self-fertile varieties planted in conjunction with self-sterile varieties, flowering at the same time, will cross-pollinate the self-sterile varieties. Early flowering sorts will also cross-pollinate mid-season flowers and mid-season bloomers cross-pollinate late bloomers, as the flowering seasons overlap somewhat.

SELF-STERILE AND RARELY SELF-FERTILE VARIETIES

Early Flowering	Mid-season Flowering	Late Bloomers
Beurré d'Amanlis Beurré Clairgeau Beurré Diel Beurré Hardy Comte de Lamy Doyenné d'Eté Jargonelle Souvenir de Congrés	Catillac Emile d'Heyst Joséphine de Malines Winter Nelis	Bosc Clapp's Favourite Doyenné du Comice Fertility Glou Morceau Nouveau Poiteau Passe Colmar

TWELVE GOOD VARIETIES OF PEAR

Beurré Superfin	Durondeau	Laxton's Superb
Bon Chrétien (Williams)	Emile d'Heyst	Louise Bonne of Jersey
Conference	Glou Morceau	Pitmaston Duchess
Doyenné du Comice	Joséphine de Malines	Winter Nelis

SELECTION OF PEARS IN ORDER OF RIPENING
Early (August–September)

Variety	Garden or Orchard	Dessert or Cooking
Bon Chrétien (Williams)	Garden or Orchard	Dessert
Doyenné d'Eté	Garden	Dessert
Dr. Jules Guyot	Garden or Orchard	Dessert
Laxton's Superb	Garden or Orchard	Dessert
Souvenir de Congrés	Garden	Dessert

Mid-Season (October–November)

Variety	Garden or Orchard	Dessert or Cooking
Beurré Clairgeau	Garden or Orchard	Dessert or Cooking
Beurré d'Amanlis	Garden	Dessert
Beurré Diel	Garden	Dessert
Beurré Hardy	Garden or Orchard	Dessert
Beurré Superfin	Garden	Dessert
Conference	Garden or Orchard	Dessert
Doyenné du Comice	Garden	Dessert
Durondeau	Garden	Dessert
Emile d'Heyst	Garden	Dessert
Fondante d'Automne	Garden	Dessert
Louise Bonne of Jersey	Garden	Dessert
Marguerite Marillat	Garden	Dessert
Marie Louise	Garden	Dessert
Marie Louise d'Uccle	Garden	Dessert
Pitmaston Duchess	Orchard	Cooking or Dessert

Late Season (November–December, etc.)

Variety	Garden or Orchard	Dessert or Cooking
Beurré Alexandre Lucas	Garden or Orchard	Dessert
Beurré Naghin	Garden or Orchard	Cooking
Beurré Rance	Garden or Orchard	Dessert
Catillac	Garden or Orchard	Cooking
Glou Morceau	Garden or Orchard	Dessert
Joséphine des Malines	Garden	Dessert
Passe Colmar	Garden	Dessert
Nec Plus Meuris	Garden or Orchard	Dessert
Vicar of Winkfield	Garden or Orchard	Cooking
Winter Nelis	Garden or Orchard	Dessert

SOME PEARS FOR MARKET

Variety	Season	Dessert or Cooking
*Beurré Clairgeau	October–November	Cooking or Dessert
Beurré d'Amanlis	September	Dessert
*Catillac	December–April	Cooking
*Conference	October–November	Dessert
Dr. Jules Guyot	September (Early)	Dessert
Doyenné du Comice	November	Dessert
*Durondeau	October–November	Dessert
*Emile d'Heyst	October–November	Dessert
*Fertility	September–October	Dessert
Fondante de Thirriot	November–December	Dessert
*Joséphine de Malines	December–February	Dessert
Laxton's Superb	September	Dessert
Louise Bonne of Jersey	October	Dessert
*Marie Louise	October–November	Dessert
Pitmaston Duchess	October–November	Cooking or Dessert
*Roosevelt	November	Dessert
Williams	September	Dessert

* Varieties suitable for orchard cultivation as standards.

ESPECIALLY HARDY PEARS

Variety	Garden or Orchard	Dessert or Cooking
Beurré Hardy	Garden or Orchard	Dessert
Beurré Superfin	Garden or Orchard	Dessert
Catillac	Garden or Orchard	Cooking
Chalk	Orchard	Dessert
Conference	Garden or Orchard	Dessert
Emile d'Heyst	Garden or Orchard	Dessert
Jargonelle	Garden	Dessert
Louise Bonne of Jersey	Garden or Orchard	Dessert
Lammas	Orchard	Dessert
Pitmaston Duchess	Garden or Orchard	Dessert or Cooking

THE PLUM *(Prunus domestica)*

SOIL AND SITUATION

In some districts plums do well on stiffish loams over a chalk subsoil, and on chalky loams over a clay subsoil. In fact, so long as they are not planted on the most extreme forms of clay, sand, or chalk, plums can be made to do well on almost any well-drained soil.

On high open land they are less liable to frost damage when in blossom, but need shelter from the east winds. Wall trees may be artificially sheltered by some form of protective covering as recommended for peach trees (page 85).

FORM OF TREE

The plum, like the cherry, produces fruit spurs freely on one- and two-year-old wood. Hence the best form is that in which plenty of new shoots can be allowed to grow full length every year without unduly crowding the tree. The bush, half-standard and standard are the most suitable forms where large yields and regular cropping is required. Where fruit size and quality are the first consideration, the fan-trained tree on a south wall is likely to give the best results. Nothing is easier or more productive of bad results than to under-estimate the space required by stone fruits when planted against a wall. The espalier and cordon forms are sometimes used for plums, but the hard cutting back of new laterals to maintain tree shape in these very artificial forms reduces the number of fruit-buds and unduly stimulates excessive growth of new laterals.

PROPAGATION

The usual nursery practice is to bud plums in July or August on to plum stocks raised either vegetatively or from seed. *Myrobolan B* has shown itself to be the most satisfactory stock where strong growth, combined with regular cropping, is required. The *Common Plum* has a partially dwarfing effect and can be safely recommended for the variety *Victoria* and most of the gages as a suitable stock for a wall tree or bush trees at comparatively close distances such as would be suitable for garden culture. This stock, however, cannot be universally recommended because certain varieties, notably *Czar*, the popular cooking variety, show marked incompatibility between stock and scion when worked on it. *Brompton*, *Damas C* and *Common Mussel* are sometimes used.

PLANTING

Trees should be planted at distances of from 15 to 30 feet apart according to the variety, form, and rootstock, and should be as young as possible ; i.e., bush, pyramid and half-standard trees may be safely planted as maidens and the head formed when and where desired. Standards may be planted as two-year-old or three-year-old trees, but should not be older than this. The artificial forms of trained tree, such as the fan, if bought already trained to the required shape, are likely to be four or five years old when they come from the nursery, and will require correspondingly greater care in looking after for the first year or so.

PRUNING

In general, plum trees, like cherries, should be pruned as little as possible in the winter. Both these fruits are susceptible to attack by the Silver Leaf fungus, the spores of which frequently infect the tree in wet weather through the wounds caused by large cuts. Such shoot pruning as may be necessary for plums and cherries should be carried out in late spring, and branch-thinning in summer when large wounds heal best and conditions are least favourable for infection. On wall trees, when fan training is completed as in the manner described in Chapter VI (page 62), the main pruning operation consists of summer pinching out the tips which are not needed for tying in. This pinching should be done when the shoots have made from six to eight leaves. As soon as possible after the crop has been picked, the extension shoots, the replacement shoots, and those for which there is still space on the wall, are tied in, all dead shoots are cut off, and the superfluous shoots which were pinched back in summer are cut back to short stubs of a few inches in length.

ROOT PRUNING

Plum trees grown on walls or against fences will have to be root-pruned, if they are to be kept within reasonable bounds. On a 6-foot wall they should be root-pruned about three years after planting, and again in three or four years' time, as described for peaches.

MANURING

Plums, like all the stone fruits, give the best results under high nitrogen conditions. If it is not possible to get ample supplies of dung, shoddy, meat-meal, hoof and horn or other organic nitrogenous fertilizers, light dressings of one form of these should be applied in the winter, supplemented in the spring by sulphate of ammonia, nitrate of soda, nitro-chalk or some similar form of inorganic nitrogenous fertilizer applied at the rate of $1\frac{1}{2}$ to 2 cwt. per acre ($\frac{1}{2}$ to 1 oz. per square yard) and pricked in lightly. Cases of potash deficiency have been known in plums, but this is the exception rather than the rule. On sandy soils sulphate of potash at the rate of 1 cwt. per acre (1 oz. per square yard) should be applied at any time in the winter and dug in. When no organic manures can be got, $\frac{1}{2}$ ton per acre of a standard compound artificial fertilizer should be given.

THINNING AND SHORING

On trees that have set a very heavy crop, fruit size may be increased by thinning out the young fruits when they are about half an inch long, leaving one fruit to every $2\frac{1}{2}$ to 3 inches length of shoot. On wall trees thinning should be a gradual process, first removing misshapen and badly-placed fruits, then reducing the clusters to singles, and lastly spacing these out to $2\frac{1}{2}$ to 3 inches apart.

Strong wooden supports, with a pad between them and the branches they support, should be placed firmly under the branches that appear liable to suffer from an extra heavy crop of fruit, or a tall pole should be tied to the trunk and hop string supports to each branch are then tied to it in " Maypole " fashion.

This shoring should be done early in the season, before the fruit becomes too heavy.

CULTIVATIONS

Whenever possible plums should be kept under conditions of clean cultivations because maximum shoot growth and large leaves are best obtained under such conditions.

GATHERING AND STORING

Dessert fruit should be left on the tree until thoroughly ripe and never gathered too soon. Each individual fruit should be snipped off with scissors with the stalk attached and carefully placed in the picker's basket with as little handling as possible. On no account should the fruit be gathered wet. Cooking plums are gathered as soon as they begin to turn colour, the trees being gone over several times and the largest fruits only being removed, until the plums are eventually all picked. Dessert fruits, if gathered a few days before they are dead ripe, may be stored for a few days, laid out and not touching in the store room. Cooking fruit is usually sent straight off to market.

MARKETING

Most plums are now sent to market in 12 lb. chip baskets. Some growers pack in a non-returnable wooden box resembling a tomato box and holding 14 lb. of plums, and gage and other dessert plums go well in 2-lb. punnets.

INSECT PESTS OF THE PLUM AND DAMSON

LEAF-CURLING PLUM APHIS *(Anuraphis padi)*

The young of this greenfly hatch out in February and March from small, black shining eggs, laid on the twigs the previous autumn. They give rise to successive generations which feed on the leaves till midsummer, when they migrate to other plants, returning to the plum only in the autumn.

This insect, by its feeding, causes the leaves to curl. Attacked shoots are stunted and the fruit remains small or drops to the ground.

Control.—Although these aphides are easily killed by contact with nicotine sprays, it is not always easy to wet them, as they are protected by the curled leaves. The winter eggs are, however, easily destroyed by means of tar-oil washes. A winter application of tar-oil should never be omitted from plums and damsons. *Victoria* plums rarely suffer from aphis.

MEALY PLUM APHIS *(Hyalopterus arundinis)*

Although less harmful than the Leaf-curling Aphis, this insect can be very troublesome. It becomes abundant in the summer, and produces a sticky, waxy secretion which falls about on the leaves and fruits.

Control.—Although the Mealy Aphis does not curl the leaves, it is nevertheless not particularly easy to wipe out with nicotine sprays, since the mealiness serves to some extent as a protection. Like the Leaf-curling Aphis, however, it spends the winter in the form of an egg on the twigs and is thus easily killed by winter washing with tar-oil sprays.

HOP DAMSON APHIS *(Phorodon humuli)*

This pest occurs on sloes and damsons, but rarely on other plums. The eggs are laid on the twigs in autumn. The aphides hatch in the spring and feed on the leaves until May or early June, when winged forms appear which migrate to hops. Return migrants lay eggs on the damsons in the autumn.

Control.—The eggs of this, like those of the foregoing species, are readily killed by tar-oil winter washes, but the summer generations on the hop have to be tackled with nicotine.

RED SPIDER *(Metatetranychus ulmi)*

The life history of this pest has been described in the chapter on apple pests (see page 126). It is even more serious on plums than on apples ; in bad cases the fruit fails to develop properly and premature leaf and fruit drop occurs.

Control.—Lime-sulphur at 1 per cent. can safely be applied to plums about ten days after petal-fall (at the time when most of the apple petals have fallen) and should not be omitted where Red Spider is at all troublesome. The eggs can be killed by spraying in winter (say in February) with a winter petroleum-oil emulsion, which, unless new invasions of spider occur in the following summer, provides the most effective means of control.

SAWFLY *(Hoplocampa flava)*

In some districts Plum Sawfly takes a heavy toll of the crop. In appearance and habits it resembles the Apple Sawfly. The eggs are laid in the flowers at blossom time and the resulting grubs feed within the growing fruits, passing from fruit to fruit and leaving holes in their sides from which wet, black frass exudes. Attacked fruits invariably drop off whilst they are small and green. When fully fed the larvæ enter the soil, where they pupate in the spring, emerging as adult " sawflies " at blossom time.

Control.—The best results have been obtained by spraying twice with derris root, once about a week after petal-fall (when the " cots " or receptacles are beginning to split) and again a week later. Care should be taken to wet the developing fruits very thoroughly with the spray.

CATERPILLARS

See Winter Moths under Apple, page 121.

RED PLUM MAGGOT (*Cydia funebrana*)

This pest is related to the Codling Moth and has somewhat similar habits.

Eggs are laid on the fruits early in July. From these arise minute caterpillars, which enter the green fruits and tunnel within them in an inconspicuous manner. Usually no sign of the pest is apparent until one eats a ripe fruit of perfectly sound appearance, when a mass of excrement is discovered near the stone, together with a large, red maggot.

Control.—It is not safe to apply arsenical sprays for the control of this pest. Any spraying carried out should be confined to non-poisonous materials such as derris or D.D.T.

Affected fruit ripens prematurely and thus some good can be done by collecting and destroying the first fruits which drop. Some of the larvæ can also be caught in sack bands placed around the tree trunks.

PESTS : DIAGNOSIS TABLE

THE PLUM

Damage	Probable Cause
Branches and Twigs	
Small, round holes in trunk	Shot Hole Borers
Shoots and Foliage (Including Blossom)	
Leaves, opening buds and blossom attacked by small, green, " looping " caterpillars	Winter Moth
Leaves spun together by small brown, green or yellowish caterpillars, which wriggle quickly backwards when disturbed	Tortrix Moth
Leaves curled, shoots stunted and infested with aphides	Leaf-curling Plum Aphis or Hop Damson Aphis
Sticky, waxy secretion on leaves and fruit in summer	Mealy Plum Aphis
Leaves turning brownish ; premature leaf fall	Red Spider
Fruit	
Remains small and drops	Leaf-curling Plum Aphis or Red Spider
Sticky waxy secretion on fruit	Mealy Plum Aphis
Fruits drop when small and green—hole in side with wet mass of black frass exuding	Sawfly
Early-matured ripe fruit drops; mass of frass near stone and large red maggot	Red Plum Maggot

SHOT-HOLE BORERS

Small, round holes in the trunks of the trees are made by various species of wood-boring beetles, which have at times been regarded as major pests of plums. There seems little doubt now that such beetles are a secondary trouble only, since they undoubtedly show a preference for trees in an unhealthy state.

MINOR PESTS

Case Bearers, Leaf-eating Weevils (*Phyllobius spp.*), and one or two other pests sometimes occur in sufficient numbers to cause alarm, but the damage they do scarcely justifies the trouble of spraying.

DISEASES OF PLUMS AND DAMSONS

BACTERIAL CANKER AND LEAF SPOT (*Pseudomonas mors-prunorum*)

This serious disease of young plum trees is very similar to Bacterial Canker of cherry, caused by the same organism, but there are a few important differences. It is less usual in plum to get cankering of individual branches ; the tree stem is more commonly attacked, though branch cankers do occur. Gumming at the site of the canker is not nearly as copious in plum as in cherry, and the leaf-spot phase usually does not appear in quantity till summer. Infection, as with cherry, is most likely to occur in late autumn and winter. The canker does not become readily visible, however, until spring, when the dead, cankered area is revealed as flattened and slightly sunken. It can usually be felt quite readily then by running the fingers around the stem, and incisions at the edge of the cankered area will show a very sharp line of demarcation between the brown, diseased area of the canker and the healthy adjacent tissue. Bacterial Canker can be suspected when the foliage on some or all of the branches is yellow, sickly, and wilting soon after growth starts in spring. As with cherry, the bacteria, which are swarming in the bark at the edge of the canker in early spring, usually die out when summer comes, and thus the canker is annual. If the tree is not girdled in the one season it will probably recover, though its vigour will be curtailed for a time. Trees that have recovered from stem cankers can often be recognized by a deep depression, sometimes several feet long, surrounded by vigorous new callus growth, running more or less vertically up the stem and frequently with a slight spiral twist. The varieties *Victoria, Czar, Giant Prune,* and *Early Laxton* are very susceptible, particularly during their early years before cropping.

Control.—The method of attack suggests the means of prevention of at least the serious stem-canker phase, and experiments have proved its value. It is the use of a resistant " stem-builder " variety on which the susceptible variety required for cropping is high-worked. *Myrobolan B* has proved highly resistant and a satisfactory nursery stock. This should be run up to the required height, usually that of a 5 or 6 feet standard, in the nursery, and be allowed to form the initial branch-system, which is then top-grafted with the susceptible variety. For existing plantations containing susceptible varieties some other means of treatment must be employed. Up to the present a satisfactory spray-programme has not been developed, since the spray treatment recommended for cherry (see page 110) does not appear to meet the requirements of plum. Summer spraying, beginning towards the end of May, has proved effective in controlling Leaf Spot, and Bordeaux Mixture at 4–6–100, though likely to cause some leaf-spotting in wet weather, is recommended. The addition of 6 pints per 100 gallons of edible cotton-seed oil will render the spray safe. Bordeaux Mixture should not be used on cropping trees within six weeks or so before picking, since this spray will leave an unsightly deposit on the fruits ; a colloidal copper preparation should be used instead at not more than 0·03 per cent. of copper when diluted, otherwise severe spray-damage to the foliage may result.

Since the bacteria are readily able to invade wounds made in autumn and winter, branch-thinning and the cutting-out of dead or dying wood, which leaves large wounds, is best done during the " safer " summer months when the risk of infection is greatly reduced (see also Silver Leaf, page 242).

BACTERIAL SHOOT WILT *(Pseudomonas prunicola and P. mors-prunorum)*

A disease of young, green, sappy shoots, the causal organisms (especially *P. mors-prunorum*) are the same as those of Bacterial Canker in cherry, and plums. The bacteria obtain entry into the leafy shoots, especially in damp weather, and cause long black streaks to appear, often on only one side of the shoot. When infection girdles the shoot, it droops at the tip and dies, and is in this phase very similar to Wither Tip caused by one of the Brown Rot fungi (see below). It is rarely of economic importance, but could be controlled by spraying the trees with Bordeaux Mixture (4–6–100) as soon as the petals have fallen. All wilted shoots should be cut out and burnt.

BROWN ROTS *(Sclerotinia fructigena and S. laxa)*

Fruit Rot.—This is caused by *S. fructigena* and *S. laxa*. Infection usually occurs through a wound, such as an insect puncture, and this acts as the centre for a progressive soft rot which ultimately invades the entire fruit. More or less concentric rings of cushions or " pustules " of fungous tissue (buff-coloured with *S. fructigena* and greyish with *S. laxa*) appear on the fruit, and produce innumerable spores that serve to carry the disease to healthy fruit. A diseased fruit is able to infect a healthy one by persistent contact, so that one diseased fruit allowed to remain in a bunch can rapidly result in the loss of them all. Bunches of " mummied " fruits are often seen hanging on the trees long after the sound fruits have been gathered. The early collection and destruction of such fruits is strongly advised to reduce the losses caused by this disease.

Wither Tip and Spur Blight.—These are caused by *S. laxa*, which infects the leaves, usually through a wound. The fungus grows down the leaf-stalk and into the main stem, causing it to wilt. The tip of the stem droops, thus giving rise to the " wither-tip " condition. The tissues harden and the leaves turn brown and persist throughout the winter. In early spring, greyish " pustules " of the fungus appear and produce spores which are able to bring about infection of the new season's leaves, flowers (see " Blossom Wilt ") and fruits. It is therefore important that diseased shoots should be removed before the fungus fructifies on them. Spur Blight is caused in a similar manner to Wither Tip ; infected leaves occur on a spur arising from a branch. The fungus may then grow down the spur into the branch, causing it to canker and die.

Blossom Wilt and Twig Blight.—These are caused by *S. laxa*, which infects the flowers and grows back into the spur and sometimes into the young twigs and branches on which the flower-trusses are borne, often girdling and thus killing them above the seat of infection. A similar disease attacks cherries, especially Morellos (see page 163).

Control.—Perhaps the best way to control diseases caused by *S. laxa* is, where practicable, to remove and burn the dead and dying twigs and shoots in the summer and autumn before leaf-fall. Once the leaves have fallen, it is very difficult to distinguish the dead shoots, which, if left on, will carry the " pustules " of the fungus during the following spring. All " mummied " fruits should also be removed and burnt for the same reason, but these can best be seen in winter when the trees are bare.

In plantations where the losses from *S. laxa* are serious and cutting-out is impracticable, winter spraying with a tar-distillate wash (5 per cent.) and pre-blossom spraying (just before flowering) with Bordeaux Mixture (6–9–100) or lime-sulphur (2 per cent.) will give good control, provided the applications are thoroughly made so as to wet the " pustules " and thus to sterilize them. The application of tar-distillate must be made when the trees are quite dormant, but the later in the dormant period the better. Even then all the fungus " pustules " might not have pushed through the bark, and the spring spraying would probably be necessary in addition to the winter one to sterilize the more recently-formed "pustules." The spray treatment recommended for the control of diseases caused by *S. laxa* are ineffective against Fruit Brown Rot caused by *S. fructigena*.

SILVER LEAF (*Stereum purpureum*)

The foliage produced by an infected branch, or possibly by a whole tree if infection has entered the trunk, is characteristically of silvery sheen, the silvering being caused by the presence of a layer of air just below the upper surface of each leaf. A brown stain will be found in the wood of an affected branch, though this stain may occur only in the lower part of the branch remote from the silvered leaves. The presence of the brown stain serves to distinguish the true Silver Leaf disease from False silver leaf, a condition that may arise as a result of some growth disturbance in the tree.

The fungus can cause infection only through wounds. Death does not always result ; natural recovery is known to occur, especially under good cultivation and manurial treatment when the trees are induced to grow strongly.

Affected branches or trees should be removed only when wilting occurs, but before death ensues. Silvered leaves are not sources of infection. Fructifications of the fungus occur *only on dead wood*, particularly in autumn after wet weather. These are most commonly in the form of overlapping brackets horizontal to the branch, and often thickly placed along most of its length. They can frequently be seen on the trunk of a dead tree as well as on the branches. The brackets are leathery, they have a wavy edge, and are up to 2 inches across. The upper surface is yellowish- or greyish-brown, often showing concentric zones of colour, and it is rough and slightly hairy. The lower surface is smooth and, when fresh, purple in colour. Occasionally flattish brackets are found, attached more closely and more nearly parallel with the branch, and showing the purplish, spore-bearing surface outwards. Many other kinds of fruit trees and bushes, as well as forest trees (e.g., Poplar) and shrubs (e.g., Rhododendron), are attacked, among them apple, pear, cherry, gooseberry, currants. Certain other, and comparatively harmless, fungi produce fructifications not unlike those of *Stereum purpureum* in some respects, so it is important that *Stereum* be correctly identified. Spores are produced in large numbers from the purple surfaces of the fructifications, and these serve to spread the disease. During June, July, and August, infection does not readily occur, for the tree is then best able to resist attack by the formation of a "gum-barrier," which prevents the fungus from progressing in the host tissue.

All dying and dead wood should, therefore, be removed and burnt early in summer ; The Ministry of Agriculture's Silver Leaf Order of 1923 makes it compulsory to do this by 15th of July every year. It is important to cut back well into healthy wood, for brown-stained wood contains the fungus-mycelium. The wounds should immediately be protected with a white-lead paint.

Victoria and *Czar* are the two most susceptible plum varieties, while *Yellow Egg, Purple Pershore,* and *Green Gage* are resistant though not immune.

Trees on the Common Plum rootstock are said to show a measure of resistance to the disease.

DISEASES : DIAGNOSIS TABLE

THE PLUM

DAMAGE	PROBABLE CAUSE
Branches and Twigs	
Cankered area on trunk or branch, sometimes with gumming ; tree may wilt and die if trunk cankered	Bacterial Canker
Shoots and Foliage (Including Blossom)	
Leaves turn yellow and wilt in spring and summer Leaf-spot phase—small, circular, brown spots, which eventually fall out and leave " shot-hole " effect	Bacterial Canker and Leaf Spot
Young green, sappy shoots droop at the tips and die	Bacterial Shoot Wilt
Tips of shoots and leaves on spurs droop and wilt ; leaves turn brown and persist often throughout winter	Brown Rot, Wither Tip and Spur Blight
Blossoms wilt, spurs and young twigs become cankered and die, dead leaves and flowers hang stiffly	Brown Rot Blossom Wilt and Twig Blight
Small, slightly raised, orange-yellow spots, later turning dark brown, mainly on undersides of leaves	Rust
Silvery sheen foliage on affected branch—brown stain in lower part of wood	Silver Leaf
Fruit	
More or less concentric rings of " pustules " of fungous tissue on fruit, may be grey- or buff-coloured	Brown Rots

Note.—Once the trouble has been diagnosed, the reader should refer to the paragraph dealing with the particular disease or pest, and should also consult the Guide to Spraying, page 111.

DESCRIPTIVE NOTES ON VARIETIES

DESSERT PLUMS

Bryanston Gage. A medium-sized, roundish, greengage-like plum, a yellowish-green, spotted with red when ripe. Of delicious, sweet flavour. Ready mid-September. Early flowering. Self-sterile. Cross-pollinates with Green Gage.

Cambridge Green Gage (Chivers). A medium-sized, roundish, greengage-like fruit. Of delicious flavour. Ready early in September. Early flowering. Partially self-fertile. Probably a seedling of Green Gage.

DESSERT PLUMS (*continued*)

Coe's Golden Drop. A medium-sized to large, oval, golden-yellow fruit, spotted with red, with marked constriction at the stalk end. Of delicious flavour. Ready late in September and will keep in a cool fruit room for some little time. Suitable for culture on east, south or west walls even in the northern districts, or as a bush or standard in the open in the warmer districts. Early flowering. Self-sterile, but cross-pollinates well with Cambridge Gage, President, or Comte d'Althan.

Comte d'Althan's Gage. A medium-sized, roundish, red-purple plum, of fine, rich gage-like flavour. Ready mid-September. Crops well when grown on a wall in sheltered gardens. Early flowering and self-sterile. Cross-pollinates well with Rivers Early, Coe's Golden Drop, or Jefferson. Incompatible with Myrobolan B rootstock when budded.

Denniston's Superb Gage. A medium-sized, round, yellowish-green fruit. Of excellent greengage-like flavour. Ready in August. Specially recommended for a north or east wall in sheltered gardens. Self-fertile.

Early Transparent Gage. A small to medium-sized, round fruit, a rich yellow and crimson spotted. Of delicious, sweet flavour. Ready mid-August. Early flowering and self-fertile.

Golden Transparent Gage. A very large, roundish, golden-yellow fruit dotted with red. Of delicious gage-like flavour. Ready early in October. Suitable for wall culture in sheltered gardens. Self-fertile.

Green Gage (Reine Claude). A medium-sized, round fruit, green, spotted with red when ripe and flattened at the ends. Of delicious flavour. Ready August to September. Makes a strong tree. Notoriously unreliable cropper. Best grown on garden walls and netted against birds. Early flowering and partially self-fertile.

Jefferson's Gage. A large, oval, golden-yellow fruit, spotted with red. Of delicious rich, sweet, gage-like flavour. Ready in September. Early flowering and self-sterile. Cross-pollinates well with Rivers Early, Monarch, Victoria.

Late Transparent Gage. A large, roundish, oval, yellow fruit, golden russet. Of delicious rich juicy flavour. Ready towards the end of September. Self-sterile. Pollinated by Denniston's Superb or Early Transparent. Makes small tree.

Laxton's Gage. A medium-sized, oval, yellow fruit, the result of a cross between the old Greengage and Victoria plum, and somewhat resembling Transparent Gage. Ready late in August, a hardy and prolific cropper in all forms. Late flowering and self-fertile.

Magnum Bonum. See Warwickshire Drooper.

Ontario. Medium to large, roundish oval, marbled yellow, vigorous. Ready mid-August. Very prolific. Gage flavour.

Oullins Golden Gage. A medium to large, roundish, oval, golden-yellow fruit, of gage-like flavour. Ready mid-August. Picked early, it is excellent for cooking and bottling. Late flowering and self-fertile. Incompatible with Myrobolan B when budded. Grown commercially in Kent.

Pond's Seedling. See list of Cooking Plums.

Red Myrobolan (Cherry Plum). A small, round, red plum of pleasant flavour. Makes a strong tree useful for shelter belts. Will not stand tar-oils. Flowers earlier than any other plum ; hence very susceptible to frost. Crops freely when the flowering season is mild and fine. Ready in July. Self-fertile. A good plum for bottling and canning. Can be grown on its own roots or budded on Myrobolan B.

Reine Claude de Bavay. A large to medium-sized, roundish, oval, greenish-yellow fruit, of delicious gage-like flavour. Ready late September to October. Hardy and prolific as a wall plant even in the northern districts. Mid-season flowering and self-fertile.

Rivers Early Prolific. See list of Cooking Plums.

Transparent Gage (Reine Claude Diaphane). A medium-sized, roundish-oval, greenish-yellow fruit flushed with pale violet. Of delicious gage-like flavour. Ready in September. Mid-season flowering and self-sterile. One of the best of all gages. Pollinated by Denniston's Superb and Early Transparent.

Victoria. A large, oval, pinkish-red fruit of delicious flavour when ripe and excellent for cooking or preserving. Ready in August. Hardy and prolific in all forms and almost anywhere. Especially partial to a chalky clay mixture. The most popular market plum, but highly susceptible to silver leaf. Mid-season flowering and self-fertile. Susceptible to Bacterial Canker.

Warwickshire Drooper. Known as Magnum Bonum in parts of the West Midlands. A medium-sized, roundish, oval plum, greenish-yellow dotted with red. Of gage flavour but not of the highest quality. Very hardy and prolific, but makes a very drooping tree. An early blossomer. Plant with River's Early, Early Laxton, or Denniston's Gage for cross-pollination. Plum hangs to September. Cans and bottles well and is also a good dessert plum in September.

Washington Gage. Large, flat at both ends, golden yellow with red flush and spots. Early September. Excellent flavour, but uncertain cropper.

COOKING PLUMS

Belle de Louvain. A large, egg-shaped red plum, ripening to a dark purple. Of juicy, rich, acid flavour. Ready late in August. Late bloomer and self-fertile. Very strong grower. Does well on heavy soils.

Blaisdon Red. A medium-sized, oval, red plum, much grown in Gloucestershire for jam. Ready in September. Hardy and prolific and almost immune from silver leaf. A fine market fruit for orchard cultivation on grass. Easily propagated by means of suckers. Mid-season bloomer and self-fertile.

Czar. A medium-sized, roundish, oval, purple-black fruit of splendid flavour. Ready early in August. A reliable and prolific cropper in all forms even in the colder northern districts. Also suitable for orchard culture and for marketing. Late-season flowering and self-fertile. Susceptible to bacterial canker.

COOKING PLUMS (*continued*)

Early Laxton. A small- to medium-sized, oval fruit, yellow flushed red, sweet and juicy. Ready mid-July, being the earliest of all plums. Recommended for wall culture, as well as a bush or half-standard in the open. Suitable for marketing. Early flowering and partially self-fertile. Subject to bacterial canker.

Early Prolific. See River's Early Prolific.

Giant Prune. A large, longish, oval, deep reddish-purple fruit of moderate flavour. Ready towards the end of September. Hardy and prolific as a bush or standard and recommended for market culture. Mid-season flowering and self-fertile. A good pollinator of many self-sterile sorts. Highly susceptible to bacterial canker and brown rot.

Monarch. A very large, round, dark purple plum, of fine flavour, good enough for dessert when ripe, and one of the best for cooking. Ready in late September. Early flowerer and self-fertile. A very uncertain cropper in Kent.

Pershore (Yellow Egg Plum). A medium-sized, egg-shaped, yellow plum, of fine quality. Ready towards the end of August. A hardy and prolific cropper in all forms and one of the most profitable market plums. Usually propagated by means of suckers. Late flowering and self-fertile. One of the most noted plums for jam, canning, and bottling.

Pond's Seedling. A very large, long, oval, deep red plum, of excellent flavour, and when ripe good enough for dessert. Ready late in September. In wet weather the fruit is somewhat liable to crack, and it is susceptible to brown rot and silver leaf. Late flowering and self-sterile. Cross-pollinates with Czar and Belle de Louvain.

Purple Pershore. A medium to large-sized, egg-shaped, deep purple fruit, of fine quality, somewhat similar to Pershore, but purple instead of yellow. Ready mid-August. Hardy and prolific in all forms and a profitable market fruit. Late-season flowering and self-fertile. One of the plums which respond to potash manuring. Widely planted.

Rivers Early Prolific. A small to medium-sized, oval-shaped, deep purple-black plum, of good flavour, for cooking, bottling, or jam making, and when ripe, considered good enough for dessert. Ready late in July or August. Hardy in all forms in districts which suit it—calcareous clay and gravel soil mixed—a profitable market fruit. Seems almost immune from silver leaf. Early bloomer, partially self-fertile. Cross-pollinated by Monarch and Warwickshire Drooper. An uncertain cropper. Plant with early-blossoming varieties.

Schwitchen (Quetsche) (Zwetsche) (German Prune). The Schwitchen is a species of plum common to eastern Europe. It produces a small, longish, oval, dark blue plum of good flavour when cooked in September. It is much grown in Germany and used chiefly for cooking and bottling. Has been planted in Kent for market purposes.

Victoria. See list of Dessert Plums.

Wyedale. A small to medium-sized, oval, reddish-purple fruit of good quality. Ready in October. Hardy and prolific in all forms and all districts. A popular market fruit. Self-sterile.

FERTILITY GUIDE TO ENSURE CROSS-POLLINATION

When only one plum tree is planted, it is essential to select one of the self-fertile varieties unless, of course, other plum trees, flowering at the same period, are growing in other gardens close by.

SELF-FERTILE VARIETIES

Early Flowering	Mid-season Flowering	Late Flowering
Denniston's Superb Gage Early Transparent Gage Monarch Warwickshire Drooper	Blaisdon Red Egg Plum Reine Claude de Bavay Victoria	Belle de Louvain Czar Golden Transparent Laxton's Gage Oullins Golden Gage Pershore Purple Pershore

PARTIALLY SELF-FERTILE

Early Flowering	Mid-season Flowering	Late Flowering
Cambridge Green Gage Rivers Early Prolific	Old Greengage Reine Claude Violette	Farleigh Damson

Any of these fertile or partially self-fertile varieties planted in conjunction with self-sterile varieties, flowering at the same time, will cross-pollinate the self-sterile varieties. Early-flowering sorts will also cross-pollinate mid-season flowers, the mid-season bloomers will cross-pollinate late bloomers, as the flowering seasons overlap somewhat and the plum blossoms last a long time.

SELF-STERILE VARIETIES

Early Flowering	Mid-season Flowering	Late Flowering
Black Diamond Coe's Golden Drop Comte d'Althan's Gage Jefferson's Gage President	Bryanston Gage Transparent Gage	Kirke's Blue Pond's Seedling

THE BEST-FLAVOURED PLUMS

Variety	Dessert or Cooking	Season
Bryanston Gage	Dessert	September
Cambridge Green Gage	Dessert	Early September
Coe's Golden Drop	Dessert	Late September
Comte d'Althan's Gage	Dessert	Mid-September

THE BEST-FLAVOURED PLUMS (continued)

Variety	Dessert or Cooking	Season
Denniston's Superb Gage	Dessert	Mid-August
Early Transparent Gage	Dessert	Mid-August
Golden Transparent	Dessert	October
Green Gage	Dessert	August–September
Jefferson's Gage	Dessert	September
Late Transparent Gage	Dessert	End of September–October
Reine Claude de Bavay	Dessert	September
Transparent Gage	Dessert	September
Washington Gage	Dessert	Early September

SELECTION OF PLUMS IN ORDER OF RIPENING
DESSERT

Variety	When Ready	Colour
Denniston's Superb Gage	August	Yellowish-green, tinged Red
Early Transparent Gage	Mid-August	Yellow and Crimson spotted
Oullins Golden Gage	Mid-August	Golden-yellow
Laxton's Gage	Late August	Yellow Fruit
Green Gage	August–September	Green, spotted Red
Cambridge Green Gage	Early September	Green, spotted Red
Victoria	August	Pinkish Red
Washington Gage	Early September	Gold, Red Spots
Bryanston Gage	Mid-September	Yellowish-green, spotted Red
Reine Claude de Bavay	September–October	Greenish-yellow
Comte d'Althan's Gage	Mid-September	Red-purple
Jefferson's Gage	September	Golden-yellow, spotted Red
Transparent Gage	September	Greenish-yellow
Coe's Golden Drop	Late September	Golden-yellow
Late Transparent	End of September	Yellow
Golden Transparent Gage	Early October	Golden-yellow

COOKING PLUMS

Variety	When Ready	Colour
Rivers Early Prolific	Late July–August	Purple-black
Czar	Early August	Purple-black
Purple Pershore	Mid-August	Deep Purple
Belle de Louvain	Late August	Dark Purple
Pershore	End of August	Yellow
Victoria	August	Pinkish-red
Blaisdon Red	September	Red
Giant Prune	End of September	Reddish-purple
Monarch	Late September	Dark Purple
Pond's Seedling	Late September	Deep Red
Schwitchen	September–October	Dark Blue
Wyedale	October	Reddish Purple

GOOD MARKET PLUMS

Variety	Cooking or Dessert	Ready
Belle de Louvain	Cooking	Late August
Blaisdon Red	Cooking	September
Czar	Cooking	August
Giant Prune	Cooking	September
Monarch	Cooking or Dessert	Late September
Oullins Golden Gage	Dessert	Mid-August
Pershore (Yellow Egg)	Cooking	End of August
Pond's Seedling	Cooking or Dessert	Late September
Purple Pershore	Cooking	Mid-August
Rivers Early Prolific	Cooking or Dessert	Late July–August
Schwitchen	Cooking	September–October
Victoria	Cooking or Dessert	August
Warwickshire Drooper	Cooking or Dessert	August–September
Wyedale	Cooking	October

PLUMS FOR GROWING ON WALLS

North Walls		South Walls	
Denniston's Superb Gage	(D)	Coe's Golden Drop	(D)
Early Transparent Gage	(D)	Denniston's Superb Gage	(D)
Jefferson's Gage	(D)	Early Transparent Gage	(D)
Oullins Golden Gage	(D)	Golden Transparent Gage	(D)
Victoria	(D)	Jefferson's Gage	(D)
		Late Transparent Gage	(D)
		Reine Claude de Bavay	(D)
		Washington Gage	(D)

East Walls		West Walls	
Coe's Golden Drop	(D)	Bryanston Gage	(D)
Comte d'Althan's Gage	(D)	Coe's Golden Drop	(D)
Denniston's Superb Gage	(D)	Denniston's Superb Gage	(D)
Early Transparent Gage	(D)	Early Transparent Gage	(D)
Oullins Golden Gage	(D)	Jefferson's Gage	(D)
Victoria	(D)	Oullins Golden Gage	(D)
		Victoria	(D)

PLUMS FOR EXHIBITION

Variety	Dessert or Cooking	Ready
Belle de Louvain	Cooking	Late August
Giant Prune	Cooking	End of September
Kirke's Blue	Dessert	Mid-September
Monarch	Cooking	Late September
President	Dessert	October

THE QUINCE *(Cydonia vulgaris)*

SOIL AND SITUATION

The quince thrives in moist soil, and does particularly well when planted near a pond or stream.

The tree itself is very beautiful and lives to a great age, requiring very little attention when once established. Its natural habit is that of a rather low, twisted tree, and it is difficult to persuade it to make a good straight standard, or to adapt its peculiarly untidy habit of growth to any of the artificial forms of tree.

The quince is particularly hardy and thrives in a sunny, open situation or against a wall, even in the colder northern districts, but it is only in the milder districts of the south and west that it ripens its fruit in the open.

PROPAGATION

The quince may easily be propagated by means of layers, stools, or hard wood cuttings or suckers.

The stooling method is the one usually adopted for the production of stocks. (See page 28.)

PLANTING

The best time to plant is early in the autumn. Standard forms should be put in 20 feet apart, half-standards 12 to 15 feet apart, and bushes about 10 feet apart.

PRUNING

The tree should be shaped in early years by cutting out unwanted branches, but after that pruning should be reduced to a minimum.

GATHERING AND STORING

The fruit should be left on the tree until thoroughly ripe, and should not be gathered until the end of October, unless the autumn is unusually frosty. On no account should it be gathered when wet. The ripe fruits are strongly aromatic and when gathered they should be stored by themselves (otherwise the aroma will affect the flavour of other fruit with which they are stored) in a cool, frost-proof place on layers of straw on a shelf, until they have turned yellow. Here they will keep for from two to three months. They are then fit for use. (See also Gathering and Storing, page 87.)

MARKETING

Very large quinces are marketed in 12-lb. chip baskets, and the smaller ones in wicker half-sieves.

VARIETIES

Some of the best-known varieties of quince are the *Angers* and the *Common*, the *Apple-shaped*, the *Pear-shaped*, the *Bereczki*, *Vranja*, *Champion*, and *Portugal*. The *Bereczki* is not quite such a good cropper as the others. The *Pear-shaped* and the *Portugal* are especially recommended for garden culture by the Royal Horticultural Society. The former is the kind in common cultivation, but its pear-shaped fruits, though plentiful, are not as large or of such good flavour as those of the *Portugal*.

INSECT PESTS

Codling Moth (see Apple, page 125), Slugworm (see Pear, page 222), and various Caterpillars (see Apple, page 121) occur on quinces but are seldom of any importance.

PESTS : DIAGNOSIS TABLE

THE QUINCE

DAMAGE	PROBABLE CAUSE
Shoots and Foliage (Including Blossom)	
Leaves, opening buds and blossoms attacked by small green, " looping " caterpillars	Winter Moth
Leaves spun together by small, brown, green or yellowish caterpillars, which quickly wriggle backwards when disturbed	Tortrix Moths
Circular, reddish-brown spots on leaves and fruit	Leaf Blight
Intervenal tissue of leaves eaten by black, slug-like larvæ, leaving brown patches ; leaves may turn brown and fall	Slug worm
Fruit	
Small fruits eaten by small, green " looping " caterpillars	Winter Moth
Maggoty fruit. May drop before ripe	Codling Moth
Circular, reddish-brown spots on fruit and leaves	Leaf Blight

Note.—Once the trouble has been diagnosed, the reader should refer to the paragraph dealing with the particular disease or pest.

DISEASES

LEAF BLIGHT (*Fabræa maculata*)

The fungus causes circular, reddish-brown spots on the leaves and fruits. In severe attacks on the fruit, the spots are so close that they run together, and Brown Rot (*Sclerotinia fructigena*) often gains entry and rots the fruits. Severely-affected leaves drop prematurely. The fungus lives on the twigs through the winter, being present on roughly circular, reddish-brown areas with dark margins. To control the disease, remove any infected twigs and spray post-blossom with Bordeaux

Mixture or a colloidal copper preparation as recommended for pears (see Pears).

The spray protects healthy leaves and fruits from infection, and therefore should be applied before the disease makes its appearance. The disease occasionally attacks pears and medlars, and can be troublesome on unworked quince rootstocks in the nursery.

MILDEW *(Podosphaera leucotricha)*

This sometimes attacks quinces as well as apples, and can be controlled by the same treatment (see Apple Mildew, page 131).

THE RASPBERRY *(Rubus Idæus)*

SOIL AND SITUATION

Raspberries do best in deep, rich, well-drained soil which holds moisture but does not waterlog. In the autumn, before planting, the soil should be well dug and a liberal dressing of manure (preferably farmyard dung, cow or pig manure) should be incorporated with it. The plants are very hardy and, given satisfactory soil and good drainage, they do well in almost any situation and aspect.

FORMS OF CULTURE

The raspberry grows in the form of single canes which shoot up annually from the base of the plant, the fruit being borne on short fruit-bearing laterals of the current season which grow out from the main stem.

PROPAGATION

In these days when the virus disease known as mosaic has infected such a large percentage of the raspberry plants in the United Kingdom, the most hopeful method of obtaining healthy raspberry canes is to apply to the local advisory officer in horticulture for information as to a reliable source of supply.

The length of life of a raspberry plantation is almost entirely governed by the health of the plants. *If kept free from mosaic*, the canes should last for nine to ten years in profitable bearing.

PLANTING

The young canes are best planted in November, though when this has been impossible, they may be planted in February. The plants should be planted singly, 2 to 3 feet apart, in rows 6 to 8 feet apart. The top roots should be an inch below the surface, the ground being made thoroughly firm at the time of planting. It is usual to cut down the newly-planted canes in March to about 12 inches from the soil.

During the summer new canes will be produced from the base, and these will bear fruit the year after.

In gardens the canes may also be put in in clumps of three, the clumps being set from 3 to 4 feet apart.

PRUNING

In autumn all old canes that have borne fruit should be cut down to the ground. All weak young shoots should be cut out at the same time, about six of the strongest on each plant being left to bear fruit the following season. In the spring these canes should be cut back to a height of about 3 feet from ground level, as this is believed to encourage an even break of fruiting laterals throughout the entire length of each cane.

The autumn-fruiting varieties bear their fruit on the current season's growth, and they should have their new canes cut down to about 4 inches from the ground in February or March. Summer-fruiting raspberries may be made to bear a crop of fruit during September and October in the following way. As soon as suckers show them-

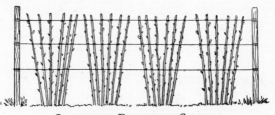

SUPPORTING RASPBERRY CANES.

selves in June, the old canes should be cut away entirely, and a mulch of well-rotted manure should be applied in June.

SUPPORTING THE CANES

Raspberries need some form of support, the simplest consisting of three wires strained horizontally at heights of about 2 feet, 3½ feet, and 5 feet from the ground. To these wires the canes should be tied in autumn, about 9 inches apart from each other. The new canes should not be tied up during the summer, as the wood ripens better if left untied. Raspberry canes grown on commercial plantations are often supported by either one or two double strands of wire or coir yarn fastened to crosspieces on support posts (see sketch). In this case there is no tying of individual canes.

CULTIVATION AND MANURING

The ground should be hoed in spring, but the soil should not be deeply stirred as the roots are very near the surface. In gardens a mulch of lawn mowings or old rotted dung put along the rows in May or June will help to keep the moisture in the soil. The best way to manure raspberries is to dig in a good dressing of dung *before* planting, and to give yearly applications of sulphate of potash at the rate of 2 to 3 cwt. per acre (1½ oz. per square yard) in winter. In alternate years nitrogen should be given, preferably in organic form, cow manure, pig manure, or failing this, in inorganic form, at the rate of 2 cwt. per acre applied up the row in early spring.

GATHERING

Berries for dessert and immediate home use should be picked as they ripen, without the " plug." For market they should be gathered before they are fully ripe, being picked with the " plug," and for jam-making the whole crop is usually left on the plants as long as possible, being gathered in one picking, fully ripe, without the " plug."

However gathered, the fruit should never be picked when wet.

When grading fruit for market, skilled pickers go over the canes in advance of the gang and pick the choice berries, placing them direct into punnets or chip baskets as required for market. Dessert fruit is usually marketed in No. 1 or No. 2 punnets ; main crop fruit in 2-, 3-, or 4-lb. chip baskets (with handles).

Fruit for jam making is sent in tubs, drums, or shallow lined wooden trays.

DISEASES OF RASPBERRY

MOSAIC *(Virus)*

This is by far the most serious disease of the raspberry and is the cause of serious loss of growth and cropping. Being in the sap of an affected plant it is impossible to eradicate the virus or to control it by spraying. A yellow mottling of the leaves is the most characteristic symptom : affected leaves are often curled downwards. More than one virus is involved, and varieties differ greatly in their response to infection. *Baumforth's Seedling B* and *Lloyd George* are susceptible to and severely affected by one or more of the viruses, while *Preussen* is susceptible to infection but may show little or no evidence of it, or be severely affected by it.

Red Cross shows obvious leaf-mottling but little ill effect, and *Norfolk Giant* is resistant though it deteriorates when it does become infected. The natural mode of spread of this disease in this country is at present unknown, but insects are suspected. Raspberry plants severely affected by mosaic should be grubbed, together with all their " spawn " or new canes, and destroyed. Virus-free stock should be used to start new plantations.

DWARF *(Virus)* (see Blackberry, page 155)

CANE SPOT *(Elsinoë veneta)*

The disease caused by this fungus is sometimes called "anthracnose." It is characterized by the presence of purplish spots on the young canes in early summer. As these spots get larger, their centres become grey. The leaves and leaf-stalks are affected in a similar manner, and the disease can severely disfigure the fruits. On susceptible varieties, notably *Baumforth's Seedling B* and *Lloyd George*, the spots on the canes are sometimes very crowded and run together, forming cankers that may be large enough to kill them. The new canes become infected from the fruiting ones on which the fungus has passed the winter. The best means of checking the disease is to spray, just as the buds begin to move, with lime-sulphur at 5 per cent. or Bordeaux Mixture at 10–15–100. An alternative, or additional, method of control is to spray immediately pre-blossom with Bordeaux Mixture at 4–6–100, or a colloidal copper preparation.

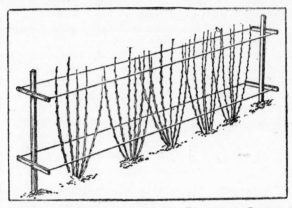

ANOTHER METHOD OF SUPPORTING RASPBERRY CANES.

VERTICILLIUM WILT *(Verticillium Dahliæ)*

In summer, the older leaves of young canes infected with this disease turn yellow and show brown discoloration between the main veins, while a broad, brownish-blue stripe is sometimes present on one side of the cane, usually towards the base. This stripe may be over a foot long. On affected fruiting canes there is no bluish stripe, but where the cane has survived, dead buds are present usually on one side of the cane and corresponding to the blue stripe of the previous year. When the cane is cut across, a brown discoloration will be found on the same side as the dead buds. The fungus occurs in the soil, and infects the root-system, ultimately growing upwards in the new canes. This disease is rarely serious enough to justify special control measures but stools with dead canes should be grubbed out and burnt with all their spawn. Natural recovery frequently occurs.

CANE BLIGHT *(Leptosphæria Coniothyrium and associated fungi)*

This is a fungus disease that appears to be increasing in economic importance. The fungi, which persist on snags left on the plants near ground level, and possibly also in the soil, attack the young canes usually near the ground. In the first year an elliptical, purplish area, an inch or two long, is the only sign of attack, but by the second year this area has become a canker which may girdle the cane and kill it. Affected fruiting canes can then readily be seen because the leaves wilt and die. Such canes, when bent sideways, often snap off at the canker. This is discoloured brown and loosely covered by the bark, which has flaked into strips. Spores are produced in clusters of small, spherical, blackish, fungal bodies that arise on the surface of the canker, and they can infect the new canes. The disease is frequently in association with the Raspberry Cane Midge.

Control.—There is so far no known spray-treatment for this disease. All affected canes should be severed, preferably below ground level, and burnt ; merely snapping off the canes is useless because infected snags are left behind. Spawn for planting up should not be taken from affected plants, and it is inadvisable to replant the gaps. Keeping the rows clear of weeds is helpful in promoting free circulation of air around the plants.

DISEASES : DIAGNOSIS TABLE

THE RASPBERRY

DAMAGE	PROBABLE CAUSE
Canes	
Purplish spots on young canes in early summer, getting larger and having grey centres	Cane Spot
Broad, brownish-blue stripe near base (see also under leaves)	Verticillium Wilt
Purple areas on young canes, cankers on fruiting canes. Leaves wilt and die if cane girdled. Cane readily snaps off at canker	Cane Blight
Shoots and Foliage	
Yellow mottling of leaves ; often curled downwards	Mosaic
Older leaves show brownish discoloration between main veins, broad, brownish-blue stripe on canes, usually at base	Verticillium Wilt

PESTS OF THE RASPBERRY

RASPBERRY BEETLE *(Byturus tomentosus)*

See page 201.

RASPBERRY MOTH *(Incurvaria rubiella)*

This pest is widely distributed and does serious damage to raspberries and loganberries. When the buds grow out in the spring many of them will wither and die when they have grown about an inch owing to a small red caterpillar feeding within them. These caterpillars move from shoot to shoot and thus destroy a great many fruiting laterals. When fully fed they pupate in the shoots or between leaves spun together, and in June turn to moths. These are small, brown in colour, with a silvery sheen and several yellow spots on the wings. They lay their minute eggs in the blossoms. Small, pale caterpillars hatch out and feed within the berries, without, however, causing appreciable damage. When the berries ripen the half-grown caterpillars, now red in colour, leave them and drop to the ground, where they spin silken cocoons just below soil level.

In these they remain until the following April, when they ascend the canes and attack the developing shoots.

Control.—On the Continent some success has been claimed for the use of tar-distillate winter washes, but, as the caterpillars spend the winter in the soil, it is doubtful whether the ground would be soaked well enough to kill them.

Attacked shoots should be pinched out and destroyed, a procedure which can be adopted in gardens.

On a larger scale the best plan is to cut down the whole of the fruiting cane before flowering time. This stamps the pest out, but sacrifices a year's crop.

MINOR PESTS

Although a great many insects feed on raspberries, few can be reckoned as pests. In addition to the above, losses are also caused occasionally by the Cane Gall Fly (*Losioptera rubi*), which produces swellings on the cane, and the Cane Midge (*Thomasiniana theobaldi*), which sometimes causes the cane to snap off at the base, is on the increase. Removal of attacked canes is a good plan and some success has followed spraying with D.D.T. in April or May.

PESTS : DIAGNOSIS TABLE

THE RASPBERRY

DAMAGE	PROBABLE CAUSE
Canes	
Swellings on canes	Cane Gall Fly
Foliage and Shoots	
Buds, when about 1 inch long, wither and die, eaten by small red caterpillars	Raspberry Moth
Fruit	
Fruit maggoty, often deformed	Raspberry Beetle

Note.—Once the trouble has been diagnosed, the reader should refer to the paragraph dealing with the particular disease or pest and should also consult the Guide to Spraying, see page 112.

VARIETIES OF THE RASPBERRY

Lloyd George is still the best red raspberry to plant provided canes free from virus can be obtained. The most popular commercial variety to-day is *Norfolk Giant* and this can now be obtained with a government certificate of health.

For those who want a succession of varieties to ripen through July into August there are *Red Cross, Park Lane, St. Walfried, Newburgh, Preussen, Brocket Hall*, to be followed by *Hailsham Berry*, the Autumn-fruiting variety.

If several varieties are grown in the same garden or plantation virus disease is almost certain to come in, and the only wise policy is that of a " short life and a gay one," grubbing and replanting as soon as the canes begin to lose vigour.

SUMMER FRUITING

Name	Size and Shape	Season	Qualities
Baumforth's Seedling A	Medium to Large, Round	Summer	Soft, acid flavour, prolific, best for jam
Baumforth's Seedling B	Medium, Conical	Summer	Good flavour and very sweet
Brocket Hall	Large, Round	Summer	
Laxton's Bountiful	Medium to Large, Roundish, Conical	Summer	Sweet and luscious
Lloyd George	Very Large, Conical	July–Autumn	Vigorous and prolific. Frequently crops on young canes in the autumn
Malling Enterprise	Very Large, Roundish	Mid-prolonged	Canes few but vigorous, bright red colour
Malling Landmark	Very Large, Round	Late-prolonged	Very vigorous, fruit soft, light bright red, slightly acid
Malling Promise	Very Large, Conical	Early	Very vigorous, fruit bright, good flavour
Newburgh	Large	Summer	Good cropper, vigorous. Subject to Cane Blight
Norfolk Giant	Medium to Large, Roundish	Late Summer	Heavy cropper
Preussen	Large to Very Large, Round	Summer	Rather soft, sweet, fine flavour
Pyne's Royal	Very Large, Conical	Summer	Slightly acid. Good for jam; good quality. Makes few canes
Reader's Perfection	Medium to Large, Roundish, Conical	Summer	Prolific
Red Cross	Large, Roundish, Conical	Summer	Good flavour and prolific
St. Walfried	Long, Conical	Summer	New promising Dutch variety

YELLOW FRUITING

Name	Size and Shape	Season	Qualities
Golden Hornet	Large, Round	Mid-season	Fine flavour
Yellow Antwerp	Large, Round	Mid-season	Sweet, pleasant flavour
Yellow Superlative	Large	Mid-season	

AUTUMN FRUITING

Name	Size and Shape	Season	Qualities
Belle de Fontenay (Red)	Very Large	October–November	Prolific. Short canes
Hailsham Berry (Red)	Large, Round	October–November	Vigorous grower
Lloyd George (Red)	Large	Summer and Autumn Lloyd George can be easily converted into an autumn-fruiting variety by cutting the fruiting canes hard back to the ground in February or March	Good flavour
November Abundance (Red)	Large	November	Good flavour
October Red (Red)	Large	Autumn	Prolific

Most of the autumn-fruiting varieties bear in October and November.

RASPBERRIES TO GROW FOR MARKET

Lloyd George
Malling Promise
Newburgh
Norfolk Giant

Preussen
Pyne's Royal
Reader's Perfection
Red Cross

RASPBERRIES FOR JAM AND BOTTLING

Baumforth's Seedling A
Lloyd George

Pyne's Royal
Reader's Perfection

Red Cross

THE STRAWBERRY (*Fragaria*)

SOIL, SITUATION AND ASPECT

The strawberry may be considered fairly catholic in regard to soil requirements. A good humus content is essential to the production of a shallow fibrous root-system like that of the strawberry. In gardens, the season of picking may be lengthened by planting varieties which ripen at different times, and by planting in borders with different aspects.

PROPAGATION

Starting with a small number of healthy and vigorous parent plants it is possible to produce new plants to stock a fair-sized garden plot in a single season. Raising strawberry plants is comparatively simple owing to the habit, possessed by most varieties, of sending out long, threadlike stolons from June or July onwards, from which young "runner" plants grow naturally at distances of anything from 6 to 12 inches apart. If these runner plants are left undisturbed, quite a number of them will throw out roots into the ground and will continue growing. If they are "hand-laid," that is to say, if they are pushed gently down into the soil and held firmly in place with a wire pin or stone, they start rooting more quickly, and, if the season is favourable, quite a number of them will be ready to plant out from July onwards in their permanent quarters. Experiments have shown that all the runners from a healthy parent plant will ultimately make good plants provided they all receive equally good treatment.

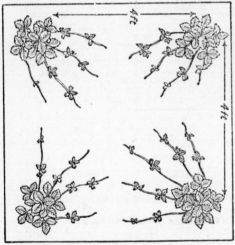

BLOCK METHOD OF RAISING STRAWBERRY RUNNERS.

For large-scale planting strawberry runners are best raised in a runner nursery bed laid down on the lines shown in the diagram. When the runners are all laid into separate blocks like this, the whole batch of plants in the block affected can be pulled up and got rid of should they develop symptoms of virus disease.

PLANTING

The ideal conditions for planting strawberry runners are those which provide a warm soil which has been heavily manured with farmyard manure some time previously and deeply dug. Planting should take place immediately after a shower, and the soil should continue warm but well supplied with moisture for as long as possible after planting. In the west of England it may be possible to get rooted runners in July by the methods described above, but in the east of England the only way to make certain of getting rooted runners early enough for August

planting is to layer them in pots early in July from healthy parent
plants, preferably from maidens (i.e. plants which were runners the
previous season). Three or 3½-inch pots filled with good potting soil
are plunged to the rim in the ground close to the parent plants. The
runners from the parent plants are pegged down with a hairpin or piece
of wire, one into each pot, the rest of the stolon being then nipped off
to ensure that the potted runner is well provided with plant food by
the parent. Opinion differs as to the number of runners to be taken
from each plant. Provided the parent is healthy and vigorous there
is no reason why at least 12 runners should not be potted up from each.
If ideal conditions for planting out are to be obtained, speedy rooting
of runners is desirable. Rooting may be encouraged by earthing up
round the base of the runner and even by judicious watering in very
dry weather. All runners not required for planting may be cut off.
Runners potted in early July under these conditions should have made
sufficient roots in three to four weeks. The stolon connecting each
runner with the parent plant is then cut off and the pots removed to
a shady place, where they are kept moderately watered. When the
site is ready and conditions for planting appear favourable, the runners
may be given warm water treatment (see page 267), and are then planted
out without the ball of soil round the roots being broken. Distance of
planting varies, the maximum for strong-growing varieties being 3 feet
between the rows, and 18 inches between the plants in the row.

With potted runners it should be easy to complete planting by
September, but with ordinary runners, if planting cannot be carried out
by the end of October, it is usually wise to postpone planting until
March or early April of the following year, when the soil will again be
warming up. The runners will then have a chance to grow on con-
tinuously with little or no check.

In many seasons, however, planting conditions are far from ideal.
The main points are to get well-rooted runners from healthy plants,
and to transplant them with as little check as possible into soil conditions conducive to rapid root growth. From this latter point of view
potted runners are to be preferred, but *potted plants are no better than
any others unless they come from healthy, vigorous parents free from virus,
and unless they are planted in a situation which is isolated from strawberry
plants that are already diseased*. Under present-day conditions the wisest
plan is to dig up the whole strawberry bed every three years, burn the
plants, and start again with a supply of healthy runners holding a
government certificate. Here again, as in the case of mosaic-free
raspberries, advice should be sought from the local advisory officer.

Method of Planting.—Where the number of runners to be planted is
comparatively small, a trowel may be used. A hole is made large
enough for the roots to be well spread out, a fine covering of soil is then

thrown over the roots, and the hole filled up and firmly trodden down with the heel.

When planted, the crown of the runner should be just above the surface of the ground.

When planting strawberry runners on a commercial scale, a dibber is generally used, and the roots are put straight downwards into a vertical hole, care being taken to see that they are not turned upwards. If severe frosts occur during the winter, autumn-planted runners may be partially lifted. Such plants should be trodden well in during the following March, and any gaps where runners have died should be filled.

CULTIVATION

From March to mid-May the ground should be kept well hoed to keep down the weeds. In hoeing, great care should be taken to draw the soil towards rather than away from the plants, and not to go too deep with the hoe.

STRAWING

As soon as the fruit is well set and beginning to swell, clean wheat or oat straw is laid along the rows and fitted close in under the leaves of the plants in order to protect the berries from being splashed with mud when it rains. After the crop has been picked, all runners are cut off from the parent plants and the straw litter is either raked up and carried off or it may be burnt over. At the time of burning, there should be a light following wind blowing down the rows.

MANURING

Experiments have shown that potassium and phosphorus are both very important for strawberries, and that nitrogen must not be given *in excess*.

Once strawberry runners have been planted, it is impossible to dig in organic manures without injuring the roots. Hence, the ideal practice is for really short-littered dung or shoddy to be ploughed or dug well in to the soil some weeks before the runners are planted, or even for the previous crop. Horse manure from stables where peat moss litter is used is excellent for the purpose. Since nitrogenous manures alone tend to produce excessive leaf growth, potash and phosphate should be given every winter by pricking in sulphate of potash at the rate of 2 to 3 cwt. per acre (1 to 1½ oz. per square yard), and either steamed bone flour or superphosphates at the rate of 4 to 5 cwt. per acre (2 to 2½ oz. per square yard).

PROTECTION AGAINST BIRDS

Birds are very fond of ripe strawberries, and in gardens it is, therefore, necessary to provide protection in the form of the usual bird scarers or netting suspended over the plants. In the latter case, the netting should be supported well away from the plants, otherwise it is liable to damage the plants and fruit.

GATHERING

Strawberries should never be gathered while they are wet, or rotting will set in very quickly. For home use the berries are picked when fully ripe. For marketing as dessert fruit they are picked just before they are fully ripe, each berry being picked with a short stalk. A good method is for each picker to carry one punnet to hold either 1 or 2 lb. of extra-selected fruit, and one chip basket to hold either 3 or 4 lb. of selected fruit. As soon as the fruit is picked, the receptacles must be put in a shady place or the fruit may be over-ripe by the time it reaches the retailer. Ripe fruit for jam may be gathered and marketed in receptacles known as tubs and holding 56 lb. of fruit. These may be either returnable or non-returnable packages.

Canning factories often supply flat trays for strawberries. These are stacked in lorries and taken straight from the farm to the factory.

MARKETING

Extra-selected fruits may be marketed in non-returnable punnets or in small chips holding 1 or 2 lb., and the selected fruits for the main crop in 3- or 4-lb. chip baskets. These containers are lined either with strawberry leaves or with lining paper, or they may be bought ready-lined with greaseproof paper. A convenient way of transporting small punnets in bulk is to place them in flat trays specially designed for the purpose. Cellophane covers, provided they allow for ventilation, give an added attraction to the appearance of small punnets.

In certain strawberry districts the railway authorities provide speci-ally-fitted vans for transporting strawberries to the London markets, particulars of which are available at the local railway stations.

ALPINE STRAWBERRIES

These grow well on any chalky or light soils and respond to generous cultural and manurial treatment. Raised from seed sown in spring or autumn, they should be planted at least 1 foot apart in the row, in rows of 1 foot to 18 inches apart. Fresh plants should be raised from seed every other year. Varieties that do not send out runners are the most convenient for garden culture.

PERPETUAL-FRUITING STRAWBERRIES

These fruit from early summer into December in favourable situa-tions. Cultivation is the same as recommended for large fruited berries, except as regards the autumn crop of fruit which is produced on rooted runners from the main plant. This, of course, necessitates more room being allowed between main plants when making a bed, as the runners which spring from the centre plant must be pegged down around it. The main plants should be put in 2 to 2½ feet apart. The summer fruit is borne on the main plant and the runners must be pegged down and stopped as soon as a single plant has formed on each. Some growers destroy the centre or main plant before it summer fruits, to encourage the runners' development for autumn fruiting. The original bed should be renewed annually in autumn, planting selected runner plants as main plants for next year.

DISEASES OF THE STRAWBERRY

MILDEW (Sphærotheca Humuli)

This is a " powdery " mildew, attacking the leaves and sometimes the berries, to which it gives a whitish, mealy appearance. The presence of the disease can readily be recognized by the up-curled margins of the leaves, usually the younger ones. The effects of attack can be serious, particularly in dry seasons, but the disease can usually be controlled by dusting two or three times with " flowers of sulphur " at seven- to ten-day intervals up to the setting of the fruits. Fruits intended for canning should not be dusted with sulphur or they will not be acceptable to the canners. Where the disease is persistent and is likely to impair the vigour of the plants, dustings can be continued after the crop has been gathered. Maiden plantations and runner beds should also be protected by dusting in summer during likely periods of infection (dry weather after recent growth has been rapid). Spraying with a 2 per cent. lime-sulphur solution before blossom and a 1 per cent. afterwards is also an effective remedy, but it is not as convenient to use as the dusting method.

Burning-over the plantation in autumn tends to reduce the source of infection for the following year by destroying the fungus already present on the plants.

LEAF SPOT (Mycosphærella Fragariæ)

This disease has been known to cause occasional losses in this country, but it is not usually of serious economic importance. The result of attack by the fungus is the appearance on the leaf of circular spots, the centres of which ultimately turn grey, but remain surrounded by a purplish-red halo. The tufts of spores produced on the spots are whitish, and serve to spread the disease. The fungus passes the winter on the old leaves ; hence, burning-over the plantation would reduce the sources of infection in this case also.

LEAF SCORCH *(Marssonina Fragariæ)*

In its early stages this disease is similar to Leaf Spot in that small, purplish spots appear on the leaves. They are more irregular than those of Leaf Spot, and do not develop a pale centre. The older leaves are usually the worst attacked, and, when severe, the disease can kill them. The fungus produces spores on the spots in shiny, black blisters, which burst to free the spores. The disease is not often severe, but the variety *Sir Joseph Paxton* is very susceptible. Control as for Leaf Spot.

GREY MOULD *(Botrytis cinerea)*

This mould can be severe in persistent wet weather. The fruits, usually when nearly ripe, develop a soft, squashy rot, around the margin of which grows a copious grey fungal weft bearing spores. Under a hand-lens, the spores can be seen clustered together on stalks, and they resemble bunches of grapes. Rain-splashes from the soil are likely carriers of infection, which can thus be prevented to some extent by adequate strawing of the beds. Overcrowding of plants should be avoided, and care should be taken that they have sufficient aeration.

ROOT ROT *(Non-parasitic)*

When strawberries are planted in badly-drained, wet soils, many of the roots often rot and turn black through lack of aeration. This weakening of the root-system naturally debilitates the plants, which may then fall victims to certain fungi that are weakly parasitic on the roots. Such fungi would not prove fatal to a healthy strawberry plant, but under unsuitable growth-conditions they are likely to accelerate the death of the root-rotted plants. The remedy lies in improving the drainage and aeration of the soil.

As there are certain parasitic fungal diseases, notably Red Core *(Phytophthora)* and Verticillium Wilt that can have superficially similar effects to those caused by waterlogging, sickly plants should be shown to an expert for examination wherever possible.

VIRUS DISEASES

Attention has already been drawn (page 261) to the serious nature of virus diseases, for which, as they are carried in the sap, there is no cure except the drastic one of roguing, i.e., the removal and destruction of all affected plants as soon as they are seen. Failure to do this exposes neighbouring healthy plants to risk of infection.

YELLOW-EDGE

The outstanding cause of the failure of strawberry plantations, especially those of the variety *Royal Sovereign* in the eastern parts of the country, is this virus disease, which is characterized by a dwarfed, flattened, sickly appearance in the plant, the young leaves of which are small, often cupped upwards, and have short stalks. At certain periods of the growing season these leaves have bright yellow edges, from which the common name of the disease is derived. The disease is carried from affected to healthy plants by aphides, which, when they puncture the leaf to suck the sap, transmit the virus. This gets into the sap of the plant and thus affects all the runners from it.

Control.—All affected plants and their runners must be promptly taken up and burnt as soon as the disease is seen. As a precaution, near neighbouring plants and their runners also should be destroyed. New plantings should be made only from certified virus-free stock, and should be well isolated from existing sources of infection. It must be borne in mind that the varieties *Huxley* and *Oberschlesien* are " tolerant " of the disease, i.e., they can be infected without showing any symptoms, and infected *Tardive de Leopold* often does not show them, so that these varieties are a special source of danger for *Royal Sovereign*.

CRINKLE

This is another serious virus disease, and it is specially prevalent in western parts of the country. It can be recognized by the presence of small, pale areas on the leaves, which are often wrinkled and puckered. The yellow areas become reddish or purple and eventually brown, and may at first glance resemble damage by capsids. Plants may be mildly infected, when they suffer little ill effect ; or severely infected, when degeneration is rapid.

Control.—The methods applicable to Yellow-Edge should be practised also for Crinkle. *Royal Sovereign* is very susceptible.

DISEASES : DIAGNOSIS TABLE
THE STRAWBERRY

DAMAGE	PROBABLE CAUSE
Foliage	
Up-curled margins of leaves with powdery mildew	Mildew
Circular spots, centres turn grey and are surrounded by purplish-red halo	Leaf Spot
Irregular purplish spots scattered over leaves	Leaf Scorch
Dwarfed and flattened appearance of entire plant ; small, curled, bright yellow-edged leaves on short stalks	Yellow Edge
Yellowing or reddening of leaves in small localized areas, crinkling and puckering	Crinkle
Fruit	
Whitish, mealy appearance	Mildew
Soft, squashy rot ; grey fungus on stalks and berries	Grey Mould

Note.—Once the trouble has been diagnosed, the reader should refer to the paragraph dealing with the particular disease or pest, and also the Guide to Spraying, page 270.

INSECT PESTS OF THE STRAWBERRY

Strawberries suffer from a great many pests, any of which can be very serious and some of which can easily be kept in check.

STRAWBERRY APHIS (*Capitophorus fragariæ*)

This pest frequently causes serious malformation of the leaves and stunting of the plants, resulting in loss of crop and, very often, the loss of valuable plants. The insects are pale green, rather long-legged, and attain a length of about $\frac{1}{12}$ inch. They feed on the leaves and leaf stalks, where they multiply at a great rate, and suck the sap. From time to time winged forms appear and these spread the infestation. Not only is the Strawberry Aphis important by reason of the direct damage it does, but it is also a vector (carrier) of the dreaded virus diseases.

Control.—One can make sure of starting a plantation free of aphis either by warm water treatment of the runners (see below), or by dipping these in a strong solution of nicotine and soap. A look-out should be kept for the appearance of aphis and the plants should then be sprayed as often as is necessary with nicotine and soap or dusted frequently with nicotine dust. In some districts plantations can be fumigated with nicotine by special machinery.

TARSONEMUS MITE (*Tarsonemus pallidus*)

This creature is minute, intermediate in size between its near relatives the Gall Mite of the black currant and the fruit tree Red Spider, and lives between the folds of the very youngest leaves. It is of a pallid, almost colourless hue, and lays large numbers of small, round eggs. The damage it does much resembles that caused by Aphis. Indeed, Aphis damage, Tarsonemus damage, and the symptoms of the virus disease " Yellow Edge " are so much alike that even the expert often finds it difficult to differentiate between them. The mite spreads about chiefly by crawling along the stolons from plant to plant. The use of infested runners has in the past been the means of transporting it from district to district.

Control.—Little can be done to check this pest when once it has become established, and badly-infested plants are best ploughed in. All runners for planting should be submerged for twenty minutes in warm water, maintained at a temperature of 110° F. to kill the mites and their eggs. Suitable apparatus for carrying out this treatment can readily be obtained or devised and one arrangement is shown in our diagram on page 268.

The plants are stacked in a wire-mesh or wicker basket (or even in a loosely-woven sack), and immersed in a tank of water heated by steam from a boiler or in any other convenient manner. The temperature of the water, naturally, drops somewhat when the plants are plunged into it, and it is, therefore, important that the prescribed temperature be reached as soon as possible and maintained for the full length of time. After treatment the plants are best cooled off with cold water.

EELWORM *(Aphelenchoides fragariæ)*

At one time almost all the little-understood troubles to which the strawberry plant is prone were laid at the door of the eelworm. Latterly it has received less attention. The whitish worms, which measure some three hundredths of an inch in length, live and breed in the plants, and

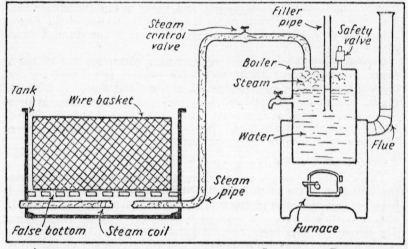

APPARATUS FOR WARM WATER TREATMENT OF STRAWBERRY RUNNERS.

if sufficiently numerous, cause the stems to swell and the flowers to develop into an abortive cauliflower-like mass.

Control.—No effective remedy can be suggested. " Cauliflower " plants should be destroyed, as they can never be expected to recover. Warm water treatment can be relied on to destroy eelworm present in runners intended for planting.

GROUND BEETLES *(Carabidæ)*

These ground beetles are normally beneficial and feed on slugs, caterpillars and the like, but a few species have developed a taste for strawberries and eat the skin of the green and ripening berries. They are black, shiny insects, half an inch or more in length, long in the leg, and very active.

Control.—No satisfactory means of preventing these attacks has been devised. The beetles can readily be trapped in jam jars let into the soil and baited with meat, but such a procedure can scarcely be adopted on a large scale. They can be killed with D.D.T. dust and it might help to spread this amongst the straw.

BLOSSOM WEEVIL *(Anthonomus rubi)*

This insect is closely related to the Apple Blossom Weevil, which it much resembles. It is rather smaller, however, and wholly black in colour. It lays its eggs in unopened flower-buds, the stems of which it then punctures at the base, causing them to wilt and, ultimately, to shrivel. The eggs hatch and the resulting grubs feed in the damaged buds. Later a new generation of weevils emerges and does further damage to leaves and petioles.

Control.—A 5 per cent. D.D.T. dust should be applied as soon as the green flower buds can be detected and again 7 to 14 days later.

STRAWBERRY RHYNCHITES *(Rhynchites germanicus)*

This is a blue-green, squarish weevil that behaves in a similar fashion to the Blossom Weevil but damages whole trusses instead of single buds.

Control.—D.D.T. dust should be applied as soon as the first blossom truss is visible at the rate of about 28 lb. per acre. Where both weevils occur a second dusting 10 to 14 days later should give good results.

OTHER PESTS

Among other pests which sometimes occur may be mentioned a weevil (*Exomias araneiformis*), which has been found to feed on the green berries, and the caterpillars of a moth (the Strawberry Tortrix, *Peronea comariana*). The latter feed chiefly on the leaves and in some districts do a great deal of damage. They are normally kept in check by parasitic insects. Red Spider (*Tetranychus telarius*) also occurs, but is kept in check by the sulphur dusting carried out for mildew. Several root-feeding insects such as Wireworms, Chafer Beetle grubs and Leather-jackets, also occur.

PESTS : DIAGNOSIS TABLE

THE STRAWBERRY

DAMAGE	PROBABLE CAUSE
Plants	
Plants wilt, fail to develop properly, or die Evidence of insect damage to roots	Wireworm, Chafer Beetle Grubs, or Leather Jackets
Shoots and Foliage (Including Blossom)	
Leaves and leaf-stalks malformed, and infested with pale-green rather long-legged aphis	Strawberry Aphis
Leaves and leaf-stalks malformed, and infested by tiny, almost colourless mite	Tarsonemus Mite
Stems of flower-buds wilt and shrivel ; leaves eaten	Strawberry Blossom Weevil
Leaves eaten by caterpillars	Strawberry Tortrix
Blossom develops into abortive cauliflower-like mass	Eelworm

THE STRAWBERRY: PESTS (*continued*)

Fruit DAMAGE	PROBABLE CAUSE
Skin of green and ripening berries eaten; fruit withers and goes mouldy	Ground Beetle

STRAWBERRY. GUIDE TO SPRAYING

Time of Application	Treatment	To Control
Before planting	Warm water treatment (20 minutes at 110° F.)	Tarsonemid Mite, Aphis Eelworm and Red Spider
Early May (before flowering and as necessary after fruit picked)	Sulphur dust	Mildew and Red Spider
August–September	Roguing	" Yellow-edge " and " Crinkle " viruses

SOME STRAWBERRY VARIETIES

Variety	Colour	Season	Qualities
Cambridge Early	Dark red	Early	Fairly large, conical, sub-acid. Moderate vigour
Climax	Bright Red	Late	Large, bluntly conical, sub-acid. Vigorous. Resistant to red core
Deutsch Evern	Bright Red	Early	Medium-fair quality. Good cropper. Small
Huxley (Brenda Gautrey)	Reddish	Mid-season	Very strong grower. Good cropper. Fruit large but coarse and of leathery texture
King George V	(*See* Royal Sovereign)		
Little Scarlet	Light Red	Early	Small. Good flavour. Fine for jam-making. Very old variety, difficult to obtain
Oberschlesien	Varies from Pink to Scarlet	Mid-season	Large. Heavy cropper. Needs a pollinator
Perle de Prague	Bright Red	Mid-season	Medium to large, bluntly conical. Moderate vigour
President	Scarlet	Mid-season	Large
Royal Sovereign	Bright Scarlet	Early	Large. Good flavour. Prolific on most soils, especially light or medium. Best market sort if free from virus
Sir Joseph Paxton	Dark Red	Mid-season to Late	Large. Good flavour. Hardy and prolific on heavy soil. Market fruit
Stirling Castle	Red	Mid-season	Small but good flavour. Used to be widely grown for jam-making and market. Susceptible to virus diseases
Tardive de Leopold	Dark Red	Late	Large. Fine flavour. Strong grower. Needs a pollinator
Waterloo	Very Dark Crimson	Late	Large and good flavour
Western Queen	Crimson	Mid-season	A promising new variety

ALPINE STRAWBERRIES

Variety	Colour	Season	Qualities
Alpine Improved	Deep Red	Summer and Autumn	Small. Good flavour. Hardy and prolific
Baron Solemacher	Red	Late	Very large. Makes no runners
Belle de Meaux	Red	Late	Large and long fruits. Good flavour and cropper. Fruits until October—forms runners
Bush White (de Gaillon Blanc)	White	Summer and Autumn	Small to medium in size. Good flavour. Makes no runners. Useful for borders
Des Quatre Saisons (La Brillante)	Bright Red	Summer and Autumn	A vigorous grower
Gaillon Rouge Amélioré	Pale Red	July-October	Large fruits. Crops well. Makes no runners. Plant in borders. Excellent flavour.
Cresta	Bright Red	June–November	Large. Good flavour. Vigorous—many runners

PERPETUAL FRUITING STRAWBERRIES

Variety	Colour	Season	Qualities
St. Antoine de Padoue	Bright Red	Autumn	Large. Prolific
St. Fiacre	Deep Red	Summer and Autumn	Medium. Good flavour. Hardy and prolific
St. Joseph	Light Red	Summer and Autumn	Medium. Good flavour and prolific

THE WALNUT *(Juglans regia)*

SOIL AND SITUATION

The walnut grows well in a variety of soils of fair depth, provided drainage is adequate. A moderate amount of lime or chalk is beneficial. Freedom from spring frosts is of the utmost importance, since the walnut " leafs out " or starts into growth moderately early and the tender young growth is extremely susceptible to frost.

PROPAGATION

Walnuts should always be grafted on *Juglans regia* or *Juglans nigra*, but as grafting must be done in this case under glass it is usually more profitable for the fruit grower to obtain trees ready worked from the nursery.

PLANTING

Walnut trees grown as standards should be planted in autumn from 40 to 50 feet apart. A good hole should be dug to take the tree without cramping the root-system. The tap root should be cut back to within about a foot of the base and the rest of the main roots are trimmed with a long, sloping cut on the under side. Short lateral roots are left full length and spread out evenly. The earth is rammed well home to promote rapid growth of new roots.

CULTIVATION

Walnut trees do not transplant as easily as most fruit trees, and need very careful after-treatment for the first few years. The ground within a radius of 3 or 4 feet from the stem should be kept hoed in spring and summer and dug over in the winter yearly until the tree has become well-established. If it is found that the tender young shoots are killed by frost every spring when they have made a few inches growth, it would be wise to move the tree to higher ground. Special attention should be paid to careful tying, staking, and guarding against cattle and vermin.

A top dressing of well-rotted dung should be applied every spring for the first few years.

There are three important and little-known facts about the pollination of the walnut. First, nutlets and catkins are normally borne on the same tree, the pollen from the catkins being carried by the wind to cross-pollinate the nutlets. Unless the nutlets are thus pollinated, they will drop off when the size of a pea. Secondly, on young trees nutlets are often produced for some years before catkins appear. Thirdly, although nutlets and catkins may be present on the same tree, the nutlets may not be in a receptive condition when the pollen is ripe on the catkins.

Hence it follows that single isolated trees of walnuts may remain unfruitful unless and until some other tree bearing catkins is planted near them. Some varieties, such as Meylanaise and Charberte, are useful pollinators because they carry catkins from an early age.

PRUNING

As little pruning as possible should be done to a walnut tree, apart from the cutting out of dead or crossing branches. Such pruning should be done in late spring or in August, all pruning wounds being pared over and covered with a good white-lead paint.

GATHERING AND STORING

Walnuts should be harvested from the ground as soon as they fall. After removing the green outer husk, the crevices of the shells must be freed from every trace of fibre as it is here that moulds begin to grow. The fibre can be easily removed by scrubbing the nuts with a soft nailbrush in water. The nuts should be removed from the water after a few moments, and spread out in single layers to dry at room temperature. Clean nuts which are well sealed may be bleached by dipping in a bleaching solution for about 3 minutes. The walnuts may then be stored in earthenware crocks filled with alternate layers of a storage medium—equal quantities of common salt and slightly damp coco-nut fibre.

The crocks should be kept in a cellar as recommended for cobs and filberts.

VARIETIES

The following French varieties of the *Juglans regia* bear large nuts of excellent quality, and are at present under trial in this country : Franquette, Mayette, Meylanaise and Parisienne. The following English varieties are of first-rate quality : Northdown Clawnut, Stutton Seedling, Champion of Ixworth, Excelsior of Taynton and Lady Irene. The English varieties, Leeds Castle, Secrett, and Patching, grow in clusters and are specially valuable for pickling green early in July. All the varieties named above come into leaf comparatively late in the spring and should escape all but the most exceptionally late frosts.

DISEASES OF THE WALNUT

BACTERIAL BLIGHT *(Pseudomonas Juglandis)*

The earliest symptoms of this disease are small black spots on the leaves, from which the bacteria spread to all the current year's growth. Later symptoms are lesions or long black markings on the shoots and leaf-stalks, and black spots on the nutlets. The latter may drop if badly affected. Shoots showing the lesions should be cut out in winter, and, where small trees are affected, they should be sprayed the following spring, as soon as the leaves open, with Bordeaux Mixture (6 lb. copper sulphate, 9 lb. hydrated lime to 100 gallons of water) and later as necessary.

WALNUT LEAF BLOTCH *(Gnomonia leptostyla)*

This disease is caused by a fungus that produces brown, roughly circular patches on the leaves.

Similar patches are found on the green husk which surrounds the young nut. The best way to control this disease is to collect and burn the leaves from infected trees as soon as they fall in autumn, thus destroying the fungus, and preventing reinfection of the new leaves in spring.

DISEASES : DIAGNOSIS TABLE

THE WALNUT

(It is chiefly young trees in the nursery that are attacked.)

DAMAGE	PROBABLE CAUSE
Shoots and Foliage	
Small black spots ; later long black markings on shoots and leaf stalks	Bacterial Blight
Circular brown patches on leaves	Walnut Leaf Blotch

INSECT PESTS OF THE WALNUT

Walnuts suffer little from insect attack, the few insects that feed on them seldom occurring in sufficient numbers to matter.   In addition to various species of greenfly, there occasionally occur Codling Moth (see Apple, page 125), a microscopic mite, *Eriophyes tristriatus* var. *erinea*, which causes small swellings on the leaves, and the Common Green Capsid (see Black Currant, page 179).

PESTS : DIAGNOSIS TABLE

THE WALNUT

(It is chiefly young trees in the nursery that are attacked.)

DAMAGE	PROBABLE CAUSE
Shoots and Foliage	
Shoots and young leaves stunted and infested with aphides	Greenfly
Small swellings on leaves	*Eriophyes tristriatus*
Leaves torn and distorted, shoots stunted and may be killed	Common Green Capsid Bug
Fruit	
Maggoty nuts	Codling Moth

Note.—Once the trouble has been diagnosed, the reader should refer to the paragraph dealing with the particular disease or pest.

INDEX

	PAGE
American Blight	122
Aphides. See Greenfly.	
Apple	113
Aspect	113
Cross-pollination	147
Diseases of	127
Apple Mildew	131
Armillaria Root Rot. . .	132
Bitter Pit	136
Blossom Wilt and Spur	
Canker	130
Brown Rot of Fruit . . .	131
Brown Rots	130
Canker	129
Chlorosis	135
Crown Gall	133
The Death	133
Diagnosis Table	138
Glassiness	137
Leaf Scorch	135
Lenticel Spot	137
Scab	127
Silver Leaf	133
Sun Scald	137
Water-core	137
Waterlogging	133
Form of Tree	113
Fruit Garden	114
Gathering Fruit.	119
Grass Orchard	113
Grease Banding	121
Insect Pests of	120
Blossom Weevil	123
Capsid Bug	124
Diagnosis Table	138
Sawfly.	124
Sucker.	123
Manuring	118, 119
Marketing	92
Method of Bearing . . .	48
Nitrogen Deficiency . . .	118
Plantations	113
Planting	80
Planting : Square Plant . .	79
Planting : Triangular Plant .	79
Phosphorus for	118

	PAGE
Apple (*Ctd.*)	
Potassium Deficiency . . .	118
Propagation 27,	114
Pruning	115
Pruning, Light	117
Rootstocks for	114
Rootstocks, Vegetative Pro-	
pagation of	114
Soil and Situation	113
Spraying Guide	109
Square Plant	79
Storing	89
Thinning.	119
Triangular Plant	79
Varieties	139
Blossoming, Early and Late	147
Cooking	145
Cordon	150
Dessert	140
Dwarf Pyramid	150
Espalier	148
Flavoured, Best	150
Garden	148
Orchard	151
Ripening, Order of . . .	149
Scab Resistant	129
Triploid	147
Wall	148
Apricot	151
Bearing, method of. . . .	48
Diseases of	152
Brown Rot	151
Silver Leaf	152
Form of Tree	151
Gathering	152
Insect Pests of	152
Marketing	152
Planting	151
Planting Distances	151
Pollination	151
Propagation	151
Pruning	152
Soil and Situation	151
Thinning Fruit	152
Varieties	152
Ripening, Order of . . .	153

PAGE

Armillaria Root Rot 132
Aspect 14

Bacterial Blight 273
Bacterial Canker and Leaf
    Spot 162, 239
Bark and Trunk Borers . . . 152
Bark-ringing 45
Bearing, Methods of 48
Bedded Stocks. 28
Bees, Danger to 99
Big Bud 178
Birds, Protection from . . . 85
Bitter Pit 136
Blackberry 153
  Diseases and Pests . . . 155
    Cane Spot. 155
    Common Green Capsid Bug. 155
    Diagnosis Table . . . 155
    Dwarf 155
    Greenfly 155
    Spraying Guide . . . 109
  Manuring 154
  Method of Bearing . . . 48
  Planting Distances . . . 154
  Propagation 153
  Pruning 154
  Soil and Situation . . . 153
  Training 154
  Varieties 156
    Hybrid Berries . . . 156
Black Currant. See Currant, Black.
Blossom Wilt and Spur Canker . 130
Blossoming, Time of . . . 78
Blue Bug 122
Bordeaux Mixture 107
Boysenberry 156
Bramble Shoot Webber . . . 201
Brick Earth 21
Bridge Grafting 37
Brown Rot of Apples . . . 131
Brown Rots . . . 130, 163, 240
Budding 29
  Choosing the Buds . . . 30
  Time for 30
Bush Fruit 157
Bush, Open-Centre Form . . 50

Cane Blight 256
Cane Spot 202, 255
Canker 129
Case Bearers 126
Caterpillars 172, 192
Cattle as Grazers 17

PAGE

Chafer Beetle Grubs 126
Chalk 20
Cherry 157
  Diseases 162
    Bacterial Canker and Leaf
      Spots 162
    Brown Rot and Blossom Wilt 163
    Cherry Leaf Curl . . . 164
    Diagnosis Table . . . 164
    Leaf Scorch 162
    Silver Leaf 164
  Gathering 160
  Insect Pests 160
    Black Fly. 160
    Fruit Fly 161
    Fruit Moth 161
  Manuring 158
  Marketing 160
  Method of Bearing . . . 48
  Packing for Exhibition . . 95
  Planting 158
  Pollination 167
  Pruning Sour Cherries . . 159
  Pruning Sweet Cherries . . 159
  Rootstocks for Cherries . . 157
  Soil and Situation . . . 157
  Spraying Guide 110
  Varieties 164
    Cooking 167
    Dessert 164
    Fan-trained Trees . . . 158
    Flowering Early . . . 167
      ,,   Mid-season . . 168
      ,,   Late . . . 168
    For Growing in Pots . . 169
    Leading Sorts, Twelve . . 169
    Pollinator 167
    Ripening, Order of . . . 168
Chlorosis 135
  ,,   Lime-induced . . . 20
Clay 19
Clay-coloured Weevil . . . 126
Clearwing Moth 126
Cluster Cup Rust 195
Cobnut 169
  Aspect 169
  Cultivation 170
  Gathering and Storing . . 171
  Insect Pests of 172
    Spraying Guide . . . 109
  Manuring 171
  Marketing 171
  Method of Bearing . . . 48
  Planting 170

PAGE

Cobnut (*Ctd.*)
Planting Distances 170
Propagation 169
Pruning 170
Storing 171
Varieties 171
Codling Moth 125
" Colloidal " Copper 107
" Colloidal " Sulphur 107
Contact Insecticides 98
Copper Lime Dust 108
Coral Spot 182
Cordon Trees 55
Double Vertical 56
Grid Iron 57
Shaping and Pruning . . . 57
Single 55
Triple Vertical 57
Cover Washes 98
Cross-pollination 147
Crown Gall 133
Crown Grafting 33
Currants 173
Method of Bearing 48
Planting Distances 174
Black 175
Diseases of 182
Coral Spot 182
Diagnosis Table . . . 183
Leaf Spot 182
Reversion 183
Rust 182
Gathering 177
Insect Pests 178
Apple Capsid Bug . . 180
Big Bud 178
Black Currant Gall Mite . 178
Black Currant Shoot Moth 180
Caterpillars 179
Common Green Capsid . 179
Currant Aphis 178
Currant Clearwing Moth . 180
Currant Leaf Midge . . 181
Currant Root Aphis . . 179
Diagnosis Table . . . 181
Eelworm 181
Leaf-curling Aphis . . 179
Magpie Moth . . . 180
Spraying Guide . . . 110
Manuring 177
Marketing 177
Method of Bearing . . . 48
Propagation 176
Pruning 176

PAGE

Currants : Black (*Ctd.*)
Shaping 176
Soil and Situation . . . 175
Suitable Forms 175
Varieties 184
Red and White 173
Diseases 182
Coral Spot 182
Diagnosis Table . . . 183
Leaf Spot 182
Rust 182
Gathering 175
Insect Pests 178
Apple Capsid Bug . . 180
Common Green Capsid Bug 179
Currant Aphis 178
Diagnosis Table . . . 181
Leaf-curl Currant Aphis . 179
Spraying Guide . . . 110
Manuring 175
Marketing 175
Propagation 173
Pruning 174
Shaping the Bush Form . 174
Soil and Situation . . . 173
Suitable Forms 173
Varieties 184
Cuttings 27

Damson 185
Diseases of ⎫
Forms of Tree ⎪
Insect Pests ⎪
Manuring ⎪
Marketing ⎪
Method of Bearing ⎬ See Plum
Planting ⎪
Propagation ⎪
Pruning ⎪
Soil and Situation ⎪
Spraying Guide ⎭
Varieties 185
D.D.T. Preparations 106
" Death," the 133
Dehorning 41
Delayed Open-Centre Tree . 51, 63
Form of Tree 63
Pruning 70
Branches 74
Centre Stem 69
Feathered Maidens . . 65, 66
For Branch Formation . . 71
Maiden Laterals . . . 72, 75
Maiden Trees 64

PAGE

Delayed Open-Centre Tree:
Pruning (*Ctd.*)
    Mature Trees 74
    Non-feathered Maidens . . 64
    Older Laterals . . . 73, 76
    Side Shoots 66
    Spur Systems. 76
    Two-year-old Trees . . . 66
    Young Trees 69
Derris Preparations . . . 106
" Die-back " 195
Disbudding 206
Diseases and Pests . . . 97
D.N.C. Washes 105
Dusting. 99
Dusting Machines . . . 103
    Geared-drive 104
    Knapsacks 103
    Small Hand-operated . . 103
Dwarf Pyramid 53

Eelworms 181, 268
Espalier 58
Espalier, Shaping and Pruning . 59
Exhibiting 95

Fan-shaped Trees 61
Fan Shaping and Pruning . . 62
Fig 186
    Bush 186
    Disbudding 187
    Diseases 188
        Canker 188
        Diagnosis Table . . . 189
        Die-back 188
        Fruit Rot 188
    Fan 186
    Forms of Trees 186
    Frost, Protection from . . 187
    Gathering and Packing . . 187
    Insect Pests 188
    Method of Bearing . . . 48
    Pinching 187
    Planting 186
    Propagation 186
    Pruning, Disbudding, Pinching 187
    Root Pruning 187
    Soil and Situation . . . 186
    Varieties 188
Filbert. See Cobnut.
Forms of Fruit Trees . . . 50
Frost, Protection from . . 85, 210
Fruit Culture, Types of . . 15
Fruit Gas Storage 90

PAGE

Fruit Garden 16
Fruit Gathering 87
Fruit, Maturity of. . . . 87
Fruit, Method of Bearing . . 48
Fruit Rhynchites 126
Fruit Storing 88
Fruit Thinning 49
Fruit Trees, Artificial . . . 55
Fruit Trees, Bush Open-Centre . 50
Fruit Trees, Cordon, Single . . 55
Fruit Trees, Cordon, Double
    Vertical 56
Fruit Trees, Cordon, Triple
    Vertical 57
Fruit Trees, Delayed Open-
    Centre 51, 63
Fruit Trees, Dwarf Pyramid . 53
Fruit Trees, Espalier 58
Fruit Trees, Fan 61
Fruit Trees, Forms of . . . 50
Fruit Trees, Half-standard . . 52
Fruit Trees, Standard . . . 52
Fruit Trees, Three-quarter
    Standard 52

Gall Mite 172
Gas Storage 90
Gathering Fruit 87
Gathering, Appliances for . . 87
    ,,   for Market . . . 88
Glassiness 137
Goat Moth 126
Gooseberry 189
    Bearing, Method of. . . . 48
    Diseases of 194
        American Gooseberry Mildew 194
        Cluster-cup Rust . . . 195
        Diagnosis Table . . . 196
        Die-back 195
        Leaf Spot 196
    Gathering the Fruit . . . 191
    Insect Pests 192
        Caterpillars 192
        Clearwing Moth . . . 194
        Common Green Capsid . . 193
        Diagnosis Table . . . 194
        Gooseberry Aphis . . . 193
        Magpie Moth 193
        Red Spider 193
        Sawfly 192
        Spraying Guide . . . 110
    Manuring 191
    Marketing 192
    Planting Distances 189

PAGE

Gooseberry (*Ctd.*)
Propagation 189
Pruning 190
Shaping, Artificial Forms . . 190
Soil and Situation 189
Suitable Forms 189
Varieties 196
Green 196
Large Fruits 198
Red 197
White 197
Yellow 197
Grading 91
Grading for Uniformity of Colour 92
Grafting, Forms of 32
Bridge 37
Crown or Rind 33
Inarching 36
Oblique Cleft 34
Rind 33
Side 35
Stub 35
Tongue 32
Top 34
Whip or Tongue 32
Grass Orchard 113
Gravel 21
Grazing 17
Grease Banding 121
Green Apple Aphis 122
Greenfly 122
Greengage 244
Grey Mould 265
Ground Beetles 268
Ground Sulphur Dusts . . . 108

Hail, Protection from . . . 211
Half-standard Trees 52
Hazel Nut. See Cobnut.
High nitrogen conditions . . 23
Hoeing 84
Hop Damson Aphis 237
Horses as grazers 17
Hybridization 26

Inarching 36
Insect Pests 97
Mechanical Control . . . 97
Insecticides 98

Japanese Wine Berry 156

King's Acre Berry 156
Kitchen Garden 15

PAGE

Labelling (Exhibition) . . . 96
Lackey Moth 126
Laxtonberry 156
Layering 28
Lead Arsenate 106
Leaf-curling Aphis . . . 179, 236
Leaf-eating Weevils 239
Leaf-roller Moth 152
Leaf Scorch . . . 135, 162, 265
Leaf Spot 182, 264
Lenticel Spot 137
Lime-induced Chlorosis . . . 20
Lime-sulphur 78, 106
Loganberry 198
Aspect 198
Bearing, Method of . . . 48
Diseases of 202
Cane Spot 202
Diagnosis Table 203
Waterlogging 203
Gathering 200
Insect Pests 201
Bramble Shoot Webber . . 201
Diagnosis Table 202
Greenfly 201
Raspberry and Loganberry
Beetle 201
Raspberry Moth 202
Spraying Guide 111
Manuring 200
Marketing 200
Planting Distances 199
Planting and Training . . . 199
Propagation 198
Pruning 200
Soil and Situation 198
Lorette Pruning 44, 218
Lowberry 156

Magnesium Deficiency . . . 24
Magpie Moth 152, 180
Malling Stocks.   See Rootstocks.
Manurial Requirements . . 77, 119
Manuring 23
Classes of Fruit in Relation to 23
Climate in Relation to . . 24
Cultivation in Relation to . 25
Disease Control in Relation to 25
Pruning in Relation to . . 24
Rootstocks in Relation to . 25
Soil in Relation to . . . 24
March Moth 121
Market, Gathering for . . . 88
Marketing Fruit 91

PAGE

Marketing Packages 92
    Sieves and half-sieves . . . 95
    Standard half-boxes . . . 94
    Standard No. 1 trays . . . 94
Maturity 87
Medlar 203
    Aspect 203
    Diseases and Pests 204
    Forms 203
    Gathering and Storing . . 203
    Method of Bearing . . . 48
    Planting 203
    Planting Distances 203
    Propagation 203
    Pruning 203
    Soil and Situation 203
    Varieties 204
Mildew 264
Mosaic 254
Mulberry 204
    Aspect 204
    Diseases and Pests 205
        Canker 205
    Gathering 205
    Method of Bearing . . . 204
    Planting 204
    Planting Distances 204
    Propagation 204
    Pruning 204
    Soil and Situation 204
    Varieties 205
Mulching 84

Nectarine 211
    Spraying Guide 111
    Varieties 212, 213
Nicotine 106
Nitrogen Deficiency 118
Nitrogenous Manures . . . 23
Nut Weevil 172

Oblique Cleft Grafting . . . 34
Orchard 16
Orchard Hygiene 97

Packing Points (Exhibition) . 92
Peach and Nectarine (Outdoors) 205
    Bearing, Method of . . . 48
    Disbudding 206
    Diseases 213
        Brown Rots 214
        Diagnosis Table . . . 214
        Leaf Curl 213
        Silver Leaf 214

PAGE

Peach and Nectarine (Outdoors)
    (*Ctd.*)
    Forms of Tree 206
    Frost, Protection from . . . 210
    Fruit Thinning 211
    Gathering 211
    Hail, Protection from . . . 211
    Insect Pests 214
        Diagnosis Table . . . 214
        Green Peach Aphis . . 214
        Leaf-curling Aphis . . 214
        Peach Scale 214
        Red Spider 214
        Spraying Guide 111
    Manuring 211
    Marketing 211
    Planting 206
    Planting Distances 206
    Propagation 205
    Pruning 206
    Root-pruning Wall Trees . . 210
    Soil and Situation 205
    Summer Pinching . . . 209
    Training, Subsequent . . . 209
    Tying in after Fruiting . . 209
    Varieties 212
    Watering 211
Pear 215
    Aspect 215
    Cross-pollination 220
    Diseases 224
        Armillaria 225
        Bitter Pit 225
        Brown Rot 225
        Canker 225
        Diagnosis Table . . . 226
        Pear Scab 224
        Waterlogging 226
    Forms of Tree 215
    Gathering and Storing . . 221
    Insect Pests 222
        Apple Blossom Weevil . . 222
        Caterpillars 222
        Codling Moth 222
        Common Green Capsid . . 222
        Diagnosis Table 224
        Leaf-curling Midge . . . 224
        Minor Pests 224
        Pear and Cherry Slugworm 222
        Pear Aphis 222
        Pear Leaf Blister Mite . . 223
        Pear Midge 223
        Social Pear Sawfly . . . 224
        Spraying Guide 111

all that science can do to ensure

FINER FRUIT

Pests and diseases are never far from our fruit. But science has now found so many answers to these would-be wreckers of orchard and soft-fruit crops that the problem for the professional grower and keen amateur has become one of selection. With so many products to choose from—which are the best?

Shell sprays incorporate the latest improvements for increased pest and disease control and greater ease of application. Their use will lead to heavier crops and richer rewards.

Spring and Summer Sprays

FOLIOL (Summer petroleum) . ROTANE (derris solution)

NICOTINE . LEAD ARSENATE . LIME SULPHUR

DISPERSIBLE SULPHUR . SHELLESTOL H (wetter and spreader)

SHELLESTONE (for preventing premature fruit drop)

DITRENE B 5% DDT DUST and DITRENE WP 35% DDT WETTABLE POWDER

SHELL TOMATO-SET (for increasing setting of tomatoes) . SHELL COPPER FUNGICIDE

Winter Washes

UNIVERSAL (DNC)

DYTROL (DNC) . TEEPOLEUM (winter petroleum)

TAR OILS

SHELL SERVICE is a source of practical advice. Separate Technical Information Sheets discussing the theory and application of Shell products are available free. The Technical Service offers ready collaboration on all problems of fruit pest and disease control.

SHELL CHEMICALS LIMITED
(DISTRIBUTORS)
112 Strand, London, W.C.2   Temple Bar 4455

PAGE

Pear (*Ctd.*)
Manuring 220
Marketing 222
Method of Bearing 48
Mulching and Watering . . 220
Planting 217
Planting Distances 217
Propagation 216
Protection from Birds and
Wasps 221
Pruning 43, 44, 218
Lorette Method 218
Rootstocks for Pears . . . 216
Soil and Situation 215
Storing 89, 221
Thinning 221
Varieties 226
Cooking 230
Cordons 218
Cross-pollinator 231
Dessert 226
Twelve Good Varieties . . 232
Hardy 233
Market 233
Pruning, Needing Hard . 219
,, Needing Light . 219
Ripening, Order of . . . 232
Self-fertile 231
Self-sterile 231
Wall 221
Pests. See Insect Pests.
Petroleum-oil Washes . . . 105
Phenomenal Berry . . . 157, 198
Phosphorus 119
Picking Utensils 87
Pith Moth 126
Planning 77
Plantation 16
Planting 79
Planting Board 81
Planting Distances 80
Planting, Marking out the Ground 79
Number per Acre 80
Quincunx Plant 79
Square Plant 79
Systems 79
Time to Plant 80
Triangular Plant 79
Plum 233
Cultivations 236
Diseases of 239
Bacterial Canker . . . 239
Bacterial Shoot-wilt . . 240
Brown Rots 240

PAGE

Plum : Diseases of (*Ctd.*)
Diagnosis Table 243
Rust 243
Silver Leaf 242
Form of Tree 234
Gathering and Storing . . 236
Insect Pests 236
Case Bearers 239
Caterpillars 238
Diagnosis Table 238
Hop Damson Aphis . . . 237
Leaf-curling Plum Aphis . 236
Leaf-eating Weevils . . . 239
Mealy Plum Aphis . . . 237
Red Plum Maggot . . . 238
Red Spider 237
Sawfly 237
Shot-hole Borers . . . 239
Spraying Guide 111
Manuring 235
Marketing 236
Method of Bearing 48
Planting 234
Planting Distances 234
Propagation 234
Pruning 234
Root Pruning 235
Soil and Situation 233
Thinning 235
Varieties 243
Cooking 245
Cross-pollination 247
Dessert 243
Exhibition 249
Fertility Guide 247
Flavoured, Best . . . 247
Market 249
Ripening, Order of . . . 248
Self-fertile 247
Self-sterile 247
Wall 249
Pollination 78
Potassium 118
Poultry as grazers 17
Propagation 26
Budding 29
Cuttings 27
Grafting 32
Hybridization 26
Layering 28
Seed 26
Stooling 28
Vegetative Rootstocks . . 27
Proprietary Wetting Preparations 108

	PAGE
Protection from Birds and Wasps	85
Protection from Frost and Wind	85
Protection from Hail	211
Protection of Stem	82
Pruning	39
Bark Ringing	45
Cuts	45
Dehorning	41
Delayed Open-Centre Tree	63–76
Excessive Wood Growth	45
First Stage	39
Fruit Thinning	49
Hard	39
Instruments	44
Light	40
Lorette	44
Multi Short, Summer	44
Multi, Summer	43
Root	47
Second Stage	40
Shaping	50
Single Long, Summer	43
Summer	42
Third Stage	40
Time To	47
Winter	39
Very Old Trees	42
See also Apples, Pears, etc.	
Pyramid	53
Quetsche	246
Quince	250
Diseases and Pests	251
Diagnosis Table	251
Leaf Blight	251
Mildew	252
Gathering and Storing	250
Marketing	250
Method of Bearing	48
Planting Distances	250
Planting	250
Propagation	250
Pruning	250
Soil and Situation	250
Varieties	251
Quincunx Plant	79
Rabbits and Hares, Protection from	82
Raspberry	252
Cultivation	253
Diseases	254
Cane Blight	256
Cane Spot	255

	PAGE
Raspberry : Diseases (Ctd.)	
Diagnosis Table	256
Mosaic	254
Spraying Guide	112
Verticillium Wilt	255
Forms of Culture	252
Gathering	254
Insect Pests	256
Cane Gall Fly	257
Cane Midge	257
Diagnosis Table	257
Minor Pests	257
Raspberry Beetle	256
Raspberry Moth	256
Spraying Guide	112
Manuring	253
Method of Bearing	48
Planting	252
Planting Distances	252
Propagation	252
Pruning	253
Soil and Situation	252
Supporting the Canes	253
Varieties	258
Autumn Fruiting	259
Jam and Bottling	259
Market	259
Summer Fruiting	258
Yellow Fruiting	259
Red Plum Maggot	126, 238
Red Spider	126, 214
Refrigerated Gas Storage	90
Reversion	183
Rind Grafting	33
Root Pruning	47
Root Rot	265
Rootstocks	27, 79
For Apples	114
For Apple Trees of Medium Size	114
Broadleaf	114
Doucin	114
Malling Number One	114
Malling Number Two	114
For Apple Trees, Very Large	115
Malling Number Twelve	115
Malling Number Sixteen	115
For Dwarf Apple Trees	114
Jaune de Metz	114
Malling Number Nine	114
For Cherries	157
For Pears	216
Vegetative Propagation of	27
Rosy Aphis	122

PAGE

Rust 182

Sand 21
Sawfly 192, 237
Scab 127
Scale Insects 126
Schwitchen (Quetsche, Zwetsche
    or German Prune) . . . 246
Seed, Propagation from . . . 26
Sheep as grazers 17
Shot-hole Beetles 126
Side Grafting 35
Sieve or Half-sieve 95
Silver Leaf 133, 242
Situation 14
Size grading of fruit 91
Social Pear Sawfly 224
Soft Fruits, Packing for Ex-
    hibition 95
Soft Soap 107
Soil Auger 19
Soils 13, 19, 22
    Cultivation 22
    Types 19
        Brick Earth 21
        Chalk 20
        Clay 19
        Gravel 21
        Sand 21
Spraying 98
    Guide 109
    Machinery 100
        Barrel Pumps 101
        Bucket Pumps 101
        Double-action Syringe . . 101
        Dusting 99
        Hand-operated 101
        Headland Pumps . . . 101
        Hints 104
        Hoses 103
        Knapsacks 101
        Lances and Guns . . . 103
        Nozzles 103
        Portable Power . . . 102
        Rotary Blowers . . . 103
        Stationary Engines . . 103
        Wheeled type 102
    Requirements 77
    Washes 105
    Winter Washes 98
Spray Materials 105
    Bordeaux Mixture . . . 107
    " Colloidal " Copper . . 107
    ,,   Sulphur . . . 107

PAGE

Spray Materials (Ctd.)
    Contact Insecticides . . . 98
    Copper-Lime Dust 108
    Cover Washes 98
    D.D.T. Preparations . . . 106
    Derris Preparations . . . 106
    D.N.C. Washes 105
    Ground Sulphur Dusts . . 108
    Lead Arsenate 106
    Lime Sulphur 106
    Nicotine 106
    Petroleum-oil Washes . . . 105
    Proprietary Wetting Prepara-
        tions 108
    Soft Soap 107
    Tar-oil washes 105
    Tar-petroleum Mixture . . 105
    Thiocyanate-oil Washes . . 105
    Winter Washes 98
Spray Materials less commonly
    used 108
    Benzene hexachloride . . . 108
    Dinitrocyclohexylphenol . . 108
    Mercury Preparations . . . 108
    New Insecticides 108
Spur Systems 76
Square Plant 79
Stakes 83
Standard Boxes 92
    Half-boxes 94
    No. 1 Trays 94
    Sieve or Half-sieve 95
Standard Trees 52
Stocks, Preparing 30
    Malling, etc.   See Rootstocks
Stoolbeds 28
Stooling 28
Store Room 88
Storing Fruit 88
Stratification 27
Strawberry 259
    Alpine 263
    Aspect 259
    Cultivation 262
    Diseases 264
        Crinkle 266
        Diagnosis Table 266
        Grey Mould 265
        Leaf Scorch 265
        Leaf Spot 264
        Mildew 264
        Root Rot 265
        Virus Diseases 265
        Yellow-edge 265

PAGE

Strawberry (*Ctd.*)
Gathering 263
Insect Pests 267
  Blossom Weevil . . . 269
  Diagnosis Table . . . 269
  Eelworm 268
  Other Pests 269
  Red Spider 269
  Ground Beetles . . . 268
  Spraying Guide . . . 270
  Strawberry Aphis . . 267
  Strawberry Rhynchites . 269
  Tarsonemus Mite. . . 267
Manuring 262
Marketing 263
Number per Acre . . . 80
Perpetual Fruiting . . . 263
Planting 260
Propagation 260
Protection from Birds . . 262
Soil and Situation . . . 259
Strawing 262
Varieties 270
  Alpine 263, 271
  Perpetual Fruiting . 263, 271
Warm Water Treatment . 267
Stub Grafting 35
Sulphur. 108
Sun Scald 137
Supports 55

Tar-oil Washes . . . 77, 105
Tar-petroleum Mixtures . . 105
Tarsonemus Mite 267
Thinning Fruit 48
Thiocyanate-oil Washes . . 105
Three-quarter Standard . . 52
Time of Blossoming . . . 78
Time to Gather 87
  Plant 80
  Prune 47
Top Grafting 34
Tortrix Moths 121
Tongue Grafting 32
Transplanting 82
Triangular Plant 79
Twig Cutter 126
Tying to Stake 84

Vegetative Propagation . . 27
Verticillium Wilt 255

PAGE

Virus Diseases 265

Walled Garden 15
Walnut 271
Cultivation 272
Diseases 273
  Bacterial Blight . . . 273
  Diagnosis Table . . . 274
  Walnut Leaf Blotch . . 273
Gathering and Storing . . 272
Insect Pests 274
  Diagnosis Table . . . 274
Method of Bearing . . . 48
Planting 272
Propagation 271
Pruning 272
Soil and Situation . . . 271
Storing 272
Varieties. 273
Warm Water Treatment of
  Strawberry Runners . . 267
Washes 105
  Bordeaux Mixture . . . 107
  " Colloidal " Copper . . 107
  ,, Sulphur . . . 107
  D.D.T. Preparations . . . 106
  Derris 106
  D.N.C. Washes 105
  Lead Arsenate 106
  Lime Sulphur 106
  Nicotine 106
  Petroleum-oil 105
  Proprietary Wetting Prepara-
    tions 108
  Soft Soap 107
  Tar-oil 105
  Tar-petroleum Mixtures . . 105
Wasps, Protection from . . 85
Water-core 137
Waterlogging 133
Whip or Tongue Grafting . 32
Wind, Protection from . . 85
Wineberry. See Japanese Wine-
  berry 156
Winter Moths 121
Winter Pruning 39
Winter Washes 98
Wood Leopard Moth . . . 126
Woolly Aphis 122

Yellow-edge 265
Youngberry 157

FRUIT IN PERFECTION

To grow good crops of any fruit free from blemishes and loss caused by Insect and Fungus attacks, special control measures are essential.

Our Research Department directs all its energies to the elucidation of Pest Control problems and its work is to invent measures to assist growers to combat all avoidable blemish and loss of crop.

Our work, always up-to-date, is at the service of all growers.

Ask us for information and leaflets

Continuous work on Pest Control since 1900 has resulted in a vast store of accumulated knowledge and experience which we willingly place at your service.

BUGGÉ'S INSECTICIDES LTD.

SITTINGBOURNE, KENT

SPECIALISTS IN D.D.T. FORMULATIONS
(LIQUIDS, EMULSIONS, WETTABLE POWDERS, DUSTS, ATOMISTS.)
ASK FOR SPECIAL BOOKLET

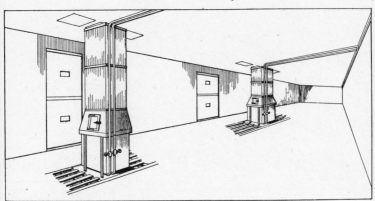

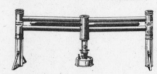
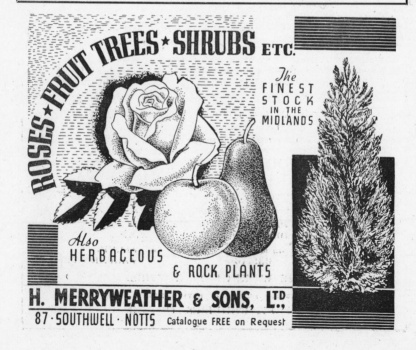

MISTIFIER
SPRAYERS

For ALL Crops the World Over

The wide range covers Hand and
Automatic WET or DRY Sprayers
for GROUND CROPS, HOPS,
FRUIT OF ALL KINDS

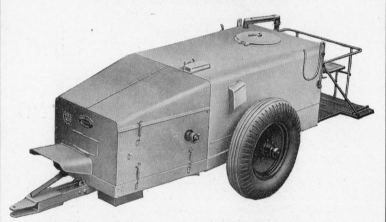

"Quadrex" Type 'S'—also with engine drive

Also GRADERS BY WEIGHT OR SIZE

Full Details & Specifications from Dept. FGH

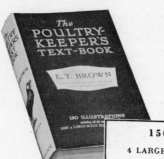

★ **The voice of experience . . .**

. . . **and the P O R O S A N Mould-on Seal**

★ *"I am so proud" . . .*

Dear Sirs,   *Penzance*

    I am so proud of my jars of fruit preserve which are the result of using ' Porosan,' and I have never heard of a more simple and successful way. E.H.H.

This is only one of the hundreds of appreciative and entirely unsolicited letters we receive from ' Porosan ' users everywhere. The reason is simple. A perfect seal is ensured because the cap and ring (in one piece) are literally moulded on to the jar rim by palm pressure alone. **THE POROSAN WAY** is both quicker and easier. You should try the squat, wide necked **POROSAN JAR**, for easy packing and storage

POROSAN JARS, CAPS and RINGS (complete)
Cost : 1-lb. 7/6 per doz. ; 2-lbs. 9/6 per. doz. ; 3-lbs. 12/6 per doz.

POROSAN CAPS & RINGS for 1/6 and 2/6; jam jars cost 3/- per doz. **RINGS ONLY,** 1/- per doz.

POROSAN PRESERVING SKIN, for all jars and bottles of odd shapes and sizes, is sold in rolls 2/- and 5/- per roll for 6 and 18 jars respectively. You cut to size and tie on, that's all. From Ironmongers' Stores and Stationers everywhere.

POROSAN *CAPS THEM ALL!*
(CAPS & RINGS OR SKIN)

The Recipe Book ' A WINTER'S TALE ' is chock full of useful hints for fruit bottlers. From address below. 3/9d. post free.

MARKETED BY
POROSAN LTD. 4-5 WARWICK COURT, HIGH HOLBORN, LONDON, W.C.1

BOOKS FOR GARDEN LOVERS

FROM WARD LOCK'S LIST

THE CULTURE OF ROSES   10/6
Edited by J. N. HART

A comprehensive and practical book by a recognised authority. Mr. J. N. Hart is a Past President of the National Rose Society.

Illustrated. 160 pages.

COLOUR ALL THE YEAR IN MY GARDEN   7/6
by C. H. MIDDLETON

A volume containing selections and cultural details of varieties of plants designed to assist the gardener in obtaining a wealth of bloom throughout the year.

Fully Illustrated.

THE COMPLETE BOOK OF GARDENING   30/-
by J. COUTTS, A. OSBORN and A. EDWARDS (Kew)

A comprehensive, detailed and practical standard work on every phase of gardening by authorities recently of the Royal Botanical Gardens, Kew.

768 pages. Fully Illustrated.

**For complete list of Ward Lock's
Gardening Books, please apply to**

WARD LOCK & CO., LIMITED, LONDON, W.C.2